Psychological Treatment in Disease and Illness

Books should be returned by the last date shown above. Renewals may be made in person, by telephone or by writing/e-mail.
Fines are charged for overdue books.

Edited by

MATTHEW HODES
STIRLING MOOREY

Psychological Treatment in Disease and Illness

GASKELL & The Society for Psychosomatic Research

Gaskell is an imprint of the Royal College of Psychiatrists,
17 Belgrave Square, London SW1

British Library Cataloguing-in-Publication Data
Psychological Treatment in Disease and
Illness
   I. Hodes, Matthew   II. Moorey, Stirling
   616.89

ISBN 0-902241-57-5

Distributed in North America
by American Psychiatric Press, Inc.
ISBN 0-88048-622-8

Phototypeset by Dobbie Typesetting Limited, Tavistock, Devon
Printed in Great Britain by Henry Ling Ltd, The Dorset Press

Contents

Contributors

Cherry Boa, Psychotherapist, St Thomas' Hospital, London

Christopher Dare, Senior Lecturer in Psychotherapy, Institute of Psychiatry, London

Ivan Eisler, Senior Lecturer, Institute of Psychiatry, London

Aleda Erskine, Head of Specialty Psychology Services, Medicine and Surgery, Camden and Islington Community Health Services Trust, London

Peter Fonagy, Freud Memorial Professor of Psychoanalysis, University College London, and Coordinator of Research, the Anna Freud Centre, London

Jackie Fosbury, Research Associate/Counsellor, St Thomas' Hospital, London

Elspeth Guthrie, Senior Registrar in Psychiatry, Manchester

Matthew Hodes, Senior Lecturer in Child and Adolescent Psychiatry, St Mary's Hospital Medical School, London

Richard Mayou, Clinical Reader, University Department of Psychiatry, Warneford Hospital, Oxford

Stirling Moorey, Consultant Psychiatrist, St Bartholomew's Hospital, and Hackney Hospital, London

George S. Moran, late Director, the Anna Freud Centre, London

Michael Murphy, Consultant Psychiatrist, Queen Mary's University Hospital, London

Shirley Pearce, Senior Lecturer in Psychology, University College London

Anthony Ryle, Senior Research Fellow and Honorary Consultant Psychotherapist, Division of Psychiatry, UMDS at Guy's Hospital, London

Tom Sensky, Senior Lecturer in Psychiatry, West Middlesex University Hospital, Isleworth

Lorraine Sherr, Principal Clinical Psychologist, St Mary's Hospital, London

Amanda C. de C. Williams, Consultant Clinical Psychologist, Input Pain Management Unit, St Thomas' Hospital, London

Preface

MATTHEW HODES and STIRLING MOOREY

There is a vast literature on a variety of psychotherapies for psychiatric disorder. However, less attention has been given to psychotherapeutic treatments for psychosomatic disorders and physical illness. These were the topics for a conference, organised by the editors of this volume on behalf of the Society for Psychosomatic Research, entitled Psychological Treatment in Human Disease and Illness, which took place in London on 26–27 November 1990. The conference provided the stimulus for this monograph. Contributors to the conference who agreed to submit a chapter to this monograph have all expanded and modified substantially their original talk. Furthermore there is one chapter on family therapy (by Ivan Eisler) that has been prepared especially for this monograph. At the conference there were some presentations that are not represented here. Some time has elapsed since the conference, but all the chapters are fully up to date at the time of going to press. It is hoped that the monograph will provide a selective perspective on contemporary psychological treatments in illness and disease. These papers represent the state of the art in the psychotherapy of psychosomatic disorders.

1 Mind, body and the psychotherapies

STIRLING MOOREY and MATTHEW HODES

Although there is a long tradition in medicine, stretching back to Hippocrates, which views the mind and body as inextricably linked, the scientific approach to medicine has tended to focus on the physical to the exclusion of psychological components of illness. The mind became the domain of philosophers and the body the province of anatomists and physiologists. This split between mind and body has been traced to Descartes' dualistic philosophy, but it is also fair to say that the advances in the natural sciences in the 19th century far outstripped any developments in the study of psychological processes, and physicians and surgeons based the clinical science of medicine on the theory and research available to them. Much of the psychological writings at the turn of the century grew out of philosophical enquiry and as such seemed of little relevance to clinicians. It was the development of psychoanalysis that provided the first coherent psychological model which could be used to understand mind–body interaction. Indeed, Freud's theories of the mind are themselves deeply rooted in a biological view of man derived from 19th-century science (Sulloway, 1979). Although Coleridge and Heinroth had both used the term 'psychosomatic' in the early years of the 19th century, it was the work of analysts such as Franz Alexander and Helen Flanders Dunbar which gave the word a substantial meaning in medicine. Alexander identified seven psychosomatic disorders: peptic ulcer, bronchial asthma, ulcerative colitis, rheumatoid arthritis, essential hypertension, neurodermatitis, and thyrotoxicosis (Alexander, 1950). The early psychosomatists believed that these disorders were related to specific emotional conflicts (Alexander, 1950) or personality patterns (Dunbar, 1935) in those who suffered from them. Apart from some evidence linking Type A personality with coronary heart disease (Rosenman *et al*, 1970) there is little research supporting this specificity hypothesis. As this form of psychosomatic medicine gradually declined in influence, developments in psychology and physiology allowed for a more sophisticated understanding of mind–body interaction

1

which superseded the narrower definition of psychosomatic used by Alexander. Research on the relationship between stress and disease has, however, shown an ever increasing number of disorders where the physical course of the illness is influenced by psychosocial factors (Brown & Harris, 1989). We feel that this focus on psychosomatic illness is too narrow. A broader definition of psychosomatic which takes account of the interaction of physical and psychological factors in all diseases is less restrictive and allows for a better integration of the different disciplines involved. This is in keeping with the statement in the very first issue of *Psychosomatic Medicine* in 1939 which saw its aims as the "study in their interrelation [of] the psychological and physiological aspects of all normal and abnormal bodily functions and thus to integrate somatic therapy and psychotherapy".

In fact, there are several ways in which psychological and physical processes can interact to produce dysfunction:

(a) Physical processes may have a direct effect on psychological functioning via their action on cerebral function. This occurs when infections such as syphilis produce mental illness, or hypoglycaemia produces confusion in someone who has diabetes mellitus.

(b) Psychological state may have a direct effect on physical functioning via some physiological mechanism. This is the classical psychosomatic illness. For instance, psychological stress can produce gastrointestinal disturbance (see the chapter in this volume by Guthrie on irritable bowel syndrome). Similarly, the course of a physical illness may be affected by psychological factors (e.g. Greer *et al*, 1979). The mechanisms for these interactions remain unclear, but may involve neuroimmunological or neuroendocrine functioning.

(c) Psychological state may indirectly influence physical functioning via its effect on behaviour. For instance, psychological factors can affect types of behaviour such as smoking which predispose an individual to cancer. Psychological factors may influence compliance with treatment regimens; Fonagy & Moran (this volume) suggest that this might be the most important mechanism for poor diabetic control in their adolescent group of patients. Anorexia nervosa is an example of a condition where dysfunctional beliefs about body shape and size lead to reduced food intake and consequent weight loss and physiological changes (see Eisler, this volume).

(d) Finally, a particular physical state may influence psychological state through the personal meaning given to it. Thus anxiety and depression are psychological concomitants of physical illnesses such as cancer or AIDS. Although there may sometimes be a direct physical cause for mental illness, in most cases it is the psychological effect of the life-threatening illness which produces the emotional disturbance.

A particular instance of the last interaction is found in hypochondriacal states. Here the physical state is usually a normal one, but is misinterpreted as a sign of serious illness. Tension headaches may be seen as symptoms of a brain tumour, or palpitations as symptoms of a heart attack. Mayou (this volume) describes the misattributions made by patients with atypical chest pain.

To separate out these interactions in this way may be conceptually useful. In real life there will be a reciprocal interaction between mind and body, and in any illness several interactions may occur together. In diabetes mellitus there may be (a) an effect on psychological functioning through hypoglycaemia, (b) a direct effect of psychological stress on diabetic control, or (c) an indirect effect on control through non-compliant behaviour, and finally (d) emotional distress may result from the negative meaning for the person of being diabetic, e.g. stigma, limitations from complications such as blindness, etc.

Development of effective treatments

The development of effective psychotherapies for psychosomatic disorders (interactions b–d as defined above) has been made possible by a number of departures from the 'psychosomatic school' of Alexander and others. There have, of course, been enormous developments in psychotherapies generally in the last few decades. New therapies such as cognitive–behavioural therapy and family therapy have flourished, in addition to changes in psychoanalytic psychotherapy. These three very widely practised psychotherapies are outlined in Part I of this book. Their application and evaluation in psychosomatic disorders have been facilitated by a number of advances.

From models of aetiology to models of treatment

One very important advance is the distinction between models of aetiology and models of treatment. While the aetiology of the psychological disorder may require a multifactorial model, e.g. anorexia nervosa (Dare, this volume), atypical chest pain (Mayou, this volume), and somatisation disorder (Murphy, this volume), the treatment rationale is not based on a reversal of the causal factors. Rather, the treatment involves the application of principles that are believed to be related to a reversal of distinct psychological processes that improve function. This discontinuity has been made most effectively in behavioural therapy, and now cognitive–behavioural therapy. While some family therapists and psychoanalysts have followed their own theoretical approaches (systems theory and psychoanalysis) in a way that has led them to eschew distinctions between models of cause and treatment, others have no difficulties accepting these distinctions (Dare & Eisler, this volume).

Outcome measures

Increasingly, psychological treatments for psychosomatic disorders are being evaluated using a variety of research designs. But however developed the treatments and sophisticated the study designs, there is still a fundamental requirement for a reliable and valid measure of outcome. In this respect, evaluation of psychological treatment in psychosomatic and physical disorders is facilitated by outcome measures that involve physiological processes and are easy to quantify, e.g. body weight in eating disorders, or HbA_{1C} in blood for diabetes mellitus.

In the treatment of some psychosomatic problems and disorders, the aim is to improve aspects of psychological functioning, without there being a known physiological measure of change. Examples are measures of pain, which have improved considerably in recent years, and changes in these are sensitive enough to reflect treatment response. The reliance on psychological and behavioural measures of change is illustrated by the chapters on treatment for pain (Williams and Pearce & Erskine, this volume). Thus, the different psychosomatic relationships outlined above are associated with different treatment goals, in terms of the difference between physiological and psychological outcome, and their respective measures.

Process measures

Recent reviews of research of a variety of psychotherapies for psychological disorders claim that replicating studies of outcome alone is wasteful, and that measures of the process of change are required (Garfield & Bergin, 1986). While evaluation of treatments in the psychosomatic field have not yet been carried out on the scale that justify this claim (with the possible exception of cognitive–behavioural therapy for bulimia nervosa), it is important to consider that outcome measures become much more meaningful when they can be linked to process changes. This facilitates the development of technique in treatment as well as theories of change.

Process measures can be concerned with psychological or intrapsychic change, interpersonal change, and change in physiological state. Unique to psychosomatic disorders is consideration of the relationship between psychological and physiological change. In each treatment study of a psychosomatic disorder, importance may be given to particular processes of change, which will enhance understanding of the most desirable therapies. For example, in a recent study comparing cognitive–behavioural therapy (CBT) with other psychotherapies for bulimia nervosa it has been claimed that CBT is superior because it tackles the 'core psychopathology', i.e. modifies disturbed attitudes to shape and weight more effectively (Fairburn *et al*, 1991). A good example of the relevance of interpersonal processes in the treatment of psychosomatic disorders is the finding that high parental expressed emotion, particularly parental criticism, is associated with dropping out of family therapy for patients with eating disorders (Szmukler *et al*, 1985). The relationships between psychological and physiological processes are investigated in a very sophisticated way by Fonagy & Moran (this volume) in their studies on the psychoanalytic treatment of children with diabetes mellitus. Other dramatic examples of these relationships come from studies by Spiegel (1989), who has shown that supportive psychotherapy groups can increase life expectancy in women with metastatic breast cancer. The women who were treated were more assertive and had better mood, which raises the possibility that the mechanisms are mediated through neuroendocrine or neurochemical changes.

Issues for the future

Many of the treatments for the conditions described here are not widely available. Indeed, the reports in this volume mostly come from research settings, although the treatments could be delivered in many clinical settings. In an era of tough cost control it is not easy for expensive research-based treatments to become widely available. Once the value of the treatments described in this book is established, the question that follows is how the findings can be used to provide effective and economic treatment to as large a number of patients as possible.

Prevention of psychosomatic disorders is an important aim, and the clinical findings of psychotherapies may have implications at this most fundamental level. Cognitive approaches have demonstrated the importance of attributions and health beliefs. To some extent conditions such as chronic low back pain and atypical chest pain are iatrogenic; the provision of information and avoidance of unnecessary investigations at an early stage might well reduce the need for the more specialist treatments described in this book. Mayou (this volume) describes the role of general practitioners at the primary care level in the early management of atypical chest pain.

An important goal for the comprehensive management of many physical disorders is the early detection of people at high risk of developing psychological difficulties. The best example is the integrated psychological and physical treatment of patients with breast cancer, using approaches described by Maguire *et al* (1980). Trained nurse counsellors provide support, education and detect early signs of psychological disturbance. Those patients seen by nurses have less psychological morbidity up to 18 months after mastectomy because psychological morbidity is detected and treated by referral to a psychiatrist. This identification of patients is essential if interventions are to be targeted on those most in need of help. Unfortunately the application of these principles to other diseases has hardly begun.

Treatment of psychological disturbance can be carried out at a number of levels. General practitioners, nurses and hospital doctors all have a role to play, and very little work has been done on educating them in basic psychological care procedures. At a secondary care level, psychiatrists, psychologists and nurses could develop and apply new skills within the services that exist for problems such as pain, somatisation disorder and anorexia nervosa. New disorders such as HIV/AIDS (Sherr, this volume) have required the development of special services for psychological management. However, there are unlikely to be many other examples of similar new services nationally.

Many of the treatments described here do not need to be carried out by psychiatrists or psychologists. More widespread provision of psychological treatments nationally could be offered by training nurse therapists, for instance. The creation of the specialty of liaison psychiatric nursing is a welcome development in this area. Nevertheless, psychiatrists will still need to play a role in the selection of patients for particular psychotherapies, and, for certain problems, such as the treatment of patients with somatisation disorder, medically qualified professionals will continue to have an important place (Murphy, this volume).

The research studies reported in this volume are only the first step towards cost-effective and widely available psychological treatments in medical and paediatric settings. Future developments will bridge the gap between outcome studies and service provision. The treatments described here demonstrate the unrealised potential of psychological approaches to human disease and illness. They show that it is possible to utilise a holistic approach to mind and body while still retaining a scientific stance.

References

ALEXANDER, F. (1950) *Psychosomatic Medicine*. New York: Norton.

BROWN, G. W. & HARRIS, T. O. (1989) *Life Events and Illness*. London: Unwin Heinemann.

DUNBAR, H. F. (1935) *Emotions and Bodily Changes*. New York: Columbia University Press.

FAIRBURN, C. G., JONES, R., PEVELER, R. C. *et al* (1991) Three psychological treatments for bulimia nervosa. *Archives of General Psychiatry*, **48**, 463–469.

GARFIELD, S. L. & BERGIN, E. A. (1986) *Handbook of Psychotherapy and Behaviour Change*. New York: Brunner/Mazel.

GREER, S., MORRIS, T., PETTINGALE, K. W. (1979) Psychological response to breast cancer: effect on outcome. *Lancet*, ii, 785–787.

MAGUIRE, P., TAIT, A., BROOKE, M., *et al* (1980) Effect of counselling on the psychiatric morbidity association with mastectomy. *British Medical Journal*, **281**, 1454–1456.

ROSENMAN, R. H., FRIEDMAN, M., STRAUSS, L., *et al* (1970) *Journal of Chronic Diseases*, **23**, 173–187.

SPIEGEL, D., KRAEMER, H. C., BLOOM, J. R., *et al* (1989) Survival of patients with metastatic breast cancer. *Lancet*, ii, 888–891.

SULLOWAY, F. J. (1979) *Freud: Biologist of the Mind*. New York: Basic Books.

SZMUKLER, G. I., EISLER, I., RUSSELL, G. F. M., *et al* (1985) Anorexia nervosa, parental expressed emotion and dropping out of treatment. *British Journal of Psychiatry*, **147**, 265–271.

Part I. Models of psychotherapy: psychoanalytic, cognitive–behavioural and family therapy

2 Aetiological models and the psychotherapy of psychosomatic disorders

CHRISTOPHER DARE

Ardent therapists seem to demand of themselves that they deal with fundamental causes. Enthusiasm for a particular therapy becomes attached to a belief in a theory which explains the treatment as though it addresses the fundamental aetiology of the condition. Exponents of behaviour therapy are likely to believe that they are dealing with psychological problems originating, for example, in conditions that arise from an unfortunate association between an activity and a reward for that activity. An ardent advocate of pharmacological treatments for psychiatric conditions is likely to have some faith in the organic nature of the conditions, in the notion of psychiatric illnesses as, ultimately, explained by neurochemistry. Psychodynamic treatments are likely to be conducted by practitioners who presume 'psychological' causes for the conditions they treat. Pause for reflection, of course, shows the flaw in these tendencies and limits them.

An example of how fallacies in this way of thinking arise is provided by the history of osteotomy and pain relief in osteoarthritis of the knee[1]. At one time orthopaedic surgeons were devising cunning operations to alter the alignment of the upper surface of the tibia and the lower surface of the femur. The argument was that by altering that alignment, undamaged portions of joint cartilage could be allowed to articulate, so diminishing the pain of the osteoarthritis of the joint. Some good results were obtained but post-operative X-rays demonstrated that the clinical improvement was not always associated with the hoped for realignment. The results were as satisfactory if the surgeon had performed an osteotomy, a cut across the tibia below the joint, but had been unsuccessful in altering the end position of the joint. It turned out that the improvement was a consequence of some effect generalising from the healing process adjacent to the joint, not to

---

1. The author is unable to substantiate this example. He recalls the anecdote from his days as a house surgeon.

physical change in the portions of articulating bone. That which 'cures' may not be explained by the rationale that led to the treatment.

A familiar fable can be woven from the well known story of the discovery of electroconvulsive therapy (ECT) and the treatment of psychotic depression. (ECT was first used by Cerletti and Bini in the treatment of schizophrenia as an extension of Meduna's original observations using camphor-induced convulsions.) A clinical observation had been made that some patients with co-existent epilepsy and schizophrenia improved as far as their psychosis was concerned, if they had an epileptic seizure. Eventually, it was realised that it was those patients with a depressive psychosis, not a schizophrenic one, that were in fact most likely to be helped by ECT (Weiner, 1985, p. 1558).

Treatments can be effective, and shown to be so, without there being any truth in the aetiological rationale, existing in the minds of the clinicians, that gave rise to the treatment.

Nonetheless the search for psychological causes comes inevitably to the mind of the psychotherapist, as do physiological causes to those prescribing medication, learned causes to those giving behaviour therapy, and to genetic causation amongst those driven to therapeutic nihilism.

This chapter discusses psychotherapeutic theories of psychosomatic disorders in general and focuses upon experiences within the psychotherapy of a particular group of conditions, namely eating disorders. We have conducted a series of investigations comparing efficacy of family therapy with individual psychotherapy across the age range of eating disorder patients (Russell *et al*, 1987; Le Grange, 1989; Dare *et al*, 1990; Dare, 1991; Dare & Szmukler, 1991; Szmukler & Dare, 1991). In summary, we have found that family therapy is an effective intervention for most cases of early onset (before 18 years), short history (shorter than 3 years) anorexia nervosa (Szmukler & Dare, 1991). For late onset anorexia nervosa (onset after the age of 18 years) individual therapy (of a supportive sort) was shown to be, in some ways, more effective than family therapy (Russell *et al*, 1987). In a subsequent trial, with as yet unpublished results, we compared family with individual therapy in a group of anorexic patients, all of whom were over 18 years of age on entry to the trial. They all had a period of weight restoration as in-patients before beginning the psychotherapeutic phase of treatment. In this trial it seems that family therapy is more effective with patients whose illness began before the age of 18 years, while individual therapy may be more effective in those whose illness began after the age of 18 years. This is despite the fact that, at the time of therapy, the patients with early and late onset anorexia were of comparable ages (they were all over the age of 18 years). We have speculated on the implications for our theory of therapy of these differences in response to family and individual therapy in anorexic patients of differing age of onset (Dare *et al*, 1990).

This chapter explores the implications for the relationship between aetiology and therapy in psychosomatic disorder, in general, and of anorexia nervosa in particular. A special emphasis is placed upon our findings about the different responses to family and individual therapy in the early and late onset cases. We presume that the close clinical similarity of early and late onset anorexia ensures that there are strong aetiological links between the disturbances arising in adolescence and those in young adulthood. The differential response to alternative forms of psychotherapy does not spring from the conditions being different in origin but is some sort of consequence of the disorder having come to acquire a different place in the psychological life of the individual and family.

Psychotherapies and psychosomatic theory

When Freud began his career as a psychotherapist he was influenced by the preoccupations of his time. His long training as a neuroscientist can be seen as having propelled him towards integrating the biological and psychological. However, his first psychological theory of the neuroses was a traumatic model (Sandler *et al*, 1973*a*). Post-traumatic psychological states were beginning to be recognised in Europe in the second half of the 19th century, perhaps because of the spread of the railway network and the concomitant increase in the number of train crashes. Freud, as a biologist, a loyal follower of Helmholtz (Sulloway, 1979) was eager to connect psychological and physical causes. In the second phase of the development of his theories (Sandler *et al*, 1972), he drew heavily upon his neurophysiological background. He emphasised the mind as an apparatus for harnessing the expression of the biologically derived, instinctual drives. He was particularly impressed by the unruliness of the sexual appetites and the need for them to conform to the demands of socialised behaviour. The most important data that he was seeking to explain were the unconscious nature of what he considered to be crucial motivational processes. He described a 'topographical' model in which a censor filtered wishes deriving from the sexually and biologically energised unconscious thoughts (Sandler *et al*, 1973*b*). The censor forced the wishes to be re-organised until they took a form that both represented the underlying sexual desire but disguised it sufficiently for it to be registered as a conscious and theoretically expressible wish. A neurotic symptom was identified as a compromise structure whereby a highly charged sexual need was met by an insistent prohibition. The symptomatic behaviour was seen as representing both the wish and the restriction of the wish. This theory was, essentially, designed to understand forms of psychological disorder presenting with physical symptoms, that is to say a special form of somatic disorder: conversion hysterias.

In the first flush of enthusiasm for psychological explanations for somatic disorder, psychoanalytic psychotherapists developed a model of physical symptomatology which extended Freud's conceptualisation of hysteria: bodily disturbance was translated as a symbolic expression of conflictual psychological processes. The origin of the illness was explained by the psychodynamic meaning; treatment consisted of the elucidation of that meaning in psychotherapy. There can be no doubt that this formulation was simply, largely, untrue. Psychosomatic symptoms are *not* hysterical conversions; the elucidation of the fantasies with which the physical symptoms are associated in the patient's mind do not reliably provide relief from the symptoms. However, by allowing for the possibility of physical symptoms being endowed with *meaning*, psychoanalysis signalled a revolution in the approach to human suffering. The discussion between psychotherapist and patient whereby the patient gains an understanding of the meaning of personal difficulties, is a continuing aspect of psychoanalysis much valued by our patients. For those who wish for that experience, it is as relevant a process within psychosomatic disorder as within the neuroses, whatever the nature of the disorder. This gives the psychoanalytic exploration an authenticity for psychoanalytic practitioners and many of their patients, a legitimacy that does not rest on the ultimate 'curability' of the disorder by means of psychoanalytic psychotherapy. The search for an understanding, a meaning of what is happening to the person, can exist alongside of, and, in some ways, is different from, the need for 'cure'.

Despite the defects of the underlying theory, psychoanalytic psychotherapists were sufficiently convinced of their therapeutic success to persist in seeing patients with somatic presentation of psychological problems. A crucial evolution of the psychoanalytic approach to psychosomatic problems came about under the impact of a move towards that which is now known as 'object relations theory'. The theory of personality development as dominated by the libidinal and aggressive drives was modified. Henceforward, and increasingly, psychoanalysis focused upon the importance of the relationship to caring figures. Rickman (1941) showed that hysterical symptoms could be seen not just as drive derivatives but also as a representation of an identification with aspects of important attachment figures. From that time the unconscious wishes and fears that were elucidated within psychoanalysis were more likely to be specifications of modes of relating rather than the expression of particular sexual or aggressive drives (of course, these two are not entirely unconnected). The endeavour of the instinctual drive, in psychoanalytic object relations theory, is construed not as the achievement of a certain sort of relief akin to orgasm but the realisation of a desire for a particular sort of relationship. A somatic symptom could be explored as having a meaning as the symbolic residue of a longed for or feared relationship within which sexual and aggressive aspects may be crucial components. This shift in the psychoanalytic theory of personal development has been accompanied by an increasing preoccupation in psychoanalytic psychotherapy with the analysis not of the unconscious mind as a reservoir of obscure and complex lusts but as the source of the unconscious determinants of the patient/therapist relationship. The technical preoccupation has come to be with the transference.

Later forms of psychotherapy, for example behavioural and especially cognitive–behavioural psychotherapy, developed different explanatory models of action for psychological interventions in psychosomatic disorder. In the classical Hullian or Pavlovian learning paradigm, or in the Skinnerian response conditioning model, a psychosomatic symptom is simply 'a behaviour', that can, in principle, be eliminated from the repertoire by altering the contingent rewards attendant on it. Cognitive theory has introduced the conceptualisation of complex mental constructs as part of the behavioural context of symptoms and enabled subtle psychotherapies to be developed. These can be effective in exploring the role of patterns of thought that allow for the maintenance or continuation of somatic symptoms within the patient's cognitive world. In the field of eating disorders, cognitive–behavioural therapy has been most extensively and successfully applied to work with bulimia in young adults (Lacey, 1983; Fairburn, 1985).

In recent years, family therapists (Minuchin *et al*, 1978) applied their techniques to so-called psychosomatic disorder. In Minuchin's model, psychosomatic symptoms occur in individuals in 'psychosomatic families'. He and his colleagues believe that there are characteristic qualities in such families, which were thought to apply to a variety of conditions extending from eating disorder, through asthma, to insulin dependent diabetes. These qualities are thought of as *structures*[2]. The important structures include patterns of alliance formation, of emotional closeness and distance, of boundaries between the generations of the family and style of dealing with conflict. Minuchin's therapy was, he believed, effective in changing these structures and hence, he argued, was the cause of symptomatic improvement. The symptoms as well as being tied to personal physiological qualities were the product of the family organisation. Other family therapists have published accounts of the management of psychosomatic problems of which the Milan Associates (Palazzoli *et al*, 1989) have been the most influential. Palazzoli, in her writings, has described anorexia nervosa as a psychological illness akin to a psychotic state which she formulates as arising because of a noxious rigidity in the family system resulting in distinctive patterns of family behaviour that are termed 'games'. Her form of family therapy is, she

---

2. David Rapaport (1951) defined structure in psychoanalytic psychology as mental processes with a slow rate of change, that is to say that they are relatively fixed patterns of thought. In structural family therapy, a structure is a relatively fixed pattern of family interactional process.

believes, addressed to undoing these specific issues. She and her colleagues also claimed therapeutic efficacy (qv. Eisler, this volume).

There are, therefore, a wide variety of psychotherapies claiming a theory for psychosomatic symptoms justifying the treatment for which success can be claimed. None of these different theories of psychotherapy would predict that family therapy and individual psychotherapy would have different efficacy in early and late onset anorexia outlined earlier.

An aetiological model for psychosomatic disorder

Figure 2.1 presents a theoretical diagram of the factors that contribute to the development of psychological disorders in general and for psychosomatic disorders in particular. It attempts to show that the symptom is derived from the interaction of sociocultural, genetic, physiological, familial and individual psychological qualities.

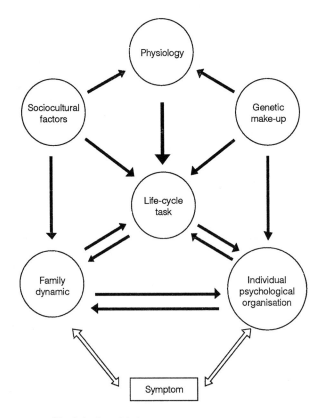

Fig. 2.1. An aetiological diagram for psychological disorder

Figure 2.1 shows that the *sociocultural factors* and *genetic make-up* are 'one-way', having both strong influences upon the individual and the family but not being affected by them. Physiological qualities are under the influence of genetic factors, as is the psychological organisation. The sociocultural context is a strong determinant of the family structure and the individual psychological organisation (Erikson, 1950) (although the diagram does not show this latter interaction). The culture and the chromosomes represent the 'givens' of the biological and social context of an individual and are not reciprocally influenced by the individual. All other elements in the system, the family, the individual, the physiological organisation, the symptom and the life-cycle processes are mutually interactive. These are essentially interactive loops. The strength or power of the connecting arrows may be more or less in different psychosomatic states. Some symptoms may require a very dominant genetic component whilst others may be determined instead by specific environmental constituents. Some symptoms may be largely physiological in origin and others more psychological and familial, but all psychosomatic states are influenced by psychological/familial and physiological factors. Psychosomatic symptoms, by definition, have a physiological expression, the subjective experience of which is influenced by psychological traits and states, by familial learned habits and communication techniques and by social customs. All symptoms are given meanings which are determined by the culture, the family history and belief systems and by the individual psychological history and experiences.

The *family dynamic* and the *individual psychological organisation* are strongly inter-connected: family dynamics structuring, in an important way, individual development, and the psychological qualities of the individual personality, in turn, interacting to form the overall family dynamic. The importance of developmental factors in the ontogeny of psychological and psychosomatic disorders is indicated by the central position given to the encircled *life-cycle task*. The concept of the life-cycle task is an important notion to establish links between psychoanalytic and family systems theories and therapies. Families undergo evolution as the couple form and children are added. As individuals change within the family, growing, maturing and going through their own crises, the family as a whole organisation has to change (Dare, 1979; Carter & McGoldrick, 1980). Each new phase in the family life cycle requires the development of appropriate structures to meet the demands of that phase. The individual, likewise, goes through a graded development, each phase being commenced in a way determined by what has occurred in the previous stage. Each stage has its own characteristic preoccupations and requires specific adjustments and orientations. These are the *life-cycle tasks*. It is characteristic for the inception of most disorders to have specific ages of maximum incidence. Developmental factors seem to be of general importance for the appearance of psychological and psychosomatic disorders and development is, in turn, impeded by these disorders.

The *symptom* (within the box), derives, on the one hand, in some way, from the psychobiological demands and occurrences of a particular phase of development and, on the other hand, reorganises or disorganises developmental phase and subsequent phases. For some symptoms, of course, the demands are almost entirely 'physiological', that is to say, the symptoms derive from a physical illness. Such a symptom will, regardless of its physiological derivation, nonetheless affect family and individual psychological organisation (diabetes would fit well into the diagram). The accomplishment of the life-cycle tasks will be altered by the presence of persistent symptoms whilst high levels of adaptability and of other psychological strengths will minimise the detrimental impact of chronic physical illness. Other symptoms may be more dominantly social/psychological in origin (the somatic symptoms associated with the separation anxiety of school phobia, for example). These, nonetheless have physiological substrates, influence family and individual development, and are, in turn, shaped by family and individual psychological organisation and patterns of tackling the demands for change at life-cycle transitions.

The diagram is both incomplete and inaccurate. Specifically, there needs to be an indicator of the genetic input to the physiological make up of the family. Likewise, physiological factors influence the psychological organisation of the individual as of all family members. It is impossible to portray the detailed and interactive relationships between the many factors.

An aetiological model for anorexia nervosa

Anorexia nervosa has been called a paradigm for psychosomatic disorder because it is possible to make some plausible guesses as to the many factors that may contribute to the development of the disorder. Figure 2.2 shows an outline of some of these potential factors, and their interactions, relevant to the development of anorexia nervosa.

Towards the top of Fig. 2.2 the *slimming culture* highlights one element of the culture that is thought to influence attitudes to food and diet in our society. The cultural context for anorexia nervosa has been suggested to be of importance. Indeed it has been suggested that anorexia is a social disease (Gordon, 1990). Epidemiological evidence can be adduced for this: the nine to one preponderance of female to male sufferers, the original but now altering class distribution, the up-to-now confinement to Western industrialised nations and so on. Apart from these rather wide social findings of an epidemiological nature it seems possible that there are more specific culturally important factors. For example, it has been noted that anorexia occurs in people who are losing weight by reasons of a restricted diet. This may seem axiomatic because it is clear that anorexia nervosa causes people to restrict their food intake. However, it is regularly observed that people who begin

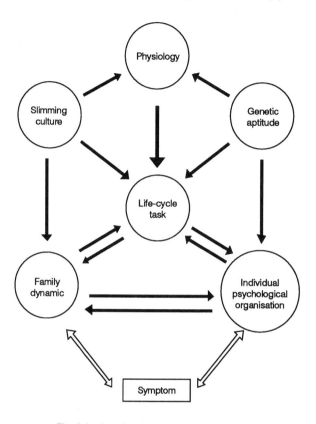

Fig. 2.2. An aetiological diagram for anorexia nervosa

to restrict their diet are at risk of becoming stuck with the habit. This may not have been initiated by the beginnings of anorexia itself. For example, historically, members of ascetic church orders seem to have been at risk of anorexia (Parry Jones, 1985) and those who attend ballet schools in contemporary culture are likewise at risk. It can be argued that the slimming culture, whereby most women in the Western world come to believe themselves to be in need of a reducing diet, is a crucial context in which anorexia develops.

Population surveys have shown that, at any one moment, a high percentage of women are convinced that they are overweight and should be slimming if they are not indeed actually slimming. This is especially so for young women from puberty to the menopause. This is a rather specific interaction, it would appear, between a slimming culture and a life-cycle task at puberty. Puberty is a signal for an individual to begin the process of identity formation (Erikson, 1950). One particular aspect of identity is physical identity. Most cultures seem to have evolved culturally specified and perhaps historically variable definitions of an ideal body shape. It has been strongly argued (Garfinkel & Garner, 1982) that the contemporary ideal body shape for women is one of increasing slimness. Moreover, this is in the context of changing nutrition patterns, consequent upon increased wealth. In the Western world this has led to a high-protein, high-fat diet. In turn, this has resulted in increasing body height. On the one hand, the ready availability of highly nutritious food makes obesity a widespread hazard. On the other hand, ideals of the body shape for women approximate to that which is common in early puberty. These two present striking conflictual demands. It can be seen how this slimming culture is likely to be influencing the whole family and not just young women at risk of anorexia nervosa. Indeed it can be argued that an unusually high level of food and dieting preoccupation is common in families within which a child of the family develops anorexia nervosa. The author has the clinical impression that this is especially so in male cases of anorexia nervosa.

The sociocultural setting within which ideal body shapes are identified can be predicted to have an effect on everyone. People going through important transitions of identity are likely to be the most influenced. Those transitions which are especially linked to necessary changes of body shape will be the most important in this respect. Body shape is also identified as part of specific gender identity and as a crucial element in sexual attractiveness. In this way the slimming culture affects the development of individual psychological organisation particularly strongly in adolescence. This impingement is in part direct on to the adolescent through media and peer influences. The family itself is a mediator of such influences. It is not the only social element that may have relevance for the development of eating problems; the different cultural expectations on young women as opposed to young men may also be important. These sociocultural influences are connected to the rest of the diagram by unidirectional arrows.

First-degree relatives of anorexic patients, as well as showing a relatively high proportion of diverse psychiatric problems (Kay & Leigh, 1954) also show an increased incidence of anorexia (Strober & Katz, 1987). This is not true for bulimic patients, whose first-degree relatives show little eating disorder but a relatively high level of affective disorder. Holland *et al* (1984) have shown that if, in a pair of identical twins, one develops anorexia nervosa, there seems to be an almost 50% likelihood of the other also developing the disorder. This appears to be strictly true for restricting anorexia, but much less so where there is a loss of control in eating, such as in bulimia. *Genetic aptitude* expresses the hereditable component in anorexia nervosa. The diagram indicates that the genetic influence is likely to affect individual psychological organisation. It might be expressed in the personality organisation, conscientious obsessional and compliant qualities that the patients are said to have. It may also be demonstrated by the capacity of the anorexic to withstand the pain of hunger, prolonged and chronic starvation. It could be argued that this hypothetical, genetically derived physiological capacity to withstand the pain of starvation could be understood to have some biological survival value in epochs when food supplies were intermittently scarce. The diagram also suggests that a genetic propensity may be particularly manifested at certain phases of the life cycle.

Figure 2.2, like Fig. 2.1, has been simplified and does not show an impingement of genetics on the family structure. Clearly, it is possible that other members of the family will have some of the genetic disposition that has led to anorexia in one person and is in a more covert way affecting other family members. This may account for the family traits of social conformity and success which has been said to occur. It has been argued that anorexic families are socially ambitious, striving and pre-occupied with food. If these factors are indeed true they may be a representation of the genetic capacity for perseverance and perhaps for restricted emotional expressivity. To show this, within Fig. 2.2, the *symptom* is portrayed as influenced by the family. The symptom is in some way within the repertoire of the family. Clinically, it sometimes appears that anorexia nervosa is occurring in a family within which food is even more than usually a prominent family preoccupation. For example it is very common that the mothers of anorexic children are high-class cooks. One family provided a striking instance: the mother was a dietician and the father an agronomist. It can be speculated that the special importance given to food as a medium of family communication and expression renders a member of that family more likely to develop food-related symptoms. Another clinical observation is that there are families containing an anorexic patient within which someone has died of a cachectic illness and the thinness of the dead person is vividly present in the minds of the family members. The pain and mourning of the family as well as the patient may then be symbolically expressed by the anorexic patient's skinniness.

It is cogent to imagine that the presence of a member of the family, voluntarily, apparently, starving herself nigh to death, has a potent impact upon, and meaning for, the rest of the family. This must be especially true for the parents: the nutritional health of the children being a prime function of parenting. The symptom is an expression of psychophysiological processes in the individual. In turn, of course, the symptom can be a powerful influence upon family organisation. For example, the life-threatening symptom, in an adolescent or adult resident within the family, returns the family, in part, to a phase of the life cycle when there is a strong demand for care and nurturance for the biological survival of the individual. What is also shown in the diagram is the fact that symptoms feed back on to the *individual psychological organisation*. Once the patient has started on the course of compulsive slimming the symptom develops self-perpetuation. By providing an apparent though detrimental solution to some personal developmental problems, it becomes incorporated as a given within the individual's repertoire of behaviour. In addition it has been speculated that there are physiological maintenance factors for slimming, specifically deriving from the genetically constituted make-up of the anorexic patient.

The emphasis in the links adduced so far has been upon the social and psychological organisation. These also affect the individual. The slimming culture can, in principle, offer the vulnerable person a solution to all the choices for identity formation available in adolescence. Preoccupation with body shape, weight and food can take over from all other choices. This is especially so if the person has the genetic aptitude to starve. A sense of fulfilment and an escape from other demands may be achieved. There is some suggestion that the state of starvation itself can be felt to be providing a sense of achievement and of elation. In this sense it has been suggested that an anorexic can become 'addicted' to self-starvation (Szmukler & Tantum, 1984). Does this model of anorexia nervosa lead to the possibility of theoretical investigation of the role of psychotherapy in the treatment of the condition? The rest of this chapter seeks to address this question.

Psychotherapeutic intervention in psychosomatic disorder (the 'mediator' paradigm – physical symptoms as interpersonal and intrapsychic processors)

When Freud first adumbrated the concept of a 'mental apparatus', he had in mind the notion of a system comparable to physiological systems, disturbance of which could be understood as underlying pathology. The traditional psychoanalytic belief has been that an interpretation was an intervention that directly affected the balance of forces within the mental apparatus. This model of psychotherapy is shown in Fig. 2.3. Subsequent generations of psychoanalytic psychotherapists have considerably modified their beliefs about the site of action of psychotherapy, whereby therapeutically effective interpretations are seen as being addressed to the relationship between the patient and the psychoanalyst. This is shown in Fig. 2.4.

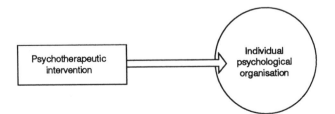

Fig. 2.3. The site of action of psychoanalytic psychotherapy (first version)

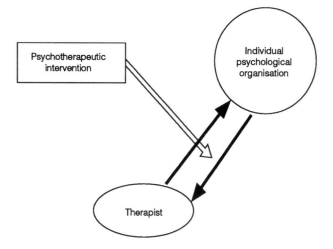

Fig. 2.4. The site of action of psychoanalytic psychotherapy (second version)

Figure 2.5 portrays a model of family therapy that is described by Minuchin and his co-workers (Minuchin *et al*, 1978). The therapy 'works' by altering the family structure.

What is the strength and reality of these three models of therapy? The model of interpretation affecting, directly, internal structure could only be shown to hold, if clear measures of mental structures in the psychoanalytic sense could be shown both to be measurable and alterable. Although the concept has endured within psychoanalysis and the idea of seeking change in such internal mental structures persists because it has clinical power, the empirical status is unclear. Psychodynamic structures are clearly not the same as anatomical structures. They can be argued to be two quite different things: (a) hypothetical constructs of a 'black box' model of the mind; (b) metaphorical or symbolic linguistic devices, translating the patient's experience into an alternative language, that is to say that they exist in a hermeneutic sense. Constructs, though hypothetical may be, in principle, of a certain magnitude, whereas translations are accurate by convention

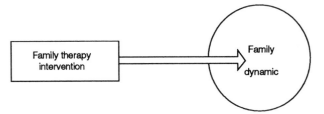

Fig. 2.5. Site of action of family therapy (third version)

rather than by their predictive mensurability. Such concerns are central to the debate as to the nature of psychoanalysis and the status of its explanations. Unresolved as this debate is, then, the idea that there can be evidence for psychic change, in the psychoanalytic sense, is bound to be dubious. With the change in emphasis embodied in the difference between Figs 2.3 and 2.4 came a considerable change in psychotherapeutic technique. The preoccupation with transference phenomena as the subject matter of psychoanalysis, and with object relations as a theory, implies that therapeutic change could be located within those psychological structures ('object relations configurations') that putatively underlie transference processes and the problem of confirmation of the theory remains unaltered. However, if transference interpretations are designed to resolve the implicit distortion of the patient's perceptions of the psychoanalyst, then, in principle, there could be a measure of change within the described paradigm of change in psychodynamic psychotherapy. As far as this author is aware, such measures have not been undertaken. Neither of the prevailing theories about the function of psychoanalytic psychotherapy, nor the 'structural change' model of family therapy, would predict the observations of the differential effects obtained in our controlled trial (Dare *et al*, 1990).

The method of using transference interpretations can be put most simply by means of a case example. This can also show the connection between a psychodynamic approach and a family viewpoint.

The patient, Alison, had been anorexic since the age of 14 years, 6 months, developing the disturbance in the context of the break-up of her parents' marriage. She had had her menarche at the age of 13 years, 9 months. At about the same time, her mother began to confide to her that she was having an affair with a man introduced to the family through Alison's friendship with his daughter. The anorexia began when the mother decided to leave Alison's father to live with her new partner. Alison was very distressed at having to live so close to her mother and the new partner in the small flat to which they moved. She was particularly disturbed by the sounds of them in their bedroom together. She was sorry for her father, but exasperated by his retreat into drink and self-pity at the marital break-up.

After 2 years of gradual weight loss, despite the care of the family doctor, Alison was admitted at the age of 17 years, 8 months, to a unit for young adults with an eating disorder. She weighed 33 kg at the time. Her symptoms were of anorexia without bulimia, laxative abuse or vomiting. The ward staff used a re-feeding programme to help her gain weight to a target of 48 kg, but were concerned that she continued to be angry and distressed about her parents. Ward family meetings had seemed encouraging, so referral to an out-patient therapist accompanied discharge from hospital. The therapist found that the patient's older brother (by 2½ years) had largely opted out of the family since going to university. Alison felt she was left to care for her father, to be the child of her mother's new home and to work for her own school career. A period of family therapy alternated meetings with Alison and her mother and step-father and meetings with Alison and her father. The main focus of these sessions was the delineation of Alison's responsibilities *vis-à-vis* herself, her mother and her father. It became clear that her mother was eager to get on with her own life, but prepared to give as much as Alison needed in a grim, exasperated manner. Her father was dourly determined to show that he could not forgive or recover from his wife's betrayal. The therapist focused on two topics: firstly, practical matters about the nature of anorexia nervosa and the re-establishment of a normal feeding programme; secondly, the need to exonerate Alison from responsibility for her father and the clarification of her role in the new family.

The family and patient committed themselves to the treatment, which appeared to be accomplishing its aims, but the patient was not losing her eating problems; her weight was stubbornly sagging from its level on discharge. After 8 months and 14 sessions the therapist decided to see Alison individually. This seemed to be appropriate to her age (now turned 18 years) and to the *impasse* of the family sessions. In the individual sessions (with the same therapist), Alison was articulate, sad about her family and insistent that she was going to conquer her problems. The therapy concentrated upon her personal relationships with her brother and his fiancée, with her father and his apparently self-destructive, excessive work and alcohol abuse and upon her struggle with herself to find a balance between her studies and her leisure interests. She also had a part-time job, seeking some financial independence and resources to travel. She was able to acknowledge and reflect upon her identification with her father, her anger at him and her mother and her sense of being totally stuck. The therapist became aware of increasing feelings of sympathy for the patient. These augmented the wish to help her and the therapist did reveal his appreciation of her struggle and unhappiness. Alison reciprocated by talking more confidentially about her longing to be able to be close and physically responsive to her boyfriend.

A curious feature developed: after several sessions, in which the therapist experienced a sense of hard, relevant work having been done, Alison became tetchy and dismissive about the therapy, saying that nothing was happening, why should she come again. The therapist felt hurt and put down. After the third such an ending to a session, the therapist made a transference interpretation of this process, at the beginning of a session. He said that he thought that Alison was seeing him as feeling compassionately about her and close to her and she was aware that he was eager to help her. She was feeling this as gratifying, which was why she came back and brought further intimacies to discuss. She also felt alarmed by the closeness that seemed to be developing with the therapist, feared that it was going to overwhelm and control her. Alison seemed moved and cheered by this discussion. It led her to talk directly of her fears of longings for sexual intimacy. The therapist talked of the way she used food to avoid the problem of wanting but fearing closeness. Eventually there was a satisfactory therapeutic outcome.

It sometimes happens that there is a sense of a significant moment in psychotherapy, experienced by the therapist as a 'turning point'. The work of Fonagy and his colleagues (this volume) with diabetic patients has shown the possibility of both demonstrating and specifying the psychodynamics of important transitions in therapy. It is suggested that the transition described as having happened with Alison revolves around the relationship with the therapist which touched upon internally significant object-related structures. In turn, these internal structures were connected with the experience of contact with figures in the family of origin.

It can be argued from the aetiological discussion, that the symptom acts to disturb the relationship between the individual and the family and disturbs the smooth accomplishment of normal life-cycle developmental tasks. Both individual and family therapies might have an effect, if successful, in eliminating the symptom from the position that it comes to take in controlling this life-cycle development. Figure 2.6 superimposes models of intervention on the aetiological diagram already elaborated. It does not necessarily rule

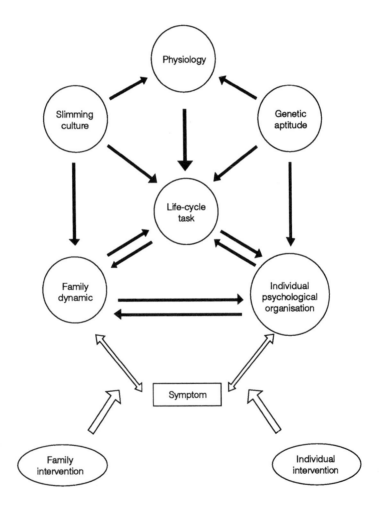

Fig. 2.6. A diagram for the psychotherapy of anorexia nervosa

out the possibility that therapy can alter directly individual or family organisation. However it implies another possible site of intervention: that is, in the relationship between the family and the symptom.

There is no body of empirical data that can be said to demonstrate this idea about the nature of psychotherapeutic efficacy. However, it is worth examining the clinical practice in successful and unsuccessful psychotherapies to see what light can be thrown on these ideas. The family therapy of anorexia nervosa will not be addressed here, in detail, because it is extensively discussed in another chapter. However, the most successful therapies in anorexia nervosa are those with young patients (under the age of 18 years), with anorexia nervosa of short duration (less than 3 years) and within families where the patient is not subject to criticism (as measured by expressed emotion (EE)) for her dieting behaviour (Le Grange *et al*, 1992). In these families, good outcome can be regularly achieved by helping the parents take control of their daughter's diet by unremitting but loving firmness. Accomplishing this is easier said than done, but when successful there is, by clinical observation, dramatic change in the family organisation as well as in the daughter's illness. The family as well as the daughter make striking moves forward in the life cycle. The main effect of the treatment can be said to be to remove the symptom from a position of rigid control over the relationship between the patient and the family. In good circumstances, the patient and the parents come to engage with each other over the myriad aspects whereby parental management of the child's life become the autonomous province of the adolescent instead of being locked into constant feeding battles and anxieties. In families within which the parents can be observed to be critical of their daughter for her anorexic behaviour ('high EE families') there will not be improvement of symptoms unless the criticism becomes reduced to a low level (Le Grange *et al*, 1992). These families remain stuck with the fear and the reality that the daughter will not be able to become a mature adult and independent from the family in the normal way. The parents are held in a pattern of relating to their daughter as though she were a little child in need of constant parental support and nurturance.

We are finding, in a current controlled trial, that two forms of individual psychotherapy produce treatment benefits in young adult anorexic patients. One form is essentially symptom focused ('supportive psychotherapy') and the other is interpretative ('focal psychoanalytic psychotherapy'). In the current trial, patients are allocated randomly to either of three therapies: the two individual psychotherapies and a form of family therapy tailored for working with this group of adult patients. A preliminary analysis of these results shows a differential effect: the individual therapies may be producing better end-of-treatment results in late onset (after the age of 18 years) anorexia nervosa; the family therapy produces significantly better end-of-treatment results in comparison with the individual therapies for those patients who, although now they are adult, began to suffer from anorexia nervosa in adolescence (before the age of 18 years). There is, at this stage of the trial, no statistically significant difference between the psychoanalytic psychotherapy and the supportive psychotherapy. In the focal, psychoanalytic psychotherapy, the focus is upon the interpretation of the transference. Such a treatment attempts to explore the registration of the early experience of family relationship in the fantasy life of the patient, especially those fantasies whereby the symptom controls the relationship between the patient and the important figures of their mental life. Focal psychoanalytic psychotherapy aims to explore the links between the personal relationships in the current life of the patient with their early infantile and childhood relationships by means of identification of evocations in the transference: the whole set of attitudes, feelings and beliefs that the patient has about the therapist, especially those that are a distortion of the actuality of the therapist (Sandler *et al*, 1973*b*). Although the therapist does not give advice or information about the nature of the anorexia as an eating disorder, the symptoms are extensively examined as they impinge upon the patient's relationship with the therapist and with others. The symptoms are construed as having a role in expressing and structuring the quality of the relationships that the patient makes in the contemporary world. At the same time, the therapist interprets the symptoms as symbolically (or, sometimes, literally) addressing unresolved conflicts with the important people of the childhood of the patient. Current relationships exist not only as representations of the current needs of the patient, as an adult, but also as attempts to correct or master childhood relationships, as they are held in the patient's current fantasy life. The process of psychoanalytic psychotherapy is thought to have a specific effect, when successful. It enables the patient to engage in a reworking of childhood relationships directly as a relationship, that with the therapist, rather than indirectly through the mediation of the symptomatology. In this sense, psychoanalytic psychotherapy and family therapy can be said to be addressing similar processes, that is, the disarticulation of anorexic symptoms from relationship patterns. It is this disarticulation that is represented in Fig. 2.6.

Conclusion

There are historical links between the psychoanalytic formulation of the role of symptoms in the psychology of the individual and the family systems view about the function of symptoms in regulating family interaction. In the mainstream of psychoanalytic thinking, a symptom is seen as a compromise formation whereby one psychological process comes into conflict with another[3]. The mental system is seen as an organisation that functions to balance opposing forces by producing character structures, or neurotic or psychotic symptoms which have properties expressing, in some form, both sides of the conflict. In both the Philadelphia Child Guidance Clinic model (Minuchin *et al*, 1978) and the Milan Systems model, the symptom is seen as a product of a family process. In both models the family processes postulated as giving rise to these symptoms are conflictual pressures, the contradictions of the conflict being in some way resolved by the symptomatic state. Both the psychoanalytic and the family systems view lead to the notion that cure of a symptom requires some form of resolution of the hypothesised, underlying conflict. What is being proposed in this chapter is that the relation between symptom and psychological and family organisation is not quite as suggested by either psychodynamic or family systems theory. The psychological structure of the individual, the transactional pattern of the family, has come to incorporate the symptom for both its behavioural qualities and its symbolic meaning. The incorporation gives the symptom a role in addressing certain, developmentally explicable, individual and family functions. In being given a role, the symptom may then appear as functioning to restrict the rate of developmental, life-cycle change in the individual and family. Psychotherapy, whether orientated towards the individual or the family, aims to facilitate the demolition of the restrictive function of the symptom, so that the demand for change that life-cycle transitions require, is faced without recourse to the psychosomatic state. Whether individual or family therapy is effective is principally an empirical question, but the specifics of the relationship between the timing of the development of the psychosomatic state and the life cycle of the individual and the family may determine whether or not individual or family therapy will be most likely to be helpful.

Acknowledgements

The author gratefully acknowledges the support of the Medical Research Council of Great Britain for funding of the controlled trials of psychotherapy of eating disorder that are the basis for this paper. The Leverhulme Trust is giving continuing support for the long-term projects deriving from this research.

---

3. Some psychoanalysts now postulate 'deficit' states as the source of some symptoms; a failure of a primary caretaking provision leading to 'something missing' from psychological organisation. A narcissistic defect, for example, might be said to come about from the failure of a parent to provide the child with the unconditional approval, that is the usual, predictable attitude of most parents towards their baby, for a period of infancy.

References

CARTER, E. A. & MCGOLDRICK, M. (1980) *The Family Life Cycle: A Framework for Family Therapy*. New York: Gardner Press.

DARE, C. (1979) Psychoanalysis and systems in family therapy. *Journal of Family Therapy*, **1**, 137–152.

—— (1991) The place of psychotherapy in the management of anorexia nervosa. In *Psychotherapy in Psychiatric Practice* (ed. J. Holmes). London: Churchill Livingstone.

——, EISLER, I., RUSSELL, G., *et al* (1990) Family therapy for anorexia nervosa: implications for the results of a controlled trial of family and individual therapy. *Journal of Marital and Family Therapy*, **16**, 39–57.

—— & SZMUKLER, G. (1991) The family therapy of early onset, short history anorexia nervosa. In *Family Approaches to Eating Disorders* (eds D. B. Woodside & L. Shekter-Wolfson), pp. 1–22. Washington, DC: American Psychiatric Press.

ERIKSON, E. H. (1950) *Childhood and Society*. New York: Norton.

FAIRBURN, C. (1985) Cognitive–behavioral treatment for bulimia. In *Handbook of Psychotherapy for Anorexia Nervosa and Bulimia* (eds D. M. Garner & P. E. Garfinkel), pp. 160–192. New York: Guilford Press.

GARFINKEL, P. & GARNER, D. (1982) Sociocultural factors. In *Anorexia Nervosa: A Multi-dimensional Perspective*, pp. 100–122. New York: Brunner/Mazel.

GORDON, R. A. (1990) *Anorexia and Bulimia: Anatomy of a Social Epidemic*. Oxford: Basil Blackwell.

HOLLAND, A. J., HALL, A., MURRAY, R., *et al* (1984) Anorexia nervosa: a study of 34 twin pairs. *British Journal of Psychiatry*, **145**, 414–419.

KAY, D. W. K. & LEIGH, D. (1954) The natural history, treatment, and prognosis of anorexia nervosa based on a study of 38 patients. *Journal of Mental Science*, **100**, 411–431.

LACEY, H. (1983) Bulimia nervosa, binge eating, and psychogenic vomiting. *British Medical Journal*, **286**, 1609–1613.

LE GRANGE, D. (1989) Anorexia nervosa and family therapy: a study of the changes in the individual and the family during the process of body weight restoration. Thesis submitted in partial fulfilment for PhD. Institute of Psychiatry, University of London.

——, EISLER, I., DARE, C., *et al* (1992) Evaluation of family therapy in anorexia nervosa: a pilot study. *International Journal of Eating Disorder*, **12**, 347–357.

MINUCHIN, S., ROSMAN, B. L. & BAKER, L. (1978) *Psychosomatic Families: Anorexia Nervosa in Context*. Cambridge, Mass.: Harvard University Press.

PARRY JONES, W. Ll. (1985) Archival exploration of anorexia nervosa. *Journal of Psychiatric Research*, **19**, 95–100.

PALAZZOLI, M. S., CIVILLO, S., SELVINI, M., *et al* (1989) *Family Games: General Models of Psychotic Processes in the Family*. London: Karnac.

RAPAPORT, D. (1951) Towards a theory of thinking. In *Organization and Pathology of Thought* (ed. D. Rapaport), pp. 689–730. New York: Columbia University Press.

RICKMAN, J. (1941) A case of hysteria – theory and practice in the two wars. In *Selected Contributions to Psycho-Analysis*, pp. 91–94. London: Hogarth Press (1957).

RUSSELL, G. F. M., SZMUKLER, G., DARE, C., *et al* (1987) An evaluation of family therapy in anorexia nervosa and bulimia nervosa. *Archives of General Psychiatry*, **44**, 1047–1056.

SANDLER, J., DARE, C. & HOLDER, A. (1972) Frames of reference in psychoanalytic psychology. II. The historical context and phases in the development of psychoanalysis. *British Journal of Medical Psychology*, **45**, 133.

——, HOLDER, A. & DARE, C. (1973a) Frames of reference in psychoanalytic psychology. IV. The affect-trauma frame of reference. *British Journal of Medical Psychology*, **45**, 265.

——, —— & —— (1973b) Frames of reference in psychoanalytic psychology: VII. The topographical frame of reference: the preconscious and the conscious. *British Journal of Medical Psychology*, **46**, 143.

STROBER, M. & KATZ, J. L. (1987) Do eating disorders and affective disorders share a common etiology? *International Journal of Eating Disorders*, **3**, 171–180.

SULLOWAY, F. J. (1979) *Freud, Biologist of the Mind: Beyond the Psychoanalytic Legend*. New York: Basic Books.

SZMUKLER, G. & TANTUM, D. (1984) Anorexia nervosa: starvation dependence. *British Journal of Medical Psychology*, **57**, 303–310.

—— & DARE, C. (1991) The Maudsley study of family therapy in anorexia nervosa. *Family Approaches to Eating Disorders* (eds D. B. Woodside & L. Shekter-Wolfson), pp. 23–48. Washington, DC: American Psychiatric Press.

WEINER, R. (1985) Convulsive therapies. In *Comprehensive Textbook of Psychiatry* (4th edn) (eds H. I. Kaplan & B. J. Sadock), pp. 1558–1582. New York: Williams and Wilkins.

3 Cognitive therapy in physical illness

TOM SENSKY

Cognitive therapy is a form of brief focused psychotherapy. Originally used in the treatment of depression (Beck *et al*, 1979) and anxiety (Beck *et al*, 1985*a*), it has been applied successfully to treat a growing range of emotional and psychological problems (Freeman *et al*, 1989; Hawton *et al*, 1989; Scott *et al*, 1989).

There are two principal reasons to expect that cognitive therapy will be effective in the treatment of psychiatric or psychological problems associated with physical illness. First, the efficacy of cognitive therapy has been demonstrated in the treatment of depression and anxiety, which are the most prevalent psychiatric problems associated with physical illness. Secondly, there is considerable evidence that emotional reactions to physical illness are more closely associated with cognitive factors than with 'disease' factors such as disease severity or symptom intensity (Sensky, 1990). Furthermore, there is some evidence that cognitive factors may determine emotional responses to illness.

The cognitive model – dysfunctional beliefs

Detailed descriptions are available of the cognitive model (Williams, 1984; Beck, 1990). Its essential feature is that a person's behaviour on the one hand, and his emotions on the other, are intimately linked with the way he construes the world. This in turn depends on the individual's beliefs. According to the cognitive model, some forms of emotional disturbance are sustained by, and may even be due to, *dysfunctional beliefs* (Beck, 1963; Beck, 1990). Such beliefs are characteristically extreme, but are usually taken as axiomatic and therefore not requiring proof or further examination. People are not normally aware of the precise nature of their dysfunctional beliefs, however extreme they might be. Despite being beyond normal awareness, such beliefs are not unconscious, and therefore exposing and working on

30

them during therapy does not require psychoanalytic techniques such as interpreting the transference or defence mechanisms. The individual's recognition of his or her beliefs can be enhanced by a variety of techniques. Helping patients to become more aware of their beliefs, and to question their accuracy and/or relevance where appropriate, is a key component of cognitive therapy (Beck, 1964).

Dysfunctional beliefs are often conspicuously false. For example, people who are depressed commonly have the conviction that nothing will ever improve, and the future is certainly hopeless. However, particularly in physical illness, dysfunctional and false are not synonymous. False beliefs are not necessarily dysfunctional, and not all dysfunctional beliefs are false. For example, denying the seriousness of one's illness or even its presence can sometimes serve a protective function (Taylor, 1983; Levenson *et al*, 1984; Levine *et al*, 1987), and is therefore not necessarily dysfunctional under such circumstances. Conversely, the belief that 'I do not have long enough to live to achieve everything I want' may be realistic for someone who is terminally ill, but might also be dysfunctional if, for example, the person can focus on nothing else and gives up trying to achieve anything. Dysfunctional beliefs form the main focus for therapeutic work in cognitive therapy for physical illness. It is not the aim of therapy either to correct *all* false beliefs, or simply to help the person to 'think positively'.

In psychosomatic medicine, dysfunctional beliefs may focus particularly on the illness itself, the management of the illness by doctors and others, and on the perceived impact of the illness on the individual's life (Table 3.1).

Although such common themes can be identified, the beliefs themselves tend to be very idiosyncratic, with considerable variation from one person to another:

A man recovering from his third myocardial infarct experienced considerable difficulty mixing with people. Discussing his difficulties revealed that he had a

TABLE 3.1
Examples of dysfunctional beliefs associated with physical illness or psychosomatic problems

(Presumed) illness	Management of illness by doctors or others	Presumed impact of the illness
Any bodily sensation which is new or unfamiliar is a sure sign that there is something seriously wrong with me. Pain which is as severe as mine must have a recognisable physical cause.	Doctors cannot really be trusted. My outlook is so bad that the doctors don't want to tell me the truth. My doctor's recommendation for me to see a psychiatrist proves that he thinks I'm imagining my problems.	Unless I can be restored to perfect health, my life will inevitably be ruined. (I know I've coped with my cancer up to now, but) if I have a relapse, I shall be unable to cope and just fall to pieces. If I can't run for a bus as well as I used to when I was fit, I must still be very unwell.

particular fear of losing consciousness, having experienced this during an early attack of angina. However, he had come to interpret a wide variety of perceptions as cues of impending loss of consciousness, including symptoms associated with anxiety or panic, as well as the loss of concentration, or boredom, which he sometimes experienced during long conversations with work colleagues. Without exploring his beliefs in depth, it would have been very difficult to understand how he equated boredom with the signs of another heart attack.

The beliefs which an individual holds, dysfunctional or not, are related to another element of the cognitive model – automatic thoughts. These share some of the qualities of beliefs; for example, they occur spontaneously and are taken as axiomatic. However, while an individual's beliefs such as those described above remain unchanged across a variety of situations, automatic thoughts are likely to vary from one situation to another. A key feature of the cognitive model is that when a person experiences a change in mood and becomes dysphoric (anxious, depressed, angry, etc.), this affect shift signals *negative automatic thoughts*. Themes which link negative automatic thoughts from different situations can help to identify the individual's underlying dysfunctional beliefs. Thus, for example, in the case of the man described above, he reported numerous situations in which he became anxious, ranging from driving on an elevated motorway from which there was no immediate exit, to some instances when he was in the company of a work colleague. The negative automatic thoughts responsible for his anxiety were different in these two circumstances, but in each case they pointed to the underlying belief that he might lose control, with disastrous consequences.

Cognitive distortions

In the above vignette, as in many other similar instances, there is clear evidence available to the patient that his beliefs are false. For example, despite numerous episodes of boredom, light-headedness, etc., the patient has not experienced a further infarct, yet his fear continues to recur. How is it that such beliefs can be sustained, even in the face of overwhelming contrary evidence?

One way in which dysfunctional beliefs are perpetuated and even enhanced is through distortions of appraisal or thinking (cognitive distortions) (Beck, 1963). Cognitive distortions can be viewed as systematic errors of logic or information processing. Among the common types, *selective abstraction* involves focusing on a particular detail of a memory or situation, even when other aspects of the memory contradict this. The detail involved usually fits with the person's dysfunctional beliefs. Thus, for example, an in-patient with a history of hypochondriasis who repeatedly sought reassurance from staff disregarded what she had been told about her problems and interpreted the nurses' reluctance to talk to her as a sure sign that they could not bring themselves to tell her face to face how bad her prognosis was. *Arbitrary inference* involves jumping to a conclusion for which there is no evidence available. Thus a woman on chronic renal dialysis who was also depressed cited the fact that she had to give up full-time employment as evidence that she had failed as a mother. *All-or-nothing thinking* might foster the belief that 'if I'm not 100% well, I must be at death's door'. *Personalisation* relates to the tendency to assume personal responsibility for everything that happens – for example, a man with cancer concluded that his situation was hopeless because he did not have a strong enough will to prevent a relapse. These and other forms of cognitive distortion have been reviewed in detail elsewhere (Beck, 1964; Beck, 1990). In therapy, patients learn to recognise their own thinking errors. It is often helpful for patients to identify what types of cognitive distortion they use most often, and under what circumstances.

For people who are depressed or anxious, and for most of those who have a physical illness or a psychosomatic disorder, the work done by patient and therapist concentrates mainly on negative automatic thoughts, dysfunctional beliefs, and cognitive distortions. However, this focus is not suitable for use in treating those with personality disorders, for whom cognitive therapists use a different approach (Beck & Freeman, 1990).

Cognitive factors in physical illness

Everyday clinical experience indicates the breadth of emotional responses to illness. Individual responses cannot be reliably predicted on the basis of intensity of symptoms, severity of the illness, its prognosis, or other 'disease' variables (Sensky, 1990). This has been the conclusion of numerous studies across different settings. For example, in a prospective study of people with cancer, perceptions of personal control were a better predictor of psychiatric morbidity than site or stage of cancer (Ell *et al*, 1989). Similarly, among in-patients referred to a liaison psychiatry service, affective disturbance correlated with health locus of control but not with a measure of seriousness of the physical illness (Wise *et al*, 1985). In another study, depression among medical in-patients was associated with perceptions of support by hospital staff and perceptions of the extent to which the illness would disrupt the individual's life (Rosenberg *et al*, 1988). Among dermatology out-patients, psychiatric morbidity was found to be related to attitudes towards appearance but not to extent, duration or site of skin disease (Wessely & Lewis, 1989). The extent to which patients on chronic haemodialysis consider that their illness can be controlled shows a strongly negative correlation with ratings of depression (Sensky, 1989*a*). Numerous other studies have supported the association in physical illness of affective disturbance with patients' beliefs that their illness or symptoms might become uncontrollable (Devins *et al*, 1982; Broadhead *et al*, 1983; Affleck *et al*, 1987; Flor & Turk, 1988). Some patients' beliefs appear benign but closer scrutiny indicates that they may be dysfunctional. For example, people with diabetes who blame their diabetes for life changes tend to have better glycaemic control than other diabetics (T. Sensky & R. Petty, in preparation). Superficially, attributing life changes to one's diabetes might therefore be seen as adaptive, in that good glycaemic control is a common therapeutic goal in diabetic clinics. However, the patients who make such attributions are also more anxious than those who do not blame the diabetes for life changes. It is unlikely that the anxiety these patients suffer is a price worth paying for good glycaemic control, since this can certainly be achieved without anxiety. Focusing too narrowly on good glycaemic control as the most important treatment objective runs the risk of failing to acknowledge such anxiety when it occurs.

Cognitive factors influence the responses of families and professionals as well as patients (Block *et al*, 1980; Sensky, 1989*b*). For example, those parents of adolescents with diabetes who attribute their child's difficult behaviours to the diabetes are less critical of the child (Sensky *et al*, 1991), although it remains to be established what impact this has on the emotional state of parent or child.

The onset of a physical illness, or its exacerbation, commonly heralds a change of circumstances for the individual. This often forces the patient and others (family, work colleagues, etc.) to reappraise attitudes. Beliefs and attitudes which had previously served the individual well might become difficult to sustain, or even dysfunctional.

> A senior scientist, very successful in her career, was given an excellent prognosis by her surgeons following removal of a relatively benign cancer. Despite this, she had great difficulty returning to her previous lifestyle. For her, success at work was the only measure of her self-esteem that mattered – being a mother or a wife or a friend were taken for granted and relatively unimportant. The belief that 'when I or others judge myself, my success in my work is the only thing that really matters' had helped her in her career. However, even a small chance that she might suffer a relapse of her cancer threatened this belief and thus rendered it dysfunctional.

Origins of dysfunctional beliefs

What sets off the cascade of erroneous beliefs and distortions of thinking? This will vary from one person to another. Depression, whatever its cause in an individual case, leads to distorted patterns of perception and memory (Teasdale, 1983). On the other hand, similar faulty cognitions can be generated using a laboratory mood induction exercise (Teasdale & Fogarty, 1979). Whatever else the impact of a serious physical illness on the individual, it involves a series of major life events, commonly involving loss or threat. For some people, the onset of an illness will represent the most threatening life event they have experienced. A particular, enduring pattern of thinking ('cognitive style') may make people more vulnerable to the effects of adverse life events (Beck, 1983; Hammen *et al*, 1989). Some people have a particular tendency to view themselves and their circumstances unfavourably; when they experience somatic symptoms, they are more likely than others to complain about these and also more likely to become distressed (Costa & McCrae, 1987; Watson & Pennebaker, 1989; Robbins & Kirmayer, 1991). People who are more sensitive than others to somatic sensation are also more likely to develop transient hypochondriacal attitudes in response to physical illness, as are those with a personality disorder (Barsky *et al*, 1990). People who make pessimistic attributions (for example, that illness and other events are pervasive and will inevitably afflict them) are not only more likely to report minor illnesses, but also less likely to take steps to deal with them appropriately (Lin & Peterson, 1990).

Responses to physical illness are often affected by the individual's (current) beliefs about illness and medical care, and these in turn may be heavily influenced by past experiences of illness, either personal or in the family. For example, patients commonly harbour beliefs about doctors' competence being less than perfect. In a study of a representative sample of patients on chronic dialysis awaiting renal transplantation, 31% spontaneously referred to mistakes made by doctors when describing how their renal failure had come to be diagnosed (Sensky, 1989*b*). Whether or not such beliefs are accurate, they do make it more difficult for patients to place their trust in their doctor, as doctors often encourage their patients to do. Where an illness runs in the family, patients may have vivid memories of the impact of treatments which have long been superseded but which continue to influence their own decisions regarding medical care.

Patients' emotions and their ability to cope can be significantly influenced by the beliefs of family and friends.

> A woman due to have a colostomy for cancer was anxious and wanted further information from her doctors. Her family considered that she would not be able to cope if she knew her diagnosis and advised the doctors that she should not be told. As a result, although the patient suspected that she had cancer, she encountered difficulties in discussing this with the doctors.

Doctors' beliefs also are not necessarily accurate (Petty *et al*, 1991). Doctors' beliefs or attitudes about individual patients or groups of patients may have a major impact on their patients' beliefs.

Cognitive therapy

In the treatment of mood disorders, cognitive therapy aims to help patients identify the relationships between their cognitions, their emotions and their behaviour, to increase awareness of dysfunctional cognitions and to address these. Although the main foci of the therapy are cognitions and behaviour, therapy results in changes in emotions also, because of the intimate associations of emotional state with cognitions and behaviour. Therapy is usually brief (often 10–20 hours in total). Patient and therapist collaborate to construct a cognitive formulation of the patient's problems, linking together beliefs, commonly used thinking errors, emotions and behaviour. This serves to guide the therapy further (Persons, 1989). The formulation is used to generate hypotheses, which can then be tested using cognitive and/or behavioural methods. The results obtained can then be used to refine the formulation.

Patient and therapist work together on a detailed investigation of specific problems, or of particular events associated with mood changes. As noted above, it is often possible by focusing on a few specific problems or events to identify themes in the individual's thinking which have a wider impact on his or her life than in the particular situation under scrutiny. The patient is encouraged not to accept his or her beliefs as axiomatic but rather to test them where appropriate, often by doing behavioural or cognitive experiments.

> A depressed woman was spending most of her time at home, where her inactivity made her feel even more depressed, and also deprived her of the opportunity of meeting other people. Because her friends did not telephone her, she concluded that they did not wish to know her any longer (an example of selective abstraction). With her therapist, she successfully challenged this conclusion by examining alternative explanations for her friends' failure to telephone her. She also believed that "it is impossible to enjoy anything unless I am with someone I like". To test this, she set herself the task of going to a play – she used to enjoy the theatre before she became depressed. Having managed to get some enjoyment from the play, this provided first-hand evidence against her original belief, allowing her to modify this and consequently also change her behaviour.

> Another example is that of an executive who became very self-conscious about dining with clients after an injury had left him with a deformity of his left hand. Further discussion revealed that his main concern was that because he was unable to hold a knife properly while eating, his clients would see him as ill-mannered. With the therapist, he worked out several ways to test this belief (for example, by directly asking close friends if they shared his interpretation of the impression he gave). Some of the experiments he could undertake were rehearsed beforehand with the therapist. Even if his concerns turned out to be realistic, he was motivated to pursue this because the strategy he had used to date to deal with this situation was not satisfactory, and getting further information was the first step in seeking more successful ways of coping.

Sometimes, it can be helpful to rehearse the outcome of a particular fear.

> A man who developed asthma in his 50s started avoiding all basement rooms following an episode of breathlessness in the basement at his work (this turned out

to be an attack of hyperventilation). His fear was of a catastrophic, possibly fatal outcome. However, examining this fear in more detail with the therapist, he acknowledged that he was usually able to cope with asthma attacks using his inhaler, and also could not identify any reason why an asthma attack in a basement should be any more severe than all others. Even if he did have a severe asthma attack, someone accompanying him could summon appropriate help. Having decided that suffering an asthma attack in a basement was not as dangerous as he had previously believed, he felt sufficiently confident to test his belief that going into a basement would inevitably bring on an asthma attack.

The cognitive approach is educational. The patient acquires skills, techniques and insights which can be applied not only to the present problems but also in the future. The patient's knowledge and insight acquired during therapy can thus be expected to have a prophylactic effect in the future. Consistent with this is evidence that cognitive therapy for depression leads to a reduced relapse rate when compared with antidepressant treatment alone (Kovacs *et al*, 1981; Teasdale *et al*, 1984; Blackburn *et al*, 1986; Simons *et al*, 1986; Hollon *et al*, 1988).

The therapist has an active role, rather than being reflective. The relationship of cognitive therapist to patient has been likened to that between research supervisor and student. As the vignettes above illustrate, the patient is encouraged to question and test beliefs and consider alternate behavioural and/or cognitive strategies where appropriate. In psychodynamic psychotherapies, the transference is the cornerstone of therapy; its development and interpretation are crucial to the therapy (Malan, 1979). By contrast, in cognitive therapy, the relationship between patient and therapist is one source of data (among many) about the patient's problems. Beliefs about the therapist are taken at face value, to be tested experimentally as are other data. By contrast, in psychodynamic psychotherapies, such (conscious) beliefs are viewed as representations of the unconscious, to be interpreted.

Although the main focus of the therapeutic work in cognitive therapy is on the present or recent past, the patient's early experiences are often relevant also. Dysfunctional beliefs often have their origins in childhood, and understanding these can be very helpful.

A woman on renal dialysis found her work and her social life very taxing but felt unable to compromise on any of her activities. She had been adopted shortly after birth, and never knew her real mother. Her adoptive mother was cold, distant and critical. The patient had developed the belief from childhood that "if I try hard enough and do everything that other people want of me, then I can earn their love". This particular belief had served her very well (not to mention her family and friends) until her illness became particularly disabling. The influence of her mother's attitude could be examined using a variety of techniques, such as role-plays of conversations between mother and daughter.

Cognitive techniques in physical illness

The importance of cognitive factors in adjustment to illness, outlined above, suggests that cognitive therapy should be helpful for people with physical illness. Therapy often begins with a detailed exploration of the patient's understanding of his or her illness. This in itself can be very therapeutic – in some instances, patients have acquired a more detailed understanding of their doctors' beliefs and attitudes than vice versa. The active role which patients assume in the therapy can be very beneficial, particularly in restoring the sense of control or mastery eroded by the illness or its consequences. That the focus of therapy is usually on present problems helps patients to recognise the relevance of the therapy to their current needs. Interventions can be rapidly effective and therefore serve to encourage the patient to pursue the cognitive model further on his or her own as well as with the therapist.

A wide variety of instruments is available to assess different beliefs about, or attitudes to, physical illness, including (amongst many others) health locus of control beliefs, beliefs about health or illness and different coping strategies (Sensky & Wright, 1993). Such instruments are particularly valuable in measuring change during and after therapy.

While the general principles of the cognitive model are widely applicable to the physically ill, as are the common techniques used in therapy, particular types of illness may benefit from more specific interventions. Descriptions of appropriate cognitive and behavioural techniques, or treatment manuals, are available for a variety of different illnesses, ranging from cancer (Moorey & Greer, 1989; Scott, 1989) and chronic pain syndromes (Turk *et al*, 1983; Hanson & Gerber, 1990) to hypochondriasis (Barsky *et al*, 1988; Warwick & Salkovskis, 1989; Clark & Salkovskis, 1992).

If, in a matter of hours, patients can learn cognitive techniques that can help them to cope better with physical illness, doctors and other professionals who are not expert cognitive therapists should be able themselves to acquire sufficient working knowledge of cognitive techniques to be able to apply them in their own work with patients. It is likely, for example, that a cognitive approach could benefit patients' adherence with medical regimens. There is already some evidence that 'Balint-style' groups run along cognitive lines can be helpful to doctors (Hartmann, 1989).

Efficacy of cognitive interventions in physical and psychosomatic illness

In the treatment of individual patients, cognitive therapy places great emphasis on measurements of change and outcome. With regard to the therapists, skill and intuition are as important and as difficult to measure in cognitive therapy as in other psychotherapies. However, instruments are available to measure the extent to which the therapist adheres to the cognitive model (Beck *et al*, 1979; DeRubeis *et al*, 1982). Although the therapist's adherence to a particular therapeutic model does not necessarily equate with competence (Dobson & Shaw, 1988), it is a prerequisite in the reliable measurement of the efficacy of a psychotherapeutic intervention (Shaw & Dobson, 1988; Elkin *et al*, 1988).

When used to treat depressed out-patients, cognitive therapy has been shown to be as effective as treatment with antidepressants, with the combination of the two treatments generally being superior to each alone (Rush *et al*, 1977; Blackburn *et al*, 1981; Kovacs *et al*, 1981; Teasdale *et al*, 1984; Beck *et al*, 1985*b*). Good outcome is associated with the patient's understanding and endorsement of the cognitive model early in therapy (Fennell & Teasdale, 1987), and may also relate to the degree to which the therapist follows the cognitive model (Hollon *et al*, 1990).

A comprehensive account of reported applications of cognitive therapy to specific physical illnesses is beyond the scope of this review. Table 3.2 gives an indication of the range of physical and psychosomatic illnesses in which clinical trials have demonstrated successful use of cognitive therapy. Extensive evaluation in bulimia nervosa has shown it to be effective (Freeman *et al*, 1988; Agras *et al*, 1989; Fairburn *et al*, 1991). In addition, pilot studies

TABLE 3.2
Examples of successful cognitive and/or behavioural interventions in physical illness

Illness	*Reference*
Ankylosing spondylitis	Basler & Rehfisch (1991)
Asthma	Maes & Schlosser (1988)
Cancer	Tarrier & Maguire (1984), Worden & Weisman (1984), Greer *et al* (1992)
Chronic pain	Turner (1982), Phillips (1987), Kerns & Haythornthwaite (1988), Pearce & Erskine (this volume), Williams (this volume)
Chronic tension headache	Holroyd *et al* (1991)
Chronic obstructive airways disease	Atkins *et al* (1984)
Inflammatory bowel disease	Schwartz & Blanchard (1991)
Migraine	Richardson & McGrath (1989)
Multiple sclerosis	Larcombe & Wilson (1984)
Osteoarthritis	Keefe *et al* (1990)
Premenstrual syndrome	Morse *et al* (1991)
Rheumatoid arthritis	Applebaum *et al* (1988)
Tinnitus	Lindberg *et al* (1989), Jakes *et al* (1992)
Type A behaviour	Friedman *et al* (1986)

This list illustrates the range of problems to which cognitive therapy has been applied. It is not intended to be exhaustive. It includes only studies reporting treatment trials; numerous other reports (some referred to in the text) have given descriptive accounts of applications of cognitive therapy to physical illnesses or symptoms.

have reported successful use of cognitive therapy in other conditions, such as atopic eczema (Horne *et al*, 1989), and in the management of eating problems associated with diabetes (Peveler & Fairburn, 1989), as well as in hypochondriasis (Salkovskis & Warwick, 1986; Stern & Fernandez, 1991). Cognitive interventions have also been shown to be beneficial in psychological preparation for cardiac catheterisation (Anderson & Masur, 1989) and in AIDS (Sherr, this volume), including reduction of risk among men at increased risk of HIV infection (Kelly *et al*, 1989).

While such work provides overwhelming support for the efficacy of cognitive therapy in physical illness, the extent to which patients' improvements are attributable specifically to cognitive interventions remains unclear. Most researchers to date have used within-group comparisons, assessing their patient sample before and after the intervention. Numerous studies have demonstrated the superiority of cognitive interventions over waiting-list control groups (e.g. Atkins *et al*, 1984) or 'treatment as usual' controls (e.g. Tarrier & Maguire, 1984). However, relatively few published studies have compared a cognitive or cognitive–behavioural intervention with other 'active' interventions. The results of such studies have been less consistent. For example, Atkins *et al* (1984) compared behavioural, cognitive and cognitive–behavioural interventions with an 'attention control' group (with therapist contact equal to the active interventions) and a waiting-list control group. The active interventions were superior to the two control treatments. Although the combination of cognitive and behavioural interventions yielded more favourable results than each alone, the differences between the three active treatments were subtle and not statistically significant, even at the 6-month follow-up. On the other hand, Turner (1982) showed that cognitive–behavioural treatment and relaxation training were equally effective in reducing some aspects of morbidity associated with chronic low back pain. However, at one-month follow-up, the relaxation group had lost some of their previous gains, while the cognitive therapy group had continued to improve, and this improvement was sustained after 1.5–2 years.

The emphasis in further intervention studies is likely to shift away from immediate post-treatment outcomes to longer-term follow-up, where cognitive therapy is predicted to be superior to other interventions. Another focus of future outcome studies is likely to be the examination of the selective efficacy of specific cognitive interventions. Sufficient data are now becoming available for this purpose, for example in pain control (Fernandez & Turk, 1989). Another research technique, familiar in cognitive therapy for depression but applied relatively little in physical illness to date, involves measurement of change in specific cognitive variables during treatment as well as the more common dependent variables such as pain or depression (Whisman *et al*, 1991). For example, in patients with chronic lower back pain, decreased pain intensity was associated with improvements in selected dysfunctional cognitions (Turner & Clancy, 1986). Such work will establish more firmly the causal link between cognitions on the one hand and pain and other outcome measures on the other, just as it has already been established that pain or depression can be predicted by cognitive variables. More research is also needed to confirm initial results which demonstrate that group cognitive therapy or treatment involving relatively little contact with the therapist can be as effective as 'conventional' individual therapy (Richardson & McGrath, 1989; Spence, 1989). Further work along these lines, together with systematic collection of data during therapy, can be expected to help to make therapeutic interventions more focused and thus even more effective.

References

AFFLECK, G., TENNEN, H., PFEIFFER, C., *et al* (1987) Appraisals of control and predictability in adapting to a chronic disease. *Journal of Personality and Social Psychology*, **53**, 273–279.

AGRAS, W. S., SCHNEIDER, J. A., ARNOW, B., *et al* (1989) Cognitive–behavioural and response-prevention treatments for bulimia nervosa. *Journal of Consulting and Clinical Psychology*, **57**, 215–221.

ANDERSON, K. O. & MASUR, F. T., III (1989) Psychological preparation for cardiac catheterization. *Heart and Lung*, **18**, 154–163.

APPLEBAUM, K. A., BLANCHARD, E. B., HICKLING, E. J., *et al* (1988) Cognitive behavioural treatment of a veteran population with moderate to severe rheumatoid arthritis. *Behavior Therapy*, **19**, 489–502.

ATKINS, C. J., KAPLAN, R. M., TIMMS, R. M., *et al* (1984) Behavioural exercise programmes in the management of chronic obstructive pulmonary disease. *Journal of Consulting and Clinical Psychology*, **52**, 591–603.

BARSKY, A. J., GERINGER, E. & WOOL, C. A. (1988) A cognitive–educational treatment for hypochondriasis. *General Hospital Psychiatry*, **10**, 322–327.

——, WYSHAK, G. & KLERMAN, G. L. (1990) Transient hypochondriasis. *Archives of General Psychiatry*, **47**, 746–752.

BASLER, H. D. & REHFISCH, P. (1991) Cognitive–behavioural therapy in patients with ankylosing spondylitis in a German self-help organization. *Journal of Psychosomatic Research*, **35**, 345–354.

BECK, A. T. (1963) Thinking and depression: I. Idiosyncratic content and cognitive distortions. *Archives of General Psychiatry*, **9**, 324–333.

—— (1964) Thinking and depression: II. Theory and therapy. *Archives of General Psychiatry*, **10**, 561–571.

—— (1983) Cognitive therapy of depression: new perspectives. In *Treatment of Depression: Old Controversies and New Approaches* (eds P. J. Clayton & J. E. Barrett), pp. 265–290. New York: Raven Press.

—— (1990) *Cognitive Therapy and the Emotional Disorders*. London: Penguin.

——, RUSH, A. J., SHAW, B. F., *et al* (1979) *Cognitive Therapy of Depression*. New York: Guilford.

——, EMERY, G. & GREENBERG, R. L. (1985a) *Anxiety Disorders and Phobias: a Cognitive Perspective*. New York: Basic Books.

——, HOLLON, S. D., YOUNG, J. E., *et al* (1985b) Treatment of depression with cognitive therapy and amitriptyline. *Archives of General Psychiatry*, **42**, 142–148.

—— & FREEMAN, A. (1990) *Cognitive Therapy of Personality Disorders*. New York: Guilford.

BLACKBURN, I. M., BISHOP, S., GLEN, A. I. M., *et al* (1981) The efficacy of cognitive therapy in depression: a treatment trial using cognitive therapy and pharmacotherapy, each alone and in combination. *British Journal of Psychiatry*, **139**, 181–189.

————, EUNSON, K. M. & BISHOPS, S. (1986) A two year naturalistic follow-up of depressed patients treated with cognitive therapy, pharmacotherapy and a combination of both. *Journal of Affective Disorders*, **10**, 67–75.

BLOCK, A., KREMER, E. & GAYLOR, M. (1980) Behavioural treatment of chronic pain: the spouse as a discriminative cue for pain behaviour. *Pain*, **9**, 243–252.

BROADHEAD, W. E., KAPLAN, B. H., JAMES, S. A., *et al* (1983) The epidemiologic evidence for a relationship between social support and health. *American Journal of Epidemiology*, **117**, 521–537.

CLARK, D. M. & SALKOVSKIS, P. M. (1993) *Cognitive Behaviour Therapy for Panic and Hypochondriasis* (in press).

COSTA, P. T., JR, & McCRAE, R. R. (1987) Neuroticism, somatic complaints, and disease: is the bark worse than the bite? *Journal of Personality*, **55**, 299–316.

DERUBEIS, R. J., HOLLON, S. D., EVANS, M. D., *et al* (1982) Can psychotherapies for depression be discriminated? A systematic investigation of cognitive therapy and interpersonal therapy. *Journal of Consulting and Clinical Psychology*, **50**, 744–756.

DEVINS, G. M., BINIK, Y. M., GORMAN, P., *et al* (1982) Perceived self-efficacy, outcome expectancies, and negative mood states in end-stage renal disease. *Journal of Abnormal Psychology*, **91**, 241–244.

DOBSON, K. S. & SHAW, B. F. (1988) The use of treatment manuals in cognitive therapy: experience and issues. *Journal of Consulting and Clinical Psychology*, **56**, 673–680.

ELKIN, E., PILKONIS, P. A., DOCHERTY, J. P., *et al* (1988) Conceptual and methodological issues in comparative studies of psychotherapy and pharmacotherapy, I: active ingredients and mechanisms of change. *American Journal of Psychiatry*, **145**, 909–917.

ELL, K., NISHIMOTO, R., MORVAY, T., *et al* (1989) A longitudinal analysis of psychological adaptation among survivors of cancer. *Cancer*, **63**, 406–413.

FAIRBURN, C., JONES, R., PEVELER, R., *et al* (1991) Three psychological treatments for bulimia nervosa. *Archives of General Psychiatry*, **48**, 463–469.

FENNELL, M. J. V. & TEASDALE, J. D. (1987) Cognitive therapy for depression: individual differences and the process of change. *Cognitive Therapy and Research*, **11**, 253–271.

FERNANDEZ, E. & TURK, D. C. (1989) The utility of cognitive coping strategies for altering pain perception: a meta-analysis. *Pain*, **38**, 123–135.

FLOR, H. & TURK, D. C. (1988) Chronic pain and rheumatoid arthritis: predicting pain and disability from cognitive variables. *Journal of Behavioural Medicine*, **11**, 251–265.

FREEMAN, A., SIMON, K. M., BEUTLER, L. E., *et al* (1989) *Comprehensive Handbook of Cognitive Therapy*. New York: Guilford.

FREEMAN, C., BARRY, F., DUNKELD-TURNBULL, J., *et al* (1988) Controlled trial of psychotherapy for bulimia nervosa. *British Medical Journal*, **296**, 521–525.

FRIEDMAN, M., THORENSEN, C. E., GILL, J. J., *et al* (1986) Alteration in Type A behaviour and its effect on cardiac recurrences in post myocardial infarct patients: summary results of the recurrent coronary prevention project. *American Heart Journal*, **112**, 653–665.

GREER, S., MOOREY, S., BARUCH, J. D. R., *et al* (1992) Adjuvant psychological therapy for patients with cancer: a prospective randomised trial. *British Medical Journal*, **304**, 675–680.

HAMMEN, C., ELLICOTT, A., GITLIN, M., *et al* (1989) Sociotropy/autonomy and vulnerability to specific life events in patients with unipolar depression and bipolar disorders. *Journal of Abnormal Psychology*, **98**, 154–160.

HANSON, R. W. & GERBER, K. E. (1990) *Coping With Chronic Pain*. New York: Guilford.

HARTMANN, P. M. (1989) A pilot study of a modified Balint group using cognitive approaches to physician attitudes about somatoform disorder patients. *International Journal of Psychosomatics*, **36**, 86–89.

HAWTON, K., SALKOVSKIS, P., KIRK, J., *et al* (1989) *Cognitive Behaviour Therapy for Psychiatric Problems*. Oxford: Oxford University Press.

HOLLON, S. D., EVANS, M. D. & DERUBEIS, R. J. (1988) Preventing relapse following treatment for depression: the cognitive pharmacology project. In *Stress and Coping Across Development* (eds T. M. Field, P. M. McCabe & N. Schneiderman), pp. 227–243. Hillside New Jersey: Lawrence Erlbaum.

——, —— & —— (1990) Cognitive mediation of relapse prevention following treatment for depression: implications of differential risk. In *Contemporary Psychological Approaches to Depression: Theory, Research and Treatment* (ed, R. E. Ingram), pp. 117–136. New York: Plenum.

HOLROYD, K. A., NASH, J. M., PINGEL, J. D., *et al* (1991) A comparison of pharmacological (amitriptyline HC1) and nonpharmacological (cognitive–behavioural) therapies for chronic tension headache. *Journal of Consulting and Clinical Psychology*, **59**, 387–393.

HORNE, D. J., WHITE, A. E. & VARIGOS, G. A. (1989) A preliminary study of psychological therapy in the management of atopic eczema. *British Journal of Medical Psychology*, **62**, 241–248.

JAKES, S. C., HALLAM, R. S., MCKENNA, L., *et al* (1992) Group cognitive therapy for medical patients: an application to tinnitus. *Cognitive Therapy and Research*, **16**, 67–82.

KEEFE, F. J., CALDWELL, D. S., WILLIAMS, D. A., *et al* (1990) Pain coping skills training in the management of osteoarthritic knee pain: a comparative study. *Behavior Therapy*, **21**, 49–62.

KELLY, J. A., ST LAWRENCE, J. S., HOOD, H. V., *et al* (1989) Behavioural intervention to reduce AIDS risk activities. *Journal of Consulting and Clinical Psychology*, **57**, 60–67.

KERNS, R. D. & HAYTHORNTHWAITE, J. A. (1988) Depression among chronic pain patients: cognitive–behavioural analysis and effect on rehabilitation outcome. *Journal of Consulting and Clinical Psychology*, **56**, 870–876.

KOVACS, M., RUSH, A. J., BECK, A. T., *et al* (1981) Depressed outpatients treated with cognitive therapy or pharmacotherapy: a one-year follow-up. *Archives of General Psychiatry*, **38**, 33–39.

LARCOMBE, N. & WILSON, P. (1984) An evaluation of cognitive–behaviour therapy for depression in patients with multiple sclerosis. *British Journal of Psychiatry*, **145**, 366–371.

LEVENSON, J. L., KAY, R., MONTEFERRANTE, J., *et al* (1984) Denial predicts favourable outcome in unstable angina pectoria. *Psychosomatic Medicine*, **46**, 25–31.

LEVINE, J., WARRENBURG, S., KERNS, R., *et al* (1987) The role of denial in recovery from coronary heart disease. *Psychosomatic Medicine*, **49**, 109–117.

LIN, E. & PETERSON, C. (1990) Pessimistic explanatory style and response to illness. *Behaviour Research and Therapy*, **28**, 243–248.

LINDBERG, P., SCOTT, B., MELIN, L., *et al* (1989) The psychological treatment of tinnitus: an experimental evaluation. *Behaviour Research and Therapy*, **27**, 593–603.

MAES, S. & SCHLOSSER, M. (1988) Changing health behaviour outcomes in asthmatic patients: a pilot study. *Social Science and Medicine*, **26**, 359–364.

MALAN, D. (1979) *Individual Psychotherapy and the Science of Psychodynamics*. London: Butterworths.

MOOREY, S. & GREER, S. (1989) *Psychological Therapy for Patients with Cancer*. London: Heinemann.

MORSE, C. A., DENNERSTEIN, L., FARRELL, E., *et al* (1991) A comparison of hormone therapy, coping skills training, and relaxation for the relief of premenstrual syndrome. *Journal of Behavioural Medicine*, **14**, 469–489.

PERSONS, J. B. (1989) *Cognitive Therapy in Practice: A Case Formulation Approach*. New York: Norton.

PETTY, R., SENSKY, T. & MAHLER, R. (1991) Diabetologists' assessments of their outpatients' emotional state and health beliefs: accuracy and possible sources of bias. *Psychotherapy and Psychosomatics*, **55**, 164–169.

PEVELER, R. C. & FAIRBURN, C. G. (1989) Anorexia nervosa in association with diabetes mellitus – a cognitive–behavioural approach to treatment. *Behaviour Research and Therapy*, **27**, 95–99.

PHILIPS, H. C. (1987) The effects of behavioural treatment on chronic pain. *Behaviour Research and Therapy*, **25**, 365–377.

RICHARDSON, G. M. & MCGRATH, P. J. (1989) Cognitive-behavioural therapy for migraine headaches: a minimal-therapist-contact approach versus a clinic-based approach. *Headache*, **26**, 352–357.

ROBBINS, J. M. & KIRMAYER, L. J. (1991) Cognitive and social factors in somatization. In *Current Concepts of Somatization: Research and Clinical Perspectives* (eds L. J. Kirmayer & J. M. Robbins), pp. 107–141. Washington DC: American Psychiatric Press.

ROSENBERG, S. J., PETERSON, R. A., HAYES, J. R., *et al* (1988) Depression in medical in-patients. *British Journal of Medical Psychology*, **61**, 245–254.

RUSH, A. J., BECK, A. T., KOVACS, M., *et al* (1977) Comparative efficacy of cognitive therapy and imipramine in the treatment of depressed patients. *Cognitive Therapy and Research*, **1**, 17–37.

SALKOVSKIS, P. M. & WARWICK, H. M. C. (1986) Morbid preoccupations, health anxiety and reassurance: a cognitive behavioural approach to hypochondriasis. *Behaviour Research and Therapy*, **24**, 597–602.

SCHWARZ, S. P. & BLANCHARD, E. B. (1991) Evaluation of a psychological treatment for inflammatory bowel disease. *Behaviour Research and Therapy*, **29**, 167–177.

SCOTT, J. (1989) Cancer patients. In *Cognitive Therapy in Clinical Practice: An Illustrative Casebook* (eds J. Scott, J. M. G. Williams & A. T. Beck), pp. 103–126. London: Routledge.

——, WILLIAMS, J. M. G. & BECK, A. T. (1989) *Cognitive Therapy in Clinical Practice: An Illustrative Casebook*. London: Routledge.

SENSKY, T. (1989*a*) Psychiatric morbidity in renal transplantation. *Psychotherapy and Psychosomatics*, **52**, 41–46.

—— (1989*b*) Cognitive therapy with patients with chronic physical illness. *Psychotherapy and Psychosomatics*, **52**, 26–32.

—— (1990) Patients' reactions to illness: cognitive factors determine responses and are amenable to treatment. *British Medical Journal*, **300**, 622–623.

——, STEVENSON, K., MAGRILL, L., *et al* (1991) Family expressed emotion in non-psychiatric illness: adaptation of the Camberwell Family Interview to the families of adolescents with diabetes. *International Journal of Methods in Psychiatric Research*, **1**, 39–51.

—— & WRIGHT, J. (1993) Cognitive therapy with medical patients. In *The Cognitive Milieu: Inpatient Applications of Cognitive Therapy* (eds J. Wright, M. Thase, J. Ludgate & A. T. Beck), pp. 219–245. New York: Guilford.

SHAW, B. F. & DOBSON, K. S. (1988) Competency judgements in the training and evaluation of psychotherapists. *Journal of Consulting and Clinical Psychology*, **56**, 666–672.

SIMONS, A. D., MURPHY, G. E., LEVINE, J. L., *et al* (1986) Cognitive therapy and pharmacotherapy for depression: sustained improvement over one year. *Archives of General Psychiatry*, **43**, 43–48.

SPENCE, S. H. (1989) Cognitive–behaviour therapy in the management of chronic, occupational pain of the upper limbs. *Behaviour Research and Therapy*, **27**, 435–446.

STERN, R. & FERNANDEZ, M. (1991) Group cognitive and behavioural treatment for hypochondriasis. *British Medical Journal*, **303**, 1229–1231.

TARRIER, N. & MAGUIRE, P. (1984) Treatment of psychological distress following mastectomy: an initial report. *Behaviour Research and Therapy*, **22**, 81–84.

TAYLOR, S. E. (1983) Adjustment to threatening events: a theory of cognitive adaptation. *American Psychologist*, **38**, 1161–1173.

TEASDALE, J. D. (1983) Changes in cognition during depression – psychopathological implications: discussion paper. *Journal of the Royal Society of Medicine*, **76**, 1038–1044.

—— & FOGARTY, S. J. (1979) Differential effects of induced mood on retrieval of pleasant and unpleasant events from episodic memory. *Journal of Abnormal Psychology*, **88**, 248–257.

——, FENNELL, M. J. V., HIBBERT, G. A., *et al* (1984) Cognitive therapy for major depressive disorder in primary care. *British Journal of Psychiatry*, **144**, 400–406.

TURK, D. C., MEICHENBAUM, D. & GENEST, M. (1983) *Pain and Behavioural Medicine: A Cognitive–Behavioral Perspective*. New York: Guilford.

TURNER, J. A. (1982) Comparison of group progressive-relaxation training and cognitive-behavioural therapy for chronic low back pain. *Journal of Consulting and Clinical Psychology*, **50**, 757–765.

—— & CLANCY, S. (1986) Strategies for coping with chronic low back pain: relationship to pain and disability. *Pain*, **24**, 355–364.

WARWICK, H. M. C. & SALKOVSKIS, P. (1989) Hypochondriasis. In *Cognitive Therapy in Clinical Practice: An Illustrative Casebook* (eds J. Scott, J. M. G. Williams & A. T. Beck), pp. 79–102. London: Routledge.

WATSON, D. & PENNEBAKER, J. W. (1989) Health complaints, stress and distress: exploring the central role of negative affectivity. *Psychological Reviews*, **96**, 234–254.

WESSELY, S. C. & LEWIS, G. H. (1989) The classification of psychiatric morbidity in attenders at a dermatology clinic. *British Journal of Psychiatry*, **155**, 686–691.

WHISMAN, M. A., MILLER, I. W., NORMAN, W. H., *et al* (1991) Cognitive therapy with depressed inpatients: specific effects on dysfunctional cognitions. *Journal of Consulting and Clinical Psychology*, **59**, 282–288.

WILLIAMS, J. M. G. (1984) *The Psychological Treatment of Depression: A Guide to the Theory and Practice of Cognitive–Behaviour Therapy*. London: Croom Helm.

WISE, T. N., MANN, L. S., PUSCHECK, E., *et al* (1985) Factors affecting anxiety and depression in psychiatric consultation patients. *International Journal of Psychiatry in Medicine*, **15**, 177–184.

WORDEN, J. W. & WEISMAN, A. D. (1984) Preventive psychosocial intervention with newly diagnosed cancer patients. *General Hospital Psychiatry*, **6**, 243–249.

4 Families, family therapy and psychosomatic illness

IVAN EISLER

Any illness and particularly serious or life-threatening illness inevitably has an impact on the family. A serious or chronic illness will often become a dominant feature of family life around which everything else revolves. The way that the family adjusts to the illness will always have important implications for the wellbeing of its individual members (including those who have not been identified as suffering from an illness) and will also affect in varying degrees the course of the illness itself. Where psychological factors play an important role in the development or maintenance of the illness, understanding the dynamics of the family can provide important insights for the clinician.

There is now a growing literature on the use of family interventions in the management of a wide range of psychosomatic and somatic illnesses which recognises the importance of psychosocial and particularly family factors. Family therapy either as an adjunct to other treatments or sometimes as the main treatment mode has been used in the management of asthma (Lask & Matthew, 1979; Gustafsson et al, 1986; Tal et al, 1990), diabetes (Minuchin et al, 1978), chronic back pain (Saarijärvi et al, 1989; Griffith et al, 1992), recurrent abdominal pain in children (Fundisgrud, 1988), pseudoseizures (Griffith et al, 1992), and intractable hiccups (Bobele, 1989). Family therapy is also increasingly used to help families cope with terminal illness (Black, 1989; Altschuler et al, 1991; Walker, 1991). The best documented and the most carefully evaluated is the use of family therapy in the treatment of anorexia nervosa (Selvini-Palazzoli, 1974; Minuchin et al, 1978; Martin, 1985; Russell et al, 1987; Stierlin & Weber, 1989; Dare et al, 1990) which is discussed in more detail in Chapter 13.

The principal aim of this chapter is to outline a conceptual framework for family therapy and to indicate how such a framework can be useful for understanding individuals with psychosomatic problems.

In very broad terms, family therapy can be defined as a therapeutic approach which focuses on the family unit, with the aim of helping the family members to find solutions to problems that interfere with their functioning as individuals in their personal relationships. Underlying this, there is a belief that individual functioning is inextricably linked to the social systems (the family being the most important of these) in which it appears. Problems and symptoms, which at one level can be understood as the property of individuals, are at the same time part of an interactional matrix, which maintains them but is, in turn, also maintained by them. Family therapy interventions are aimed at interrupting these patterns of interaction and mobilising the family's strengths, which have often become buried under layers of despair and feelings of helplessness.

In giving an account of family systems theory it is important to keep in mind that it is not simply an account of the context of dysfunction and pathology but that it is equally important for an understanding of normal development (Minuchin, 1985). Understanding the links between the symptomatic behaviour of the individual family member and family functioning can give the clinician an effective tool for intervention. This must not be taken to imply the simplistic notion that families 'cause' individual pathology. Such a view of families is not only scientifically naïve but is also clinically unhelpful, because it engenders feelings of guilt and blame.

In the following description of family systems theory equal stress will be put on the role of families in normal development as on explaining the importance of the family context in individual dysfunction.

The family as a social system

A careful observer of a family will soon discern that there are fairly stable patterns of interaction that are characteristic for that particular family. It is often striking how quickly certain patterns emerge, regardless of the topic of discussion. Descriptions of such patterns may focus on a dyad within the family ('father seldom expresses his opinion and when he does, mother generally contradicts him') or they may describe a pattern that applies to the family as a whole ('whenever any two members of the family begin to openly express disagreement a third family member intervenes by changing the subject'). Many such patterns are so well established that the participants of the interaction are unaware of them, until something happens that threatens to break the pattern. In some families these patterns appear quite fixed, whereas in other families there is a considerable degree of flexibility.

> During an initial family interview it was observed, for instance, that questions put to the family as a whole were invariably answered by mother. Father seldom joined in spontaneously. When he did speak he was soon interrupted by mother. The more mother spoke, the more father withdrew, but equally the less active father was, the more mother took centre stage. The complementarity of their behaviour was matched by the way they perceived their positions in the family.

Mother described father as uninvolved and uninterested and complained that everything in the family was dumped on her. Father on the other hand felt that he was an outsider, excluded by mother whom he saw as overbearing and intrusive.

Family systems theory views such patterns as an expression of the way the family unit functions as a whole. It goes beyond the linear description, where behaviour A causes behaviour B, but examines also the effect of B on A. At the simplest level this may just entail a description of a recursive loop $A \rightarrow B \rightarrow A_1 \rightarrow B_1$. In reality such behaviours are, of course, part of a complex matrix of behaviours, differing perceptions and expectations of how different family members will behave. Such patterns may include illness behaviour of a psychosomatically ill family member. The following clinical case example will illustrate the way that the pattern of interaction in a family can provide an insight into the way that the family functions and how that can be used for therapeutic interventions.

The Jones family was referred to a child guidance clinic by a paediatrician, who had been repeatedly asked to investigate severe colics in a 7-year-old boy, and could find no obvious physical explanation for this. In discussing the problem with the family the following pattern emerged:

Johnny would from time to time come into the parents' bedroom in the morning, complaining at first of a vague tummy ache. Mother would try to reassure him that nothing was wrong and at the same time consult father, whether they ought to make sure and call the doctor. Father would suggest that they ought to wait and see. Johnny's distress would grow visibly and mother would become more anxious that this time 'it was for real'. Eventually she would persuade father that they should take Johnny to the hospital. On the first few occasions the pain had disappeared by the time Johnny was seen by the doctor and the parents were reassured that nothing serious was amiss. When the episodes persisted, the hospital admitted the child for observations to be 'on the safe side'. Routine investigations were all negative.

The paediatrician referred Johnny to the child guidance clinic because he saw the problem as psychosomatic. In the referral letter he emphasised the mother's overprotectiveness, implying that this was the root cause of Johnny's behaviour. The mother's anxiety certainly appeared to be one of the factors that maintained the above pattern. The paediatrician had noted that the mother found it impossible to contain her anxiety, to the point where her son would try to reassure her that he was feeling better, only to start complaining in the next minute that the pain was worse. This description of the feedback loop between the mother's and son's behaviour was revealing, but was also misleading because it did not take into account the broader context. A more comprehensive picture emerges when the father's role is taken into consideration:

Like the doctors, father also felt that mother worried too much and he therefore had a tendency to play things down. This made mother feel unsupported and annoyed that he was not taking the problem seriously. She would either tell father that he should go off to work and that she would deal with things on her own, or alternatively she would redouble her efforts to involve him by persuading him that things were quite serious. In either case father would become more determined not to leave things to his wife. He could see how she was getting increasingly upset and felt that leaving things to her would just make things worse. The more father played things down the more mother emphasised their seriousness. Although they were both aware that they were pulling in opposite directions, they never clashed openly. They were very aware of Johnny's distress and they would quickly respond to any sign of his pain getting worse by dropping their disagreement.

The different components of the family system are interdependent and to single out any one of them as the starting point of a sequence of interaction is arbitrary. Moreover, there will be factors beyond the moment-to-moment interaction also influencing the transactional pattern. The behaviour of all three family members was as much determined by their anticipation of how the familiar pattern would unfold as it was by the immediately preceding behaviours. And, of course, there were other factors as well. The mother's and father's concept of themselves as parents, the quality of their relationship with their son, the marital relationship, the value that the family attached to closeness (which acted as a prohibition against open expression of disagreement) and so on.

Factors outside the immediate family system were equally important. Johnny was having a difficult time at school and often came home upset and tearful. The mother was aware that his morning tummy aches were not unrelated to his anxiety about school but felt guilty that she was unable to protect him from his bad experiences there. She had tried to go to school to complain but felt that she had not been taken seriously. She had avoided telling her husband about this, because she felt that he too would consider that she was making an unnecessary fuss. Another contributing factor was the hospital's readiness to admit Johnny 'for observation'. It had been felt that this might reassure the mother and make her less anxious. In fact, the effect was the reverse as it made both parents think that if the doctors were themselves sufficiently worried to admit Johnny to hospital, there might indeed be something wrong. Viewing the presenting problem in this broader context led to a brief intervention which altered the pattern of interaction in the family but also allowed the parents to take effective action.

The parents had been quite apprehensive about a referral to a family therapist. They both felt rather bad about the fact that they had not been able to deal with the problem on their own and covertly blamed one another for this failure. They were, therefore, relieved when the therapist expressed sympathy with their worries about Johnny and suggested that until they were absolutely certain that there was nothing physically wrong with their son they could not effectively help him with the thing that worried Johnny more than anything else – school. As the focus of the discussion shifted, the therapist encouraged Johnny to tell his father what it was like for him at school. As soon as Johnny started talking about school he became upset and mother tried to comfort him. The therapist gently dissuaded mother from intervening, saying that he was sure that father could handle Johnny's upset. This intervention dramatically altered the usual pattern of interaction. Instead of mother trying to bring in father and father effectively distancing himself, father now had to deal directly with Johnny's crying. He was at first very uncomfortable with this but as he listened to what Johnny was saying he became more and more angry when he heard how the school had mishandled a bullying incident. He immediately announced that they would have to go to the school to sort things out. When mother expressed doubts, saying that she had already tried that, and no one took her seriously, father insisted that that was why he wanted to go himself, so that he could make sure that the school would listen. If they didn't, the parents would have to find another school. At this point the discussion became quite heated and Johnny intervened by saying that it was really OK now at school. The therapist encouraged the parents to continue their discussion saying that it was up to them as parents to decide whether they needed to go to the school or not. The parents in fact made several visits to the school and eventually decided to move Johnny to another school. Johnny's tummy aches recurred just after he started at his new school but the parents were able to reassure him and the problem did not escalate as it used to in the past.

The concept of the family as a social system, which was illustrated by the above case example, draws on several related strands:

(a) Individual behaviour and individual personal characteristics need to be viewed in the specific social context in which they occur (e.g. a dominant individual can only be dominant in relationship to someone who is submissive).

(b) There is a mutual, circular, influence that individuals exert on each other (the more mother worries, the more father plays things down, the more mother worries . . .).

(c) The individual's internal world has a mediating role, which results in perceptions of the past and expectations of the future being inextricably linked with present actions.

(d) The whole is more than the sum of its parts, in that the whole also takes account of the relationship between the parts.

Family therapists often stress the apparent stability of certain aspects of family life, the repetitiveness of patterns of interaction within a given family and a tendency of families to react to changes in one part of the family by counterbalancing responses in other parts of the family. This has led to the family being likened to a complex cybernetic system with homeostatic feedback mechanisms that control the behaviour of its component parts, so that a balance in the system as a whole is maintained.

In families, where one member suffers from a psychosomatic disorder, the symptomatic behaviour will generally play a central role in such an interactive system. The physical nature of psychosomatic symptoms exerts a powerful influence, as a result of which the transactional pattern of the family can be seen to revolve around the symptomatic behaviour in a way that both maintains it and is in turn maintained by it. This is perhaps most apparent where the symptoms are severe or even life-threatening, as is the case in anorexia nervosa.

Descriptions of families with a psychosomatically ill child generally include an account of a high level of overprotectiveness (Minuchin *et al*, 1978). Indeed the level of worry, anxiety and expressed need to protect the ill child from the difficulties she might encounter are often the most striking manifestation presented to the clinician by the family. It is all too easy to view such behaviour in isolation and to see how it contributes to the symptomatic behaviour. The reverse effect, of the symptom on the overprotective attitudes, is often, however, equally powerful. As one mother of an anorexic teenager eloquently put it: "I know I hover over her all the time and it probably doesn't help. But how can I *not* do that? I can't just sit by and watch her die!" The anorexic youngster may indeed feel overwhelmed by the highly protective attitudes of her family (often including siblings, as much as parents) and have the sense that her individuality is being denied. Her anorexic symptoms become to her the only area of her life over which she has control. Her success in this, however, has the effect not only of increasing her family's anxiety and overprotectiveness but also focuses everyone's attention on the anorexia which increases the sense of a loss of individuality ("I am only a number on a pair of scales – I am not a daughter any more"). Some further aspects of the way the patterns of interaction in the family centre on the symptomatic behaviour will be discussed later in the chapter.

So far we have been discussing the concept of the family as a system observed in moment-to-moment interaction. While this perspective provides important insights into how the family functions, it gives insufficient weight to the role of the individual and also to developmental issues. The family, like all social groups has two crucial functions. It has to provide for the basic psychological needs of its members (which change over time) and at the same time has to provide a degree of stability in order to be able to survive as a social group. In order to function effectively, the family not only has to find ways of maintaining an equilibrium but also has to adapt to the changing needs of its individual members.

Psychological needs and individual development

Individual psychological needs are usually discussed within a context of individual developmental psychology but they are also quite central to the issues being considered here. Psychological needs are powerful motivators of human behaviour and the social construction and satisfaction of individual needs is what bonds people in social groups. The importance of the family stems from the fact that it plays a crucial role in satisfying the most basic psychological needs of its members. The way in which the family organises itself in order to be able to meet the needs of its members, how it deals with conflicting needs, and the manner in which it restructures itself in order to meet the challenge of developmental change are all central to an understanding of family life.

The question of psychological needs is also relevant to an understanding of psychosomatic disorders. It would be simplistic to view psychosomatic symptoms simply as somehow arising out of, or being an expression of, an unmet psychological need. There is clear evidence that psychosomatic disorders arise as an outcome of complex interaction between biological, psychological and social factors (Garfinkel & Garner, 1982). In clinical practice there is also always the danger that reducing a symptom to a psychological level will be perceived by the patient as an accusation of manipulativeness or malingering. Nevertheless, psychological needs do play an important role.

Psychological needs are defined in a variety of ways. The definition that will be used here is one that is readily integrated within family systems theory. It is derived from Langmeier & Matejcek's (1975) study of psychological deprivation in early childhood. They state:

> "We begin with the assumption that the basic developmental tendency of an organism (in addition to the biological drive for survival) is its need for active contact with the environment, which is realized by a constant widening, differentiation, subsequent concentration and repeated integration of this contact. A living organism is, by its very nature, active, and this activity is, in principle, inevitably oriented towards the world and objects in it: it takes possession of things, learns to recognize their relations and meaning, becomes attached to specific objects and ascribes values to them, and in the middle of the possessed, grasped and evaluated things and persons, eventually meets its own person and defines its status in the world of things and human beings. This basic activity develops in the process of continuous anticipation and fulfilment, by means of which the organism actively helps to create and realize itself." (p. 305)

Figure 4.1 shows the four basic psychological needs, conceptualised in a two-dimensional schema. The two dimensions of psychological needs, stability–variability and dependence–independence are the cornerstones of individual psychological development, the former underpinning cognitive development and the latter emotional development. Two things need to be noted in relation to these. The first is the active nature of the individual's striving to satisfy these needs. Even the youngest infant actively interacts with his environment, seeking out new and variable aspects of the

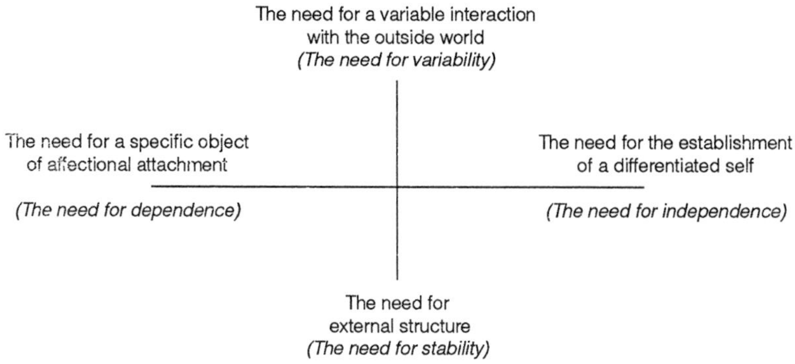

The need for a variable interaction
with the outside world
(The need for variability)

The need for a specific object
of affectional attachment

(The need for dependence)

The need for the establishment
of a differentiated self

(The need for independence)

The need for
external structure
(The need for stability)

Fig. 4.1. Psychological needs

environment and attempting to find order and predictability in them. Individuals in interaction are never merely passive recipients but actively elicit those responses that are most likely to satisfy their needs. The second point to emphasise is the interrelated nature of the above needs. Stability/variability and dependence/independence are in one sense opposites, but they are also complementary. This complementarity means that the satisfaction of one need leads to the emergence of another. On the immediate or micro level this is seen in the child, who in mother's presence will actively explore a new environment but in her absence will lose all interest in everything, other than getting back to her. At the macro level, the satisfaction of one need and the consequent strengthening of its opposite, characterises different stages of individual development from infancy, through childhood and adolescence, to adulthood and old age. Throughout their life, individuals strive to discover structure and stability in the world around them. The more they achieve this the more they will also experience the need for change. In parallel with this, individuals go through stages in life where the strength of the two opposing needs of dependence and independence also alternate. These developmental stages have been well described both in the area of cognitive development (Piaget, 1950) and emotional development (Erikson, 1950).

The consideration of the manner in which individual psychological needs are met within the family brings us back a full circle to our discussion of the process of social interaction and to the concept of the family as a social system. Earlier on it was stressed that each individual makes an active contribution to the interactive process through which he enters into social relationships; the interplay between perceptions of past interactions and relationships, current experiences and expectations of how actions will influence future events. The relationship which individuals form in this way can be seen as an outcome of attempts to satisfy individual needs. At the same time these relationships shape future development and thus also future needs. This manifests itself both in self-concept and in the partly shared concept of the family. Dare (1988) comments on this as follows:

> "In the interaction between the specific desires of the individual and that which actually happens to them in their family of origin relationships, there is a tension. This is internalised as patterns of self and other in interaction, in which there is a contrast between what actually happens and what was longed for. The extent of the differences between the ideal and the actual is associated with strong feelings negatively or positively coloured. Because of the persistence of such patterns of satisfaction and frustrations, and because the patterns are always linked to family experience, then the unfolding life-cycle, leaves innumerable traces within the structure of the adult mind. When their children go through their own life-cycle, there is a tendency for the adults to re-experience, by identification, aspects of their own life at the comparable stage."

The concept of the family as a social system can be understood as being the result of a process through which the family attempts to satisfy the major needs of its members. At any particular point in time the transactional pattern of the family will be determined by the manner in which these needs are satisfied. Thus in a family in which there is an over-riding need for closeness and dependence there will be relatively weak boundaries between individuals or between generations; there will be a strong awareness or anticipation of needs of other family members; in such families conflict may be seen as threatening and the family may develop patterns of interaction that will prevent overt conflict from developing. The balance that the family needs to achieve does not depend only on processes internal to the immediate family. A young couple setting up a new family will derive a sense of closeness from their new family while at the same time gaining a sense of autonomy and independence from making a break with their family of origin. Of course relationships at work and with friends will also play a significant role. How they experience this process will be influenced by past events and current needs which will be different for each partner.

Nevertheless, family members will gradually acquire an overall perception of their own family which they will by and large share with other family members (van der Veen & Novak, 1971). The belief system which thus evolves within the family ascribes to family members certain roles and behaviours (Byng-Hall, 1988), which provides a sense of stability but will also at times be felt as a constraint on change. The normal developmental process will lead to external or internal demands for change requiring the family to respond in such a way that the family evolves and re-establishes a new stability. Clinical observations of families with a psychosomatically ill child (Minuchin *et al*, 1978; Dare & Eisler, 1992) suggest that in these families this process comes to a standstill. The pattern of interaction in the family and the symptomatic behaviour seem to become locked together so that one reinforces the other – the family transactions having the effect of maintaining the illness and at the same time the symptomatic behaviour becoming a powerful factor preventing the family from changing. The rigidity of the observed patterns of interaction (Selvini-Palazzoli, 1974) and resistance to change which clinicians often feel frustrate their efforts to help the patient, make the family feel hopeless and powerless to cope with the problem in their midst. The power of the psychosomatic symptom is such that it will gradually become a dominant feature of family life.

Just as the psychosomatic symptom can be seen to address, as well as maintain, the individual needs of the youngster, so it can perform a similar role for the family. It brings the family together, albeit often in an uncomfortable, guilt-ridden way while at the same time it also makes it impossible for the family to move on to the next stage of the family life cycle.

A discussion of how the family develops through predictable life stages which are governed by the changing individual needs of the family members will complete the theoretical framework of the role of the family in psychosomatic illness.

The family life cycle

When a couple meet and start a new relationship they draw on their currently dominant needs and the ability to express them in a way that enables them to develop a satisfactory relationship. In some areas of their relationship there will be a 'meeting of minds'. If one partner has a tendency to lead and the other to follow, a pattern will quickly be established. There will also be differences that will need to be negotiated. The process of adaptation to one another will depend on the way each of them perceives the other, the demands of the situation, how they respond and what in turn they transmit of their own expectations, needs or wants. The way such a system evolves is quite subtle, much of the process being outside the awareness of the protagonists. In this way what occurs within a relationship becomes relatively fixed and unspoken rules and regulatory mechanisms develop that will govern individual responses. In time, the transactional pattern will itself begin to shape expectations, perceptions and individually experienced needs.

In coming together in this way to begin to form a family, both partners will have brought into their relationship their whole inner world – their perceptions of past relationships and interactions, a concept of self, a concept of the family, expectations of family roles, of how needs are met etc. All this will determine what each partner is expecting from the new relationship. The transactional pattern of the couple thus encapsulates the family of origin experiences of both partners even though some of these will remain dormant, resurfacing only at later stages of their family's development. Through their relationship with them the children in the family will gradually incorporate into their own inner world much that has been central to their parents' experience.

The harmonious state which a couple might have experienced during their courtship is soon challenged. A couple in the pre-parenting phase will increasingly come under pressure to decide whether and when to have children and start their own family. The arrival of a child will dramatically alter the family. The child's needs have to be heeded and equally, this will evoke new needs in the parents. The parents' own memories of their childhood will also come to have an influence on both of them. As the children grow, their requirements will continuously change, and so will the needs of the parents. The needs dominant at the time of courtship will in time be overshadowed by other previously dormant ones. Because of the tension that this creates the family system will have to develop mechanisms of coping with conflicting needs, adapting to changing requirements of its members and yet finding a way of regaining stability and providing satisfaction.

At each further stage of the life cycle, when children go to school, move into adolescence and later begin to leave home, further changes will be demanded (for a detailed discussion of life-cycle stages see Carter & McGoldrick, 1982). The transition points between the stages of the family life cycle are often seen as 'crisis points' during which there is an increased probability of disturbance which can be understood as a developmental block or delay (Dare, 1988).

> A family came to our out-patient eating disorder clinic because the 17-year-old daughter Anne was suffering from anorexia nervosa. Anne had been ill for several years; she had recently been discharged from an in-patient treatment programme, but was already starting to lose weight again. The family was anxious to prevent a further relapse but felt helpless and demoralised, as their efforts seemed in vain. Mother herself suffered from asthma, which had recently become worse. The family were invited to attend our out-patient clinic.

During the first family interview (attended by Anne, her 16-year-old sister Ruth and both parents), several features were noted by the observing clinical team[1]:

> Mother appeared to have a particularly close, intimate relationship with Anne, to the extent that mother often appeared to be able to anticipate Anne's wishes or fears as if she could 'read her mind'. Father related to Anne in a rather serious, matter-of-fact way, while his relationship with Ruth was joky and flirtatious. Both parents tended to speak for and about Anne, as if she were a much younger child. Anne would sometimes complain about this in a whiny, childish voice. The family presented father as the person very much in charge of what happened at home (and the only one who had much influence on Anne) but at the same time what he said was often treated dismissively, particularly by Anne. The relationship between the parents was notably less close than their relationship with their

---

1. These observations are based on clinical descriptions that were subsequently experimentally corroborated (Eisler *et al*, 1985).

daughters. The parents never openly contradicted each other but also seldom interacted together.

Father was often away from home because of his work, and mother felt that the burden of looking after her anorexic daughter fell very much on her shoulders. Whilst she did not complain about this openly, she said that the stress of trying to cope made her asthma worse, to the point of being incapacitated by it. Father was quite critical of Anne for being such a burden on her mother but also seemed at times exasperated that his wife got so involved with Anne. However, when mother got upset, father would generally step in and take over from her.

The family seemed to have a need to present itself as united and stable and as hierarchically organised with the father in control – this, however, was not matched by reality. Both Anne's and her mother's symptoms enabled the family to be organised, as if the wished for features were present. Anne's symptoms maintained her close, childlike relationship with mother. They also regulated her relationship with her father, allowing her to have a somewhat argumentative, rebellious attitude to him but in a way that did not even suggest a move towards independence for her. The family's preoccupation with Anne's illness made Ruth's growing independence from the family go virtually unnoticed. Anne's and her mother's symptoms maintained the father's involvement in the family so that his otherwise more peripheral role was less apparent. The parents were brought closer in their efforts to look after Anne but it was an uncomfortable closeness, because it raised feelings of guilt and blame which had the effect of pushing them apart again.

A major change (which, in retrospect, was the starting point of Anne's recovery) happened after about 3 months of therapy. The family arrived at the session without Ruth, who had refused to come because she wanted to go out with a friend. The mother seemed in high spirits as Anne had put on some weight, while Anne stressed that this was through her own efforts and not as a result of any pressure from the parents. Her father, in contrast, seemed uninterested and even withdrawn.

The parents reported that a week earlier they had felt that things were really looking up, after Anne had spent a weekend with an aunt and had come back having not only put on some weight but also reporting that she had enjoyed eating. A few days later, however, father returned home to the usual scene between mother and Anne. This last argument over food seemed to be the last straw for him.

Father: We've had lots of pressures recently and on Friday I did my nut. Before, when I got angry, it wasn't real anger, in so far as I did not really feel wound up inside. But this time, the show of anger turned into real anger. I didn't like it, I shouldn't have got angry.

Therapist: You shouldn't have got angry with Anne? You don't think you were justified at least a little bit, in being angry that she had not eaten?

Father: No, you don't understand. I was angry with my wife for having the row with Anne. I should have supported her, but I couldn't. I just had enough. I've got to the point where I really believe that we've done all we can and it's entirely up to her. I don't want to come home and listen to arguments.

Therapist (turning to Mother): Do you feel the same?

Mother: Well on Friday night it was pretty bad and I felt like giving up. But I couldn't, we had people coming to stay. But I felt that either things had to change or . . . I am not, after 20 years of marriage going to start arguing over her. He has had three hard weeks at work. He was mad on Friday night, really cross. We have done everything. I did think we had done everything other than throw her out.

Therapist: I am not sure whether the two of you are in agreement that there is nothing more that you can do.

Father: I've got to the stage where the hassle is affecting us to the extent that I'm not prepared to put up with that.

Mother: I can't stop caring. It hurts more when you can't shut off.

Father: If she does not care for herself, why should we care? Mind you, her age has probably got something to do with it, but if you disregard yourself, how can you expect others to care? I certainly do not feel as content as I did one year ago. Things have changed purely because of somebody's illness.

Therapist: How are things different?

Father: I don't know there are any obvious changes but you cannot come in and have a meal any more.

Therapist: The meal table was the place where you would converse as a family then?

Father: Yes, now there's just tension – is she or is she not going to eat her food? Now there's a tense atmosphere, it means a certain amount of upset because we are not talking so much.

Therapist: Is this making the two of you distant?

Mother: Not really.

Father: I don't know. The actual closeness of the family group is different, but the children are growing up and going away. There is no less closeness between my wife and I but we do tend to have different ways of dealing with the situation. I feel less able to support my wife lately. When I come in, they have been having an argument but I don't necessarily feel I can back her up now. On Friday, when there was the argument I just felt – oh, let her get on with it.

Mother: I just wanted him to make her eat. But he had had a busy day.

Therapist (turning to mother): You describe being at your wits end and he says, he doesn't want to know. What do you do?

Mother: I had a damn good cry. This attitude won't help our relationship. One day I will probably tell all of them to get on with it. But I can't stop caring. I can get mad, put pressure on Anne, withdraw finances. But I can't stop caring. And neither will he. But men are capable of shutting the door I think. Mothers will always come back for more, believing this time it will be different. I want him to be him – the same. I cannot see into the future but he has been very supportive. He has always been very supportive.

Therapist: I hear him saying that he is no longer going to be supportive over this, because he wants to wipe his hands of it.

Mother (after a pause): I can see that if we were on the opposite sides of the fence and Anne was in the middle, it could spoil a good relationship, but I won't let this happen if I can possibly help it. She will be long gone, happily married and all that and I am not going to be separated from someone I've been married to for 20 years over that.

Therapist: Well, I hear him saying that he is getting over the other side of the fence. Are you going to join him or are you going to stay over on this side?

Mother: I don't know.

Father: I don't know that it would come to that.

The metaphor, of the parents' being on the opposite sides of the fence remained a theme for the rest of the session. Father made it clear that for him there was no turning back. However, he also seemed convinced that his wife was not going to be able to do the same. When the therapist pointed out that his wife had said several times that she did not want to remain behind and that he should help her join him he seemed intent on stressing that he was not doing this to help Anne to sort out things for herself but that he simply did not want to be a parent to her any more. Anne, whose presence at times seemed almost forgotten, eventually joined in, saying that there was no way that she was going to stay in the middle; she wanted to get on with her own life.

It is impossible to identify where the changes in the family started or who they were initiated by. Father's refusal to continue to be involved with Anne's problem had been signalled for some time, but his outburst of anger, nevertheless, took everyone, including him, by surprise. The possibility that Anne's attitude to food and weight might be changing both reduced father's anxiety but at the same time her apparent slipping back increased his frustration and belief that she was capable of coping, if only she wanted to. Mother's vacillation as to which side of the fence to come down on seemed initially to be a possible stumbling block, but was in fact an important factor, helping the family to unravel the pattern that they had all got stuck in. Had she clearly taken her husband's side, they might both have found their anxiety about Anne building up again. Equally, had she firmly refused to join him, his feelings of loyalty and guilt about abandoning her might have made him give up his attempts to move on. In the session, it had been quite striking that much of the discussion focused on the parents' trying to decide how they were going to move to the post-parenting phase of their lives. Anne's anorexia at times seemed quite incidental to this.

This pattern became much clearer over the ensuing months. Anne's growing independence forced the family to renegotiate their relationships. While this was not always an easy process, it did not revolve round anorexia any more. This does not mean that Anne suddenly stopped being preoccupied with food and weight. Anne continued to struggle with this for some time but in a way that did not involve her parents any more.

Observing the uncertainty and ambivalence about what the next stage of their family life would be like can tempt one to view this as the 'heart of the problem'. This would, however, be very misleading. The process which the family was going through would be familiar to any family with adolescent children on the point of growing up and leaving home. The link between the developmental stage of the family and a psychosomatic illness such as anorexia nervosa is much more complex than that of a simple causal relationship.

Anorexia nervosa most commonly occurs in mid to late adolescence, when the youngster has a growing need for individuation and separation but is also often apprehensive of achieving independence. Leaving aside the question of why a particular individual might be susceptible to develop anorexia nervosa in the first place (for a discussion of this see Szmukler, 1985) it is clear that the symptom can be understood to play a role in addressing the need for, as well as the fear of, independence.

However, it is not just the youngster who is in a transitional developmental phase of her life. The family as a whole goes through a similar process. The family is faced with the prospect that the children will depart from home leaving the parents on their own. Inevitably, the marital relationship becomes a more central issue and there will often be a wish to return to the closeness of the early days of the couple's relationship before they became parents.

Conclusions

Clinical observations of families with a psychosomatically ill member will generally focus on how the transactional pattern of the family is organised around the psychosomatic symptom. The family therapist will use such observations to help the family to break the link between the symptom and the family organisation. This is not dependent on a belief that the family is somehow the 'origin' of the illness but rather that the symptom becomes part of the family system and the family thus becomes stuck, and unable to address the growing need for change within the family. The fact is that much of what we observe as clinicians is not pathological or dysfunctional. Because the family gets stuck at a certain developmental stage, certain aspects of the family organisation may appear exaggerated or out of place. Helping the family get 'unstuck' allows them to get back on the developmental track and start using their own resources to tackle the usual developmental issues.

Thus, the aim of treatment is to reduce the salience of the symptom in organising the family.

References

ALTSCHULER, J., BLACK, D., TROMPETER, R., *et al* (1991) Adolescents in end-stage renal failure: A pilot study of family factors in compliance and treatment considerations. *Family Systems Medicine*, **9**, 229–247.

BLACK, D. (1989) Life threatening illness, children and family therapy. *Journal of Family Therapy*, **11** (special issue), 81–102.

BOBELE, M. (1989) Interactional treatment of intractable hiccups. *Family Process*, **28**, 191–206.

BYNG-HALL, J. (1988) Scripts and legends in families and family therapy. *Family Process*, **27**, 167–179.

CARTER, E. A. & MCGOLDRICK, M. (1982) The family life cycle. In *Normal Family Processes* (ed. F. Walsh). New York: Guilford Press.

DARE, C. (1988) Psychoanalytic family therapy. In *Family Therapy in Britain* (eds E. Street & W. Dryden). London: Harper & Row.

—— & EISLER, I. (1992) Family therapy for anorexia nervosa. In *Feeding Problems and Eating Disorders in Children and Adolescents* (eds P. J. Cooper & A. Stein), pp. 147–160. Chur: Harwood Academic Press.

——, ——, RUSSELL, G. F. M., *et al* (1990) Clinical and theoretical impact of a controlled trial of family therapy in anorexia nervosa. *Journal of Marital and Family Therapy*, **16**, 39–57.

EISLER, I., SZMUKLER, G. I. & DARE, C. (1985) Systematic observation and clinical insight – are they compatible? An experiment in recognizing clinical interactions. *Psychological Medicine*, **15**, 173–188.

ERIKSON, E. H. (1950) *Childhood and Society*. New York: W. W. Norton.

FUNDISGRUD, H. P. (1988) A consultation model in a pediatric outpatient clinic: Conversations with psychosomatic children and their parents. *Family Systems Medicine*, **6**, 188–201.

GARFINKEL, P. E. & GARNER, D. M. (1982) *Anorexia Nervosa: A Multidimensional Perspective*. New York: Brunner/Mazel.

GRIFFITH, J., GRIFFITH, M. E., KREJMAS, N., *et al* (1992) Reflecting team consultations and their impact upon family therapy for somatic symptoms as coded by Structural Analysis of Social Behaviour (SASB). *Family Systems Medicine*, **10**, 53–58.

GUSTAFFSON, P. A., KJELLMAN, N. & CEDERBLAD, M. (1986) Family therapy in the treatment of severe childhood asthma. *Journal of Psychosomatic Research*, **30**, 369–374.

LANGMEIER, J. & MATEJCEK, Z. (1975) *Psychological Deprivation in Childhood*. St Lucia, Queensland: University of Queensland Press.

LASK, B. & MATTHEW, D. (1979) Childhood asthma: a controlled trial of family psychotherapy. *Archives of Diseases in Childhood*, **54**, 116–119.

MARTIN, F. E. (1985) The treatment and outcome of anorexia nervosa in adolescents: A prospective study and five year follow-up. *Journal of Psychosomatic Research*, **19**, 509–514.

MINUCHIN, P. (1985) Families and individual development: provocations from the field of family therapy. *Child Development*, **56**, 289–302.

MINUCHIN, S., ROSMAN, B. L. & BAKER, L. (1978) *Psychosomatic Families: Anorexia Nervosa in Context*. Cambridge, Mass.: Harvard University Press.

PIAGET, J. (1950) *Psychology of Intelligence*. New York: Harcourt-Brace.

RUSSELL, G. F. M., SZMUKLER, G. I., DARE, C., *et al* (1987) An evaluation of family therapy in anorexia nervosa and bulimia nervosa. *Archives of General Psychiatry*, **44**, 1047–1056.

SAARIJÄRVI, S., LAHTI, T. & LAHTI, I. (1989) Time limited structural couple therapy with chronic low back pain. *Family Systems Medicine*, **7**, 328–338.

SELVINI-PALAZZOLI, M. (1974) *Self-starvation*. London: Chaucer.

STIERLIN, H. & WEBER, G. (1989) Anorexia nervosa: lessons from a follow-up study. *Family Systems Medicine*, **7**, 120–157.

SZMUKLER, G. I. (1985) Anorexia nervosa: a clinical view. In *Eating Habits* (eds R. A. Boakes, D. A. Popplewell & M. J. Burton). New York: J. Wiley & Sons.

TAL, D., GIL-SPIELBERG, R., ANTONOVSKY, H., *et al* (1990) Teaching families to cope with childhood asthma. *Family Systems Medicine*, **8**, 135–144.

VAN DER VEEN, F. & NOVAK, A. L. (1971) Perceived parental attitudes and family concepts of disturbed adolescents, normal siblings and normal controls. *Family Process*, **10**, 327–343.

WALKER, G. E. (1991) Pediatric AIDS: Towards an ecosystemic treatment model. *Family Systems Medicine*, **9**, 211–227.

Part II. Application of psychological therapies to specific disorders

5 Psychological management of somatisation disorder

MICHAEL MURPHY

In this chapter I discuss the management and psychotherapy of patients with somatisation disorder from the point of view of a psychiatrist working in a general hospital. The experience on which it is based came from managing patients who were initially recruited for clinical research projects.

The concept of somatisation disorder

Somatisation disorder (SD) was introduced in DSM–III (American Psychiatric Association, 1980) to denote a chronic condition characterised by numerous changing physical symptoms. It is one of six disorders included in the broader category of somatoform disorders and would previously have been called hysteria. Prior to DSM–III, two decades of research on chronic hysteria (Briquet's syndrome), as operationally defined by workers in St Louis, supported the reliability and validity of the diagnosis (Perley & Guze, 1962; Woodruff *et al*, 1971; Guze, 1975). The diagnosis of SD is based on "a history of many physical complaints or a belief that one is sickly, beginning before the age of 30, and persisting for several years" (American Psychiatric Association, 1987). The diagnostic criteria require the patient to have had a minimum of 13 specifically defined symptoms from a given list of 35, restricting the diagnosis to a small minority of somatising patients (Murphy, 1989).

The diagnosis is rarely made in Britain. Despite the claims made for its validity, many British psychiatrists believe it is a peculiarly American invention. Most believe that patients who meet criteria for SD have affective disorders and anxiety disorders, often in combination with personality disorder (Stern *et al*, 1993*a*). However, our research indicates that conventional psychiatric treatment of these 'underlying' mood and anxiety disorders in SD patients fails to prevent the repeated episodes of physical symptoms which lead to further consultations, investigations and inappropriate physical treatments (Bass & Murphy, 1991). The diagnosis of SD seems therefore justified.

Somatisation disorder is classified on axis 1 (mental illnesses) as opposed to axis 2 (personality disorders) of DSM–III–R. There have been several studies of the co-existence of other axis 1 diagnoses with SD – so-called 'comorbidity'. The results show a high prevalence of mood disorders and anxiety disorders in SD patients (Orenstein, 1989; Bass & Murphy, 1991). The term 'comorbidity' is misleading. Assuming that a patient with SD and a history of depression and anxiety disorder has three different illnesses (each with its own cause and pathogenesis) is naïve realism run riot. The distinctions between these different disorders arise because of the artificial boundaries used in the DSM–III classificatory system, and not because there are three discrete types of illness. Indeed, the diagnosis of hysteria (Briquet's syndrome) according to Research Diagnostic Criteria (Spitzer *et al*, 1975) includes depressive episodes and panic attacks in its diagnostic criteria, and thus one does not detect 'comorbidity' using this classificatory system (Bass & Murphy, 1990*a*).

Somatisation disorder needs specific psychological treatment. The patient's physical complaints, illness behaviour, attitudes and beliefs all have to be addressed specifically if a patient is to be engaged and helped by treatment. Parallels can be drawn with the treatment of anorexia nervosa, repeated deliberate self-harm, and addictions. In each of these conditions anxiety, depression and personality disorders can also be diagnosed. Successful treatment, however, involves focusing on the patient's self-destructive behaviour, limit setting, containment, and the therapist's understanding of the self-destructive behaviour which informs intervention. One would not, for example, expect a depressed patient with anorexia nervosa to stop dieting in response to an antidepressant. Somatisation disorder is therefore a useful diagnosis because it alerts the clinician to the need for specific intervention in the somatisation process, however superficial the diagnosis is in terms of psychopathology.

The distinctions between SD and the other somatoform disorders have also been criticised (Vaillant, 1984). But these distinctions can be important in treatment. Consider the difference between hypochondriasis and SD. An important dimension of hypochondriasis is fear of disease. The hypochondriacal patient presents repeatedly asking for tests to reassure them they do not have serious disease. Usually the patient believes that they have a specific condition, such as a brain tumour or leukaemia. Anxiety is a striking feature and often elicits reassurance from the doctor, who may even perform tests to reassure the patient further. This may alleviate fear temporarily. However, in a behaviour therapy formulation of hypochondriasis, the temporary relief of anxiety by reassurance reinforces the behaviour that elicits reassurance. Thus, reassurance aggravates the patient's abnormal illness behaviour. The behavioural treatment of hypochondriasis that follows from this formulation therefore involves exposing the patient to illness-related stimuli and withholding reassurance, i.e. exposure therapy. The importance of accurate diagnosis is that many patients with SD are not hypochondriacal: they show no fear of illness (Murphy, 1990). Far from seeking reassurance, they become indignant or scornful if 'reassured' they do not have the diseases they say they suffer. Patients with SD usually want affirmation of their right to the sick role. These patients do not get relief of anxiety from reassurance. Thus, behavioural treatment along the lines described for hypochondriacal patients is inappropriate and ineffective.

This does not stop some patients from having features of hypochondriasis and fulfilling the criteria for SD at the same time – many do. There is no reason why the two categories should be mutually exclusive. However, while the categories of somatoform disorders overlap, the conceptual distinctions between the different types of psychopathology is important in deciding therapy (see Murphy, 1990, for a fuller discussion of the classification of somatoform disorders).

Characteristics of patients with somatisation disorder

Our findings on the social, psychopathological, and other characteristics of patients with SD are similar to those described in American studies. The prototypical SD patient is female, in her forties, has a complicated medical history, is often on invalidity benefit, has spurious physical diagnoses, is on numerous drugs, and has had a hysterectomy (60% in our series). Concurrent and past symptoms of depression and anxiety are common and most have been treated for these with antidepressants and benzodiazepines. They are generally as disparaging about their past psychiatric treatment as they are about their medical treatment. Many, but not all, fit the clinical picture of Briquet's syndrome, the features of which include a history of overdoses, substance abuse, vagueness in thinking, and histrionic behaviour.

Over 70% of SD patients have a personality disorder as assessed by the Personality Assessment Schedule (Stern *et al*, 1993*b*). This is double the rate seen in patients with most other psychiatric disorders classified on axis 1. Somatisation disorder patients are also more likely than other psychiatric patients to be rated as having severe rather than mild or moderate personality disorders.

The social lives of SD patients are often impoverished. Current and past family life is often marked by discord, acrimony and bitterness, and patients may not be able to provide adequate parental care for their children.

Fifty per cent of our SD cases grew up in families where one or both parents suffered significant physical disability to the extent that it interfered with the parent's ability to provide care. On standardised rating scales, patients with SD reported receiving less maternal care than matched controls with other forms of mental illness. Furthermore, 20% of the SD patients had suffered chronic disabling illness (rheumatic fever, insulin-dependent diabetes and asthma were examples) in childhood, bringing them into regular contact with the health care system. We have thus hypothesised that inadequate emotional care in the family combined with exposure to chronic illness and/or contact with professional health care in childhood plays a major role in the development of SD (Murphy & Bass, in preparation). This is in contrast with the view adopted in the USA where SD is often depicted as a genetically transmitted disorder. Our findings are in line with the view that chronic somatisation can be understood as abnormal care-eliciting behaviour (Henderson, 1974).

Referral

Patients with SD consult general practitioners, physicians, gynaecologists, surgeons and practitioners of alternative medicine – anyone who might alleviate bodily suffering. Rarely do they find relief, but they keep on moving from one practitioner to another. Frequently the GP or specialist recognises the psychopathology but finds it difficult to refer the patient with SD to a psychiatrist. They know that such patients often become angry and indignant when told that no organic cause can be found for their symptoms and will resent the suggestion of referral to a mental health professional. Psychiatric referral is often interpreted by the patient as meaning the doctor thinks the symptoms are not real; that the patient is imagining them or 'putting it on'. Many speak of psychiatric referral as if it were a form of punishment, as indeed do some doctors. Simply mentioning psychiatry may therefore lead to a hostile and embarrassing confrontation between doctor and patient. The doctor's wish to avoid this situation is one of the factors that maintains somatisation, as for example when a doctor opts for a referral to another medical specialty or stalls by ordering more tests rather than risk confrontation.

Physicians who have referred such patients to a psychiatrist often complain that little was achieved by the referral. Most often, the patient receives a diagnosis of depression or anxiety, and is prescribed a psychotropic drug. This generally has no impact on the patient's use of other medical resources, and they continue reporting symptoms and being referred between specialists. Our research suggests that the psychiatric out-patient clinic becomes simply another port of call in the patient's rounds of the hospital (Bass & Murphy, 1991).

Another frequent unsatisfactory result, from the physician's point of view, is when the psychiatrist says the patient has "no formal mental illness". This occurs when the patient reports no "psychological symptoms" and the psychiatrist does not believe in the validity or have experience of somatoform disorders. Having excluded schizophrenia, manic-depression etc., the psychiatrist may reassure the patient that they are psychologically normal or even "coping very well, given all the physical problems". The patient then returns triumphantly to the embarrassed physician who may conclude that psychiatric referral is counter-productive in somatising patients.

Successful referral requires an interested psychiatrist who understands the concept of liaison. Currently in Britain there is reluctance on the part of psychiatrists to recognise liaison psychiatry as a subspecialty involving particular assessment and management skills. Some of the most effective interventions in patients with SD begin with liaison – a joint consultation in which the patient sees the physician and psychiatrist together. This is arranged by the physician who tells the patient that he would like to involve a psychiatrist in the management. Physician and psychiatrist agree on what their future roles are going to be before the consultation, for example, whether the physician sees the patient again, how they should respond to new symptoms, and how to deal with requests for urgent appointments. There are additional advantages in liaison as opposed to standard consultation: the patient is less likely to feel dismissed as when "sent to see the psychiatrist", the patient is less able to dismiss a joint opinion, devalue the other doctor's expertise, or engender confusion and conflict between the doctors. Furthermore physician and psychiatrist learn from each other.

The first contact

A common striking feature of the first consultation with SD patients is their anger about their medical treatment. They are often reluctant to talk about anything else, complaining that they are being denied the help to which they are entitled, or that they have been neglected and mistreated. Their behaviour may elicit defensiveness and a range of unpleasant emotions in the interviewer, including apprehension, guilt, inadequacy and hatred. The psychiatrist may feel he is being attacked, along with previous would-be helpers. Alternatively, the interviewer may partly share the patient's view on how awful the other doctors have been, particularly if the patient combines the attack on previous helpers with praise for the current doctor being so understanding (such splitting is more likely where there is interdisciplinary rivalry). The psychiatrist has to know how not to take sides: how to have empathy without colluding. The SD patient inhabits a Manichaean universe; the psychiatrist must make contact with the patient but not cohabit this universe. The following dialogue is composed of condensed extracts from initial interviews with SD patients and illustrates some of these features:

> Patient: "I want something to be done. I can't go on like this. You must be able to do a scan to show what is causing this pain. There must be a cause."

Psychiatrist: "You are still worried there is a physical cause which has not been found despite what we have told you and all the tests you have had."

Patient: "It must be something physical. It's not in my mind; I've got no other problems apart from these pains. You can't tell me that it's my nerves – I've taken all the antidepressants and tranquillisers and they just make me worse by turning me into a zombie, but they do nothing for the pain. Anyway, why is it I never had this problem until that doctor at St Thanatoid's Hospital gave me that injection in my spine – [Sarcastically] Do spinal injections cause depression? He must have damaged something sticking that needle in me like that." (Patient becomes increasingly more animated as she describes incident. . . .)

Psychiatrist: "You are in a very difficult position – having to depend on doctors, but at the same time thinking they can make you worse and that you can't trust them."

Patient (with indignation): "He didn't even tell me that he was going to do it. He just told me to bend over. The next thing I knew was this excruciating pain, like something rupturing inside me. It must have been a cyst or something – but how can I prove it? Doctors stick together, they won't say anything against each other and once it's in your notes that your a psychiatric patient nobody believes you."

Psychiatrist: "You suspect that doctors don't believe you?"

Patient: "Well I've even had doctors blame me for being ill. How can it be my fault? Mr Cutter (the surgeon who did my gall bladder) – how dare he come and tell me, after he has operated on me, that I shouldn't have had the operation because I've still got the pain. He is supposed to be the doctor and know when to do the operation, not me. I'm the patient. And how dare he say 'Mrs K, you should be under the psychiatric department not the surgical department'. I've been a patient with Crohn's disease under that hospital for 25 years. I was one of the first patients to have Crohn's in this country . . ."

Psychiatrist: "Let me check whether I understand what you have said. You are very ill; you want something done; you have to persuade, even plead with doctors to do something, but they seem reluctant. Then, when things are done, like the spinal injection or the gall bladder operation, you end up worse than you were to begin with, and you even get the blame for it. You can't win. [Pause] Is that right?"

Patient: "Yes, but nobody will listen. You take my GP: I've been getting cystitis ever since they did the operation on my bladder and I went to see him about it yesterday and he gave me antibiotics [looking surprised] – he knows I'm alergic to antibiotics but he still gives them to me . . . there must be somebody who can do something to help me? I'm going to have to go privately if the NHS is not going to help me. It has already cost me £2000, but what else can I do?"

Psychiatrist: "You sound like you are suffering a lot – you are angry and in pain. You also sound very determined, and you can be very powerful when it comes to getting what you believe is right – to have persuaded a surgeon to do a gall bladder operation the way you did. But, perhaps you can be too powerful – the doctors might be overcome by it and then they are no longer in control of the treatment they give you. That's when things turn nasty and go wrong [Pause]."

Patient: "Are you saying that it's my fault? That I shouldn't complain?"

Psychiatrist: "I don't think it is your fault that you are angry and I think you should complain when you think something is wrong. What I'm saying is that you've had all these angry struggles with doctors and the result has always been a bad one for you."

Patient: "It's them that give me the wrong treatment."

Psychiatrist: "You must be worried that I won't be able to cope with your anger and that I'll end up doing something bad to you – give you the wrong treatment."

Patient: "I'm not angry with you, doctor. Why should I be? You haven't done anything yet."

Psychiatrist: "You want something done, like the scan you mentioned, which I'm not going to order (because it won't help you) – that could be a reason for you being angry with me."

Patient: "No. I realise it's not your job . . . there must be something somebody can do? I can't see how me seeing you is going to help [Pause] . . . How is this supposed to be helping me?"

Psychiatrist: "We need to talk about what we can realistically expect from you seeing me. I don't know whether it will help you or not."

Patient: "Dr Jones told me that the problem was depression and that you were going to help me?"

Psychiatrist: "Dr Jones and I have often worked together on your type of problem. I'd like to know more about your experiences with your illness . . ."

Patient (interrupting psychiatrist): "So you are just going to sit here and ask me questions and then you'll tell me that it's all in my mind and I'm expected to carry on like this."

Psychiatrist: "I suggest I see you for six appointments over the next 12 weeks to give us a chance to look at your problems and your history and then we can decide . . ." [Patient interrupts]

Patient: "And what am I supposed to do for the next 2 weeks? What if I carry on getting worse in the meanwhile? How can I contact you? I've already waited a month between seeing Dr Jones and this appointment and now you're telling me that there is nothing you can do."

Psychiatrist: "You seem to feel that I'm abandoning you. I recognise that you are in a lot of pain and distress. I will see you in 2 weeks. We have only just begun to talk about your illness, you are obviously anxious that I will let you down. You have been ill for years; we both know that there is no simple cure for your condition, neither a physical one, nor a psychological one. Let's spend some time looking at what's happening to you. Come back and see me on the 16th."

In this dialogue the psychiatrist addresses and legitimises the patient's anger and anxieties as they emerge. Rather than reassuring the patient, the psychiatrist acknowledges how ill she is without being drawn into a sterile discussion of cause. Despite devaluing the psychiatrist, it is clear at the end that the patient is already expressing dependency.

In a paper on taking care of the 'hateful patient', Groves describes four stereotypes to help physicians identify the dynamics of the doctor–patient relationship (Groves, 1978). The 'entitled demander' and the 'manipulative help-rejecter' are two patterns often seen in SD, elements of which can be seen in the above dialogue. Both types of behaviour are motivated by 'insatiable dependency', according to Groves. In both, the doctor is treated as an inexhaustible caregiver. The entitled demander tries to hold on to the doctor by intimidation and guilt-induction, while the help-rejecter, who asks for relief of their symptoms, cannot lose them for fear of losing the relationship with the doctor. Groves advises:

> "demanders evoke a wish to counterattack; such patients need to have their feelings of total entitlement rechannelled into a partnership that acknowledges their entitlement – not to unrealistic demands but to good medical care. Help-rejecters evoke depression; sharing their pessimism diminishes their notion that losing the symptom implies losing the doctor."

Stereotypes are oversimplifications, and Groves' categories overlap in practice. But they are useful because they alert clinicians to their own emotional reactions and suggest that these responses are important diagnostic information, and that they need to be consciously processed in the assessment and management of these patients. After this initial recognition, psychiatrists and therapists will usually want to go beyond stereotyping.

Treatment goals

Early attempts to negotiate treatment goals can lead to the impression that the patient's main goal is to reject psychological help. In most cases the patient will insist that they want physical treatment to alleviate physical symptoms, or more tests to get to the bottom of what is wrong with them. The patient should be told that this is not the psychiatrist's role, and that there will be no more tests or physical treatments (unless antidepressants are indicated or new symptoms suggest intervening organic disease). The patient often becomes angry and challenges the value of psychological treatment. If the psychiatrist or therapist takes this challenge at face value they may respond by defending psychiatry/therapy, or even apologising for its failure to have found a cure for the patient's ailments (a form of collusion). Instead, the therapist can address the patient's anger and associated anxieties (as in the dialogue above). By shifting attention to how the patient is currently feeling and uncritically accepting that they are angry, the therapist may give the patient a sense of containment (defined below). If so, the patient may feel the value of psychotherapy.

Psychiatrists of the St Louis school have written that patients with SD are 'not interested' in psychotherapy. Since proponents of this school believe there is only one kind of psychiatry – biological psychiatry – it is not surprising that they do not detect much interest in psychotherapy in their encounters with SD patients (Guze, 1989). Our experience is that once patients have experienced psychotherapeutic contact, many want the relationship to continue, and given time, some make good use of it. However, a patient with SD cannot be told to stop believing that there is something physically wrong with her before she can have psychotherapy. Yet patients may feel that this is what is being asked of them when the offer of 'psychological' help is made. For the patient to agree to an explicitly psychological treatment means accepting that psychological factors are contributing significantly to his or her symptoms. For a patient with SD being a 'physical' invalid may be a central part of her identity. Asking a patient to consider symptoms as psychological is challenging the integrity of her self-representation. She is being asked to do more than change 'dysfunctional illness attributions'. The coherence of her world may be at stake. If the SD patient could accept the advice that her illness was psychological she probably would not have SD in the first place.

So what should the therapist's agenda be? It should not be curing patients of all their ailments, and patients should be told this. One aim is to engage the patient in a relationship that reduces the need for further doctor-shopping. 'Engaging the patient' might seem like a platitude – surely this is true of any patient? True – but engaging an SD patient in a psychotherapeutic relationship, establishing a therapeutic alliance, brings one instantly in contact with the core psychopathology and requires particular skills. It is different from engaging a patient with a phobia who wants to be rid of their phobia, where a therapeutic alliance is built up as shared goals are negotiated. As one exasperated psychotherapist wrote of an SD patient, ''How do you begin to help someone who is addicted to rejecting help?'' The first step is not to reject the patient.

Engaging a patient in treatment is a goal in itself, as it can lead to a change in illness behaviour – a reduction in the number of attendances at other clinics and fewer physical investigations and treatments. To achieve this goal the psychiatrist should liaise with medical and paramedical colleagues as well as negotiating it with the patient. Doctors' anxieties about 'missing something' are often alleviated when they are offered a psychiatric formulation of the problem and informed that the patient is being offered regular appointments with a psychiatrist. Informing other professionals should be discussed with the patient first as it can be interpreted as persecutory or as deprivatory. A clear, concise, authoritative letter describing the diagnosis, its implications and the care plan can be put in the front of a patient's notes to discourage the unwary new junior doctor from performing unnecessary investigations.

Illness is a way of life for most patients with SD, and many have known no other way. A long-term commitment from a doctor (usually a GP or a psychiatrist) is necessary if the patient is not to be over-investigated and is to avoid further risk of iatrogenic physical disease, which some will already have sustained. Some psychiatrists express concerns about 'fostering dependency' by this approach. Clearly, dependency is central to the psychopathology of people who spend their lives in the sick role and seem determined to remain there. The issue is how to deal with this dependency. If one does not offer regular psychotherapeutic contact, patients continue with the hopeless alternative of 'doctor-shopping'.

Engaging the 'resistant' patient

Patients with somatisation disorder protest when it is suggested that their main problem is psychological. Some appear hurt, as if humiliated and shamed by the suggestion. Often they are scornful and dismissive of psychological treatment – "You think that me coming and talking to you is going to get rid of this pain? I know you are trying to help but I'm talking about a real pain."

The patient's protest is in part based on an interpretation of 'psychological' ('emotional', 'mental' etc.) as 'not real' – at least not as 'real' as in 'real disease'. The offer of psychiatric help is taken by the patient as proof that their physical complaints are disbelieved. This interpretation of 'psychological' usually persists despite the doctor's insistence that the psychological is as real as the physical, and despite assurances that the doctor believes in the reality of the patient's symptoms. In the language of most somatisers 'psychological' is a term of abuse. Thus, at one level, doctor and patient seem to be speaking different languages, or attaching different values to the term psychological.

At another level, regardless of what health professionals say, 'psychological' is a moral category, and belongs to a shared moral order in which the psychological (subjective) is of less value and to be taken less seriously than the physical (objective). At this level, the patient's understanding of 'psychological' is not incorrect, but rather involves its moral and metaphysical connotations. The belief that the 'psychological' is less than 'real' is not peculiar to patients with SD, since it is a metaphysical assumption of most doctors as well. This is partly why doctors sound unconvincing, even to themselves, when they try to persuade a patient they believe in the reality of the symptom despite there being no objective findings. It is difficult for doctors committed to the metaphysical assumptions of positivism, however unwittingly, to be comfortable in this situation. It is commonplace for doctors in all specialties, at all levels of experience, to talk of 'real pain' in contrast to the complaint of pain made by the patient with SD whom the doctor thinks is imagining a pain that does not exist.

Not all somatising patients reject a psychological explanation for symptoms; those presenting with acute or subacute illnesses may readily accept the doctor's psychosocial explanation of their physical symptoms, if they feel they have been taken seriously and there is mutual respect. But patients with SD are, by definition, chronically ill and unamenable to persuasion.

Faced with a reluctant patient, the would-be therapist may invoke the concept of resistance or say that the patient has no motivation to change. Formulating the problem this way conveys the idea that the patient is responsible for the therapeutic impasse, and could be seen to imply that the patient is also to blame for not getting better. Patients with SD are usually sensitive to such implications. Tackling resistance to a psychological explanation of illness directly, by asserting something like '20 doctors have failed to find anything physically wrong, so now it is time to take a psychological approach' rarely fosters a therapeutic alliance in SD. Most patients have well argued rebuttals to the logic of this imperative. In addition, most patients can cite numerous doctors who did think the patient had something wrong with them – 'a mild episode of MS', 'a small heart attack'. Many also have coexisting organic disorders that they invoke to explain symptoms.

Direct confrontation on the issue of the cause of symptoms runs the risk of unresolvable conflict, increasing the patient's resistance and impeding the development of the therapeutic alliance. Therapists also invoke resistance as a way of disclaiming responsibility for therapeutic failure and to justify a nihilistic approach to these patients. Similar consequences may follow from confronting a patient's ''lack of motivation'' or ''non-compliance with treatment'' – they are not specific to the psychodynamic metaphor of resistance.

Family therapists are familiar with alternatives to challenging resistance. These 'strategic' techniques are said to have their origins in the work of Milton Erickson, who used them with individual patients as well as families (Hayley, 1963). Erickson saw resistance as a social interaction between therapist and patient. An interaction is characterised by resistance when the therapist insists on moving in a direction that does not suit the needs or capabilities of the patient at that time. Resistance can thus reflect the therapist's rigidity or the therapist's failure to have developed an adequate formulation of the patient's problems.

The strategic psychotherapist does not 'struggle against' or try to 'breakdown' a patient's resistance, but uses interventions based on the idea of 'joining' the resistance (Marshall, 1976). These interventions are more likely to work if they are based on an understanding of the patient's cognitive–attributional processes. Kirmayer (1990) refers to a class of problem ''in which the mechanisms of symptom persistence and psychotherapeutic resistance involve the same conservative cognitive processes that act to maintain an adaptive level of coherence and consistency in the person's self-representation.'' Identifying these cognitive processes involves establishing the patient's attributions of cause and control to self and others.

Joining is not the same as empathy. In SD joining involves a cognitive reconstruction of the patient's particular experience of illness and the health care system. The therapist establishes how the patient construes her predicament and adopts her model. Rather than challenging any material that suggests resistance, the patient's view is firstly supported. The therapist communicates this support before any attempt is made to modify the patient's view by 'reframing' symptoms or behaviour (see Kirmayer, 1990, for an account of joining interventions in terms of cognitive–attributional theory). The following dialogue illustrates the use of strategic techniques.

The patient is a 45-year-old single nurse with SD who retired because of her illness 8 years ago. She lives alone and has no regular social contact with anyone other than her doctors. The following extract was recorded after her 16th session. The session began with her describing her frustration during a recent diploma exam when she developed writer's cramp. This was followed by an episode of chest pain which she links with the 'stress' of the situation. She has not previously talked about 'stress' having a role in causing her pain which she insists is 'angina' despite attempts by cardiologists to persuade her otherwise. (Comments on the process are in parentheses.)

> Psychiatrist: "I don't understand why you think stress caused your chest pain." (The psychiatrist is resisting a psychological link.)
>
> Patient: "It does. Stress can bring it on." (Somatising patient having to persuade psychiatrist that psychological factors play a role in illness.)
>
> Psychiatrist: "I don't understand how that comes about."
>
> Patient (looking bemused): "It's well known that stress can do this. You must see this kind of thing a lot, surely?"
>
> Psychiatrist: "Yes, but in your case I don't see how."

The patient explains how stress causes heart disease. I thank her for her patience, but admit that I am still puzzled. I also mention how I am struck by her careful attention to detail in relating her history and ask her if she can recall any other episodes that she thought were related to stress that might help me grasp the link. She thinks and then relates this story:

> Patient: "It was during the winter, when we were having that very cold weather. The Gas Board cut off my gas supply, so I had no heating, no hot water, could do no washing. And this was not my fault – I had sent them a cheque, but they are incompetent. So, I spoke to this idiot of a woman at British Gas and told her that another cheque was coming, and could they please *please* switch my gas back on – I was freezing to death. You know how ill I was at that time: I was

vomiting up everything I ate, my stress incontinence was very bad, I could hardly move so that I was vomiting all over myself and everything stank of urine because I had no hot water to do any washing. But she just would not listen to me and treated me as if I counted for nothing. She was prepared to let me die of hypothermia. They treat you like rubbish these people, but I was not prepared to just lie there and take it; they were in the wrong this time. I will sue you for this I thought. But now this means I have to get legal aid, so I managed to get up despite how ill I was, and go to get help from the Citizen's Advice Bureau. What do I find when I get there? A sign on the door saying 'due to staff shortage we are closed on Monday'. What is this country coming to under Thatcher? The CAB – they are supposed to be there to help you; that's the whole point. How can they be closed and help you? There I was on this bitter cold day standing in the street staring at this sign and it happened: the chest pain. 'My God!' [She puts her hands across her chest and as if to clutch her heart] I thought now I am going to die like a dog in the street and nobody will give a damn. They will probably just step over my body."

Psychiatrist: "I think I am beginning to see what you mean about the pain being linked to stress. Let me see if I've got the picture. First, you are unfairly deprived, cut off, left in the cold. A basic comfort – heating – is taken away by the Gas Board – somebody up there who doesn't give a damn. [Patient nods, agreeing cautiously.] Then not only are you deprived and mistreated, but when you turn for help, the authorities who are supposed to listen and help you are not available."

Patient: "I'm not blaming them. It wouldn't be like this if it were not for Thatcher."

Psychiatrist: "OK, let me make sure I've fully understood the stress that led to the pain . . . ." (Repeats summary of events similar to above.)

Patient: "Yes [again cautiously], I suppose that describes it."

Psychiatrist: "It sounds as if you felt completely abandoned out there on the street – that is *painful*. To be abandoned. To be so alone . . . that *hurts* . . . that is a real *heart*-felt pain . . . ." (Reframing experience of pain as painful experience, contextualising pain.)

Tears appear and the patient fights not to cry. Within a second or two the patient lets out a pained gasp and clutches her chest – she is having an attack of chest pain which continues for 5–10 minutes. During the attack she has difficulty speaking. She begins to reach for her bag where she keeps a supply of glyceryl trinitrate which she takes to alleviate her chest pain, but then decides not to (possible evidence of reattribution). The psychiatrist comments on how their discussion of her abandonment has caused her pain. There is mainly silence for the next 15 minutes.

Patient: "You see! I just have to remember it and I get so angry that it brings back the pain."

Psychiatrist: "It is very upsetting, but very important. We began by talking about how you get pain in stressful circumstances. Now we are talking about painful experiences, like the experience you have just had now. I see what you mean about getting angry – you must be angry with me for persisting in talking about how you had been let down.''

Patient: "I'm not angry with you – it's them."

This dialogue can be understood at several levels, but it is used here to demonstrate strategic techniques for opening up dialogue where resistance had previously been encountered. The process of reframing experience led in this case to re-experience, with the possibility of reattribution of symptoms for the patient. It was also necessary in this case to consider the above interaction in terms of transference and countertransference: the patient experienced pain in the therapeutic process and this might lead to her avoiding further self-disclosure or not attending future sessions. Initial attempts to talk about this and her feelings towards the psychiatrist were ignored or dismissed by the patient who talked about physical complaints instead. At a subsequent visit, however, the patient described how exposed she had felt by the psychiatrist seeing how needy she was, and how pathetic it was that she could be so hurt by ''anonymous bureaucrats''.

I am not suggesting that challenge and confrontation be eschewed in dealing with resistance in SD patients. There are times when confrontation is appropriate, e.g. when agreed limits are ignored. But before proceeding further with the discussion of psychotherapeutic technique, I will describe what we learned by studying patients with SD, since it was through research that we engaged with the patients.

We wanted patients with SD for research, and did not set out to offer them psychological help. We informed patients that we were doing a study on people with recurrent symptoms for which doctors could not find a satisfactory physical explanation. Such patients, we suggested, suffered a great deal and if we could help we would discuss it after completing the research. Our research protocol conveyed the message that we were interested in physical symptoms and that we were not immediately suggesting they should have psychological help. We did not have the answers but hoped that the patients might help us arrive at some kind of understanding of their chronic ill-health. This was not intended as a strategic approach; we wanted to get the patients' views, hear their experiences, establish their attributions and how they understood their predicaments. Although we had hypotheses and standardised methods for examining these, we were also trying to discover what other questions we should be asking. We tried not to be attached to a particular school of thought, but rather to try out different views with the patient as we went along. Thus, in addition to using a conventional psychometric approach to clinical research, we complemented this with exploratory interviews aimed at establishing the patients' understanding, attributions, concerns and attitudes. We wanted patients' own models of their illnesses. We made notes during these interviews and frequently sought clarification. Clarification was not restricted to establishing 'the facts', as it might be in taking a medical history, but also involved getting patients to elaborate as much as they could about what events meant to them, and how they felt about them. We offered summaries which we asked the patient to confirm, correct or add to. We would thus often reflect back to patients what they had told us to see if we had understood.

Since we were interested, for research purposes, in the details of each and every symptom the patient had ever had, and all the patient's experiences within the health care system – what tests they had, what the doctors said, what they thought and felt about this, what effect this had on their activities and relationships – we shared a common agenda with most patients. They were usually eager to talk about their medical histories. In most clinical settings clinicians become bored, irritated, possibly overwhelmed by these details, and in the case of psychiatrists may want to discuss other aspects of the psychosocial history. The patient with SD may be reluctant to talk about anything other than their medical experiences until they feel they have been fully heard and appreciated. Our genuine interest in these details seems to have been a key factor in engaging these patients.

Curiosity and neutrality

Adopting a stance of curiosity in descriptive clinical research is similar to maintaining neutrality in psychotherapy. Cecchin of the Milan group of family therapists has described neutrality as "the creation of a state of curiosity in the mind of a therapist" (Cecchin, 1987). Neutrality is an ideal from which a therapist strays. It is an important idea in psychoanalytic, client-centred and some forms of family therapy, having different but related meanings in each. Neutrality cannot be maintained easily with SD patients; they frequently break the ground rules, for instance, telling lies, refusing to leave the room at the end of a session, or repeatedly telephoning and being rude to receptionists. However, if neutrality is regarded as a dimension along which a therapist can move, curiosity moves one towards neutrality.

Psychiatrists or therapists may not want to pursue a therapeutic relationship with a patient who disparages them and their treatment. Professionals often feel they are being abused by patients with SD and may feel the urge to retaliate or tell the patient not to come back. Psychiatrists frequently tolerate similar attacks from patients with paranoid psychosis and deal with this by understanding it as part of the patient's illness. In psychotic patients reality testing is obviously impaired and the patient is deemed not responsible for his or her behaviour; psychotic patients can be admitted and medicated. In SD the patient's reality testing appears relatively intact and thus psychiatrists may be less ready to ascribe aggression to illness. However, if a psychotherapeutic approach to SD is adopted it must include techniques for dealing with the patient's aggression and demands. Such strategies are usually described by the spatial metaphors of containment and limit setting.

Containment and limit setting

A therapist is containing a patient when he or she tolerates the patient's aggression and other emotions while remaining empathic and emotionally available. Containment usually involves the therapist attempting to understand the patient's feelings and behaviour, and often communicating this to the patient. How the therapist understands the patient depends on their working models of people, therapy, somatisation and so on.

Limit setting means telling the patient which behaviours cannot be accepted in the course of therapy. It involves being directive and can be opposed to neutrality. It involves the therapist in actively structuring therapy to curtail potentially destructive behaviour. It is necessary to decide on limits for each individual, rather than inflexibly applying general principles.

In SD it is usually necessary to agree the frequency and length of visits, and to inform the patient that they will not usually be seen at times outside these. Despite setting these limits, many patients still telephone or arrive in the department asking for earlier appointments. The usual reason they give for this is their worsening physical condition. They should be advised to wait till their scheduled appointment. On the occasions when there is a reasonable suspicion of organic disease, the symptoms can be discussed with the GP.

Limits on telephone calls may have to be set and receptionists advised on how to respond to repeated calls. Many patients find the end of sessions difficult and suddenly report physical symptoms, demanding explanations, tests and cures. When the patient is engaged in treatment this can be used as an opportunity to point out how the physical symptoms relate to separation and to empathise with the pain and fear of isolation and deprivation.

Discussing the patient's attempts to breach set limits is useful in developing the necessary dialogue about their dependence on professional care – their fear of it being withdrawn; their ambivalence; their need to abuse it and so on. This particular thread of dialogue helps to establish whether a patient might in the future be able to use psychoanalytically orientated psycho-therapy, since it may involve examining negative aspects of transference. Setting limits is not only about preserving the psychiatrist's sanity.

What model of psychotherapy?

Our approach to the psychological treatment of patients with SD at King's College Hospital has been eclectic in several senses. We have treated the same individual using different models concurrently or consecutively, and we have selected patients for specific kinds of treatment, although always after a fairly lengthy assessment period during which a doctor–patient relationship is already well developed. We have been assisted by colleagues trained in different psychotherapeutic modalities such as psychoanalytic, cognitive–behavioural, family and group therapies. Our experience suggests that whatever gains are made in treatment, long-term supportive psychotherapy is probably necessary in most cases if any improvement is to be maintained (Bass & Murphy, 1991).

The difficulty with an eclectic approach to treatment is that the theoretical models of different therapies are often conflicting or incommensurable. For the therapist moving between models this may weaken interventions in one or other role. For the patient moving between therapists, it may lead to them receiving contradictory messages. These pitfalls must be borne in mind when deciding treatment.

Supportive non-collusive psychotherapy

A lot of the work health professionals do with patients is called supportive psychotherapy. Supportive psychotherapy is often distinguished from psychoanalytically orientated psychotherapy in terms of its methods and goals – in supportive psychotherapy defences are not challenged, unconscious conflict is not explored and acquiring insight is not a goal of treatment. It is often described as 'non-specific' in contrast to cognitive and behavioural therapies in which specific defined techniques are used to treat specific problems.

Supportive psychotherapy is traditionally indicated in patients with personality disorders. Judging from what little is written about supportive psychotherapy in the general psychiatric literature, it is regarded as a nebulous activity undertaken when there is nothing better to do. Recent descriptions of supportive psychotherapy in the psychoanalytic literature have offered clearer descriptions of technique and rationale, particularly in relation to patients with borderline personality disorder.

Although a minority of patients with SD would fulfil DSM–III descriptive criteria for borderline personality disorder, assessed psychodynamically or in terms of psychostructural level of adaptation (object relations) most would be diagnosed as borderline, rather than neurotic or psychotic. The psychodynamic criteria require the presence of certain primitive defence operations including splitting, idealisation, omnipotence and devaluation, in the context of preserved reality testing. The psychoanalytical formulation of the borderline concept is not widely accepted in general psychiatry or psychology. However, there are few other discussions of supportive psychotherapy that have as much salience to patients with SD.

For Kernberg, supportive psychotherapy involves "exploring the patient's primitive defenses in the here and now" and helping the patient to understand the consequences of these in daily life (Kernberg, 1982). This is done in a 'non-analytic' way, which means that transference is not usually interpreted or at least not traced to unconscious origins. This is in contrast to expressive or analytic therapy (see Chatham, 1985, for review).

Primitive defences are inferred by assessing a patient's behaviours, feelings and attitudes both in and outside the therapeutic relationship. It does not need much knowledge of object–relations theory to identify the pattern that emerges in the doctor–patient relationship with SD patients as borderline. Recognition may occur as SD patients describe their previous experiences with doctors and in the relationship that is developing with the therapist. A typical pattern is the patient who dismisses all previous doctors as incompetent and uncaring (evidence of devaluation) and contrasts them with the current doctor – "someone who finally listens . . . why did Dr X not believe me when I told him about my pains" (evidence of idealisation and splitting).

The techniques of supportive psychotherapy include clarification and confrontation. The therapist does not support the patient when their behaviour is destructive or maladaptive, but rather challenges the patient. The following vignette illustrates the difference between how this might be done in supportive as opposed to analytic (expressive) therapy.

> A patient with SD complained that she had recently visited her GP, who did not take her complaint seriously. She told her psychiatrist that the GP did not really care about her, and that she was considering changing her GP (thus disrupting current care arrangements). The patient then began to repeat her usual list of grievances about doctors in general.

In analytic therapy, the therapist might, at this point, interpret the patient's complaints in terms of transference, e.g. the patient is attacking the therapist and testing whether he or she can be a good enough mother to the patient. Such interpretations usually leave the SD patient bewildered or feeling attacked. In supportive psychotherapy the therapist restricts the immediate work to clarifying what happened between the patient and the GP.

> She had consulted her GP for dysuria. He had taken a urine specimen for microbiology, prescribed antibiotics and given her an appointment to return in a week. She left his consulting room thinking that he was doing this solely to appease and get rid of her. She then made an appointment with his receptionist to see him again the following day. Although the GP had told her that he thought she had a urinary tract infection and given her treatment for it, she returned demanding more tests and treatment. He showed his annoyance and told her that the result of the test would not be available until the following week and asked her not to come back until then. She left feeling even more rejected and angry than she had the previous day.

Rather than allowing the patient to deliver her usual speech on how awful doctors are, the psychiatrist kept the focus on the specific example under discussion. He clarified what was going on in the patient's mind until both he and the patient shared an understanding of what she was saying. The psychiatrist then confronted this material, pointing out how the patient had played an active part in the story and was not a passive victim. He also suggested that her behaviour made it difficult for her GP to give her good medical care, which is what she is asking for.

In supportive psychotherapy of the type described by Kernberg (1992), confrontation involves pointing out the internal contradictions in what a patient says after it has been clarified. For example the patient says she wanted tests to show what was wrong, but when they were performed she did not wait for the result before demanding more. The patient can thus be challenged to think again about what it is she is trying to get from the doctor.

By recognising primitive defences in SD patients the therapist can identify and deal with processes that disrupt management and fuel further somatisation. Although transference interpretations are not given the central role ascribed to them in analytic therapy, it is often important to address negative aspects of transference when this threatens the therapeutic alliance and the survival of supportive psychotherapy (as discussed in relation to the dialogue on pp. 76–78). Typically this involves talking about the patient's suspicion that the therapist is trying to deprive them of care by labelling them 'psychiatric', or that the therapist wants to expose and humiliate them. If these are not addressed, not only does therapy break down, but the patient may make formal complaints to the hospital authorities or pursue litigation.

Cognitive–behavioural therapy

There have been several uncontrolled studies of cognitive–behavioural therapy in patients with physical symptoms in which a positive outcome has been reported. None of these have been studies of SD patients, but they have involved treating symptoms misattributed to physical disease. They include studies of chronic pain, primary hypochondriasis and the chronic fatigue syndrome ('ME'). The cognitive aspect of these treatments involves establishing a patient's causal attributions and beliefs and, where these are misinformed and dysfunctional, helping the patient to find alternative models. Complementary behavioural strategies include reintroducing the patient to activities that they are avoiding. This may be particularly important when the avoidance is adding to the handicap, or is aggravating physical symptoms, as has been suggested of exercise avoidance in patients with chronic fatigue (Butler *et al*, 1991).

We have seen symptomatic improvement in a few SD patients treated with cognitive–behavioural strategies, but this has usually involved remission of a particular symptom, rather than the overall condition. For example, a psychologist on our team treated a 32-year-old wheelchair-bound patient. The patient was able to reattribute her inability to walk to a ''phobia'' for walking, and accepted admission to our day hospital for rehabilitation. A structured behavioural regimen helped her to establish a normal gait over a year. She continued to have numerous other physical complaints as a day patient, and a behavioural approach was adapted to these. One of these complaints was pseudoseizures. The patient had always lived with her elderly mother and dreaded separation from her. One day her mother had to be admitted to hospital, and the patient had a 'fit' while holding a pan of boiling water which she poured over herself. She was thus admitted to the regional burns unit on the same day her mother was admitted. While in hospital she was misdiagnosed as having epilepsy and started on anti-epileptic treatment.

Most SD patients are polysymptomatic at any one time. This presents great difficulties for a cognitive–behavioural approach in which selected symptoms are targeted: as one symptom declines in intensity others begin to dominate. However, the above case shows that disabling symptoms can be treated, but it also illustrates that additional measures are usually necessary to maintain improvement.

The difference between SD and primary hypochondriasis was mentioned above – hypochondriacal patients have a fear and preoccupation with a disease, usually a named condition. The cognitive treatment of primary hypochondriasis depends on accurate formulation of the patient's dysfunctional health beliefs, and proceeds in much the same way as the cognitive therapy of depression and anxiety disorders (Warwick & Salkovskis 1989; Sensky, this volume). SD patients are often much vaguer than hypochondriacal patients about what they believe is physically wrong, and are more preoccupied by what has been wrong with their care. Vagueness was indeed listed as one of the symptoms of Briquet's syndrome, and has often been described as the hallmark of the cognitive style of hysteria. Cognitive formulation becomes very difficult when a patient's attributions are ill-defined.

Most SD patients reject the idea that cognitive processes have anything to do with their bodily symptoms. However, the cognitive therapist does not work only at the level of the symptoms (manifest problems), but also on the underlying schema (inferred structure) (Beck *et al*, 1990). A schema consists of specific rules that govern information processing and behaviour. The maladaptive behaviours and attitudes of SD patients described above as symptomatic of primitive defences can be described in terms of core cognitive schemas. The basic assumptions that shape the SD patient's behaviour in relationship to carers and authority figures need to be established. Such theoretical formulations have an obvious bearing on the doctor–patient relationship and may be more important than current theories that emphasise dysfunctional health beliefs in somatisation. If we consider the SD patient with dysuria described on pages 82 and 83, part of the core schema might be something like "when you take a problem to a doctor (person in authority who has the means to help you) they will try to fob you off". Operating from this assumption the patient attends to those aspects of the doctor's behaviour in the consultation that support her assumption, ignoring those that do not. For example, the doctor can only spend a short period of time with each patient if he is to get through his surgery in time. However, the patient interprets the brevity of the consultation as meaning that the doctor does not want to see her and that he gives her a urine test and prescription to get rid of her. When she returns the following day the doctor truly does not want to see her. For the patient this is evidence that her assumption was right in the first place. This can lead to a self-perpetuating cycle in which the patient becomes increasingly demanding and the doctor increasingly disinclined to see the patient.

Patients with SD are prone to focus selectively on other aspects of their interactions with doctors that incriminate the doctors. Typical preoccupations include how doctors have contradicted themselves and each other. The patient may argue that this proves that nobody has got to the bottom of the problem and that further tests are therefore necessary.

Cognitive–behavioural therapy is more structured than supportive psychotherapy. It is likely to involve more explicit goal-setting and usually includes 'homework' such as keeping a diary or carrying out behavioural tasks between sessions. A relative or friend may be invited to participate in treatment as a 'co-therapist'. Both patient and co-therapist are given an explanation for the rationale of cognitive–behavioural treatment and the co-therapist is encouraged to come along to some of the treatment sessions with the agreement of the patient.

Family approaches

There are no published studies and little discussion of family therapy in somatisation disorder. Patients with SD and their families rarely accept referral to or attend for family therapy. Family members are more willing to attend the general out-patient clinic, where they can assume the role of concerned and exasperated relative with less threat to the family's status quo. Although seeing the family in this context can be useful, it is difficult to make use of the systemic approach when one's role is that of the patient's psychiatrist. Adopting a systemic approach is easier if the whole family is seen from the outset. It is easier to change from seeing the family to seeing the patient individually than the other way around.

Using a family systems approach to somatisation involves asking what function the patient's symptom(s) serves in maintaining the family in its present state (homeostasis). This involves eschewing a linear model of cause and effect in favour of a circular or interactive one. This entails reframing the symptom as a manifestation of the family's pathology rather than the individual's psychopathology. This can be a difficult shift to make in SD where symptoms often date back to childhood or adolescence and predate the formation of the family. A transgenerational approach that takes account of the families of origin of the patient and spouse is most likely to produce a coherent picture on which a formulation can be based. Patients with SD are more likely to have come from families in which illness and disability have afflicted parents, or to have suffered serious physical disease themselves in childhood. Physical symptoms are thus likely to have important meanings in family transactions and to influence the transactional patterns of the subsequent generation. There has been little systematic study of the spouses of SD patients who adopt the caring role in these marriages.

We have had more success treating families in which the identified patient has a less chronic type of somatoform disorder than SD, for example, cases with a recent onset with one or few physical symptoms. These have included cases of conversion disorder, such as a monoparesis or pseudo-seizures, and patients with psychogenic (somatoform) pain. This is undoubtedly the case with whatever type of therapy is used and is probably a reflection of the lower prevalence of personality disorders in those with shorter histories. Our limited experience of family therapy in SD suggests that, as with cognitive–behavioural therapy, particular symptoms may be alleviated in the course of therapy, but that other symptoms emerge once therapy ends.

Conclusions

Patients with SD can be engaged in psychological treatment. Whether they engage depends not only on the patient, but on the therapist's understanding of the patient's beliefs, fears, experiences and so on. Treatment and management should preferably only be undertaken by someone interested in such patients as the job is time-consuming, demands patience, therapeutic skill and flexibility. Psychiatrists working in liaison services and general practitioners are probably best suited to the task.

Patients with SD usually require long-term skilled supportive psycho-therapy. Without this they continue demanding and invariably receiving physical interventions. At best this is a waste of resources and at worst causes iatrogenic disease. It will be important for psychiatrists or psychotherapists to demonstrate the cost of intervention compared with the cost of not intervening, as well as any beneficial effect for patients and their families (Bass & Murphy, 1990*b*). The effects of specific types of intervention in SD still need to be evaluated and compared. Treatment outcome research will only be meaningful where follow-up assessments are carried out after long periods, given the relapsing course of the condition.

References

AMERICAN PSYCHIATRIC ASSOCIATION (1980) *Diagnostic and Statistical Manual of Mental Disorders* (3rd edn) (DSM–III). Washington, DC: APA.
—— (1987) *Diagnostic and Statistical Manual of Mental Disorders* (3rd edn, revised) (DSM–III–R). Washington, DC: APA.
BASS, C. & MURPHY, M. (1990a) Somatisation disorder: a critique of the concept and suggestions for future research. In *Somatisation: Physical Symptoms and Psychological Illness* (ed. C. Bass). Oxford: Blackwell Scientific.
—— & —— (1990b) The chronic somatizer and the government white paper. *Journal of the Royal Society of Medicine*, **83**, 203–205.
—— & —— (1991) Somatisation disorder in a British teaching hospital. *British Journal of Clinical Practice*, **45**, 237–244.
BECK, A. T., FREEMAN, A., *et al* (1990) *Cognitive Therapy of Personality Disorders*. New York: Guilford Press.
BUTLER, S., CHALDER, T., RON, M., *et al* (1991) Cognitive behavioural therapy in the chronic fatigue syndrome. *Journal of Neurology, Neurosurgery and Psychiatry*, **54**, 153–158.
CECCHIN, G. (1987) Hypothesizing, circularity, and neutrality revisited. *Family Process*, **26**, 405–413.
CHATHAM, P. M. (1985) *Treatment of the Borderline Personality*. New Jersey: Jason Aronson.
GROVES, J. E. (1978) Taking care of the hateful patient. *New England Journal of Medicine*, **289**, 883–887.
GUZE, S. (1975) The validity and significance of hysteria (Briquet's syndrome). *American Journal of Psychiatry*, **132**, 138–141.
—— (1989) Biological psychiatry: is there any other kind? *Psychological Medicine*, **9**, 315–323.
HALEY, J. (1963) *Strategies of Psychotherapy*. New York: Grune and Stratton.
HENDERSON, S. (1974) Care-eliciting behaviour in man. *Journal of Nervous and Mental Disease*, **159**, 172–181.
KERNBERG, O. F. (1982) Supportive psychotherapy with borderline conditions. In *Critical Problems in Psychiatry* (eds J. Cavenar & H. Brodie). Philadelphia: Lippincott.
KIRMAYER, L. J. (1990) Resistance, reactance and reluctance to change: a cognitive attributional approach to strategic interventions. *Journal of Cognitive Psychotherapy*, **4**, 83–104.
MARSHALL, R. (1976) "Joining techniques" in the treatment of resistant children and adolescents: a learning theory rationale. *American Journal of Psychotherapy*, **30**, 73–84.
MURPHY, M. (1989) Somatisation: embodying the problem. *British Medical Journal*, **298**, 1331–1332.
—— (1990) Classification of the somatoform disorders. In *Somatization: Physical Symptoms and Psychological Illness* (ed. C. Bass). Oxford: Blackwell Scientific Press.
ORENSTEIN, H. (1989) Briquet's syndrome in association with depression and panic: a reconceptualization of Briquet's syndrome. *American Journal of Psychiatry*, **146**, 334–338.
PERLEY, M. G. & GUZE, S. B. (1962) Hysteria: the stability and usefulness of clinical criteria. *New England Journal of Medicine*, **266**, 421–426.
SPITZER, R. L., ENDICOTT, J. & ROBINS, E. (1975) Research Diagnostic Criteria (RDC). *Psychopharmacology Bulletin*, **11**, 22–24.
STERN, J., MURPHY, M. & BASS, C. (1993a) Attitudes to the diagnosis of somatisation disorder amongst British psychiatrists. *British Journal of Psychiatry*, **162**, 463–466.
——, —— & —— (1993b) Personality disorders in patients with somatization disorder. *British Journal of Psychiatry* (in press).
VAILLANT, G. (1984) The disadvantages of the DSM–III outweigh its advantages. *American Journal of Psychiatry*, **141**, 542–545.
WARWICK, H. & SALKOVSKIS, P. (1989) Cognitive therapy of hypochondriasis. In *Cognitive Therapy in Clinical Practice* (eds J. Scott, J. Williams & A. Beck). London: Croom Helm.
WOODRUFF, R., CLAYTON, P. & GUZE, S. (1971) Hysteria: studies of diagnosis, outcome, and prevalence. *Journal of the American Medical Association*, **215**, 415–428.

6 Psychological management of patients with the irritable bowel syndrome

ELSPETH GUTHRIE

This chapter describes a randomised, controlled trial of psychotherapy of patients with chronic symptoms of the irritable bowel syndrome. For the sake of brevity, the main points and findings of the trial have been summarised, but are presented in more detail elsewhere (Guthrie *et al*, 1991). Two therapy cases are presented at the end of the chapter, to illustrate the nature of the therapy that was employed.

The irritable bowel syndrome (IBS) is a common condition consisting of abdominal pain, abdominal distension and an alteration in bowel habit in the absence of underlying gut pathology. Patients commonly describe rabbit-like, pellety stools, although diarrhoea can be a prominent feature in some cases. In addition to bowel symptoms, patients often describe a variety of other physical complaints including lethargy, backache, headaches, gynaecological symptoms, etc.

About one in ten people in the community experience mild symptoms but the majority never seek professional help. IBS accounts for up to 50% of all new out-patients seen each week by gastroenterologists in the United Kingdom. In the West, more women than men consult doctors regarding this problem, whereas in Asian countries, men are more frequent consulters.

The majority of people who consult their doctor respond to conventional medical treatment, in conjunction with explanation and reassurance (Harvey *et al*, 1987). Approximately 15%, however, are not helped by medical intervention and their symptoms persist, often resulting in extensive investigation and utilisation of health service resources (Kingham & Dawson, 1985).

The aetiology of IBS remains unclear, but there is unlikely to be one underlying cause as the condition itself is a syndrome, with many different variations and presentations. Various psychological factors have been implicated, including personality, life events and the presence of psychiatric disorder (Creed & Guthrie, 1987). In addition, underlying physiological factors such as gut motility are also relevant (Thompson, 1984). The development of the condition in any one individual, therefore, is likely to result from a combination of the above factors.

Approximately 40–50% of patients with chronic symptoms of IBS have diagnosable psychiatric illness (Creed & Guthrie, 1987) but they are often reluctant to be referred to a psychiatrist for fear that their symptoms will be viewed as being 'all in the mind'. In some cases, even if they agree to a psychiatric referral, it is unhelpful as the psychiatrist may be unfamiliar in dealing with patients who present with physical symptoms.

Although there are many single case reports and uncontrolled studies that suggest psychological intervention may be beneficial in patients with the irritable bowel syndrome, there is a paucity of methodologically sound research, employing randomised, controlled designs (Creed & Guthrie, 1989). A recent comprehensive review (Klein, 1988) of all the drug trials conducted on patients with the irritable bowel syndrome concluded that ''not a single study has been published that provides compelling evidence that any therapeutic agent is efficacious in the global treatment of the irritable bowel syndrome''.

Behavioural treatment has been tried to good effect with patients presenting for the first time with IBS symptoms at a gastroenterological clinic (Bennett & Wilkinson, 1985). The authors found that relaxation training was superior to conventional medical treatment for the reduction of anxiety and equally effective as medical treatment in IBS symptom reduction. The effectiveness of such treatment for patients with chronic symptoms of IBS remains untested.

Hypnosis has acquired a certain popularity with gastroenterologists seeking to treat IBS patients who have failed to respond to conventional medical treatment. There is no doubt that with certain groups of patients it is remarkably effective. Whorwell *et al* (1984), in a small controlled study of 36 patients with chronic symptoms of IBS, found hypnosis to be far superior to 'supportive sessions' when delivered by the same gastroenterologist. Hypnosis has also been found to be effective when delivered in a group format (Harvey *et al*, 1989). Hypnosis seems to have greatest therapeutic effect in patients below the age of 55 years, without overt symptoms of anxiety or depression and in those patients who are not psychologically minded. This may be related to the fact that in the above studies, hypnosis has been introduced to the patients almost as a medical treatment; a procedure to be undergone and learnt that will then make them better. There is little discussion of psychological issues or exploration of problems in the patients' lives. It is not surprising, therefore, that those patients who tend to deny psychological problems and view their symptoms as having a physical aetiology do well with this kind of 'medicalised' approach.

The excellent study of Svedlund (1983), involving 101 subjects, is the only controlled trial of dynamic therapy in IBS. Svedlund demonstrated that psychodynamic psychotherapy in addition to medical treatment was superior to medical treatment alone both at three months and at follow-up one year later. The study, however, may have been more influential in gastroenterological circles by the inclusion of an independent assessment by a gastroenterologist, instead of the two therapists involved in the trial rating each other's patients.

The aim of the present study was to assess the feasibility and efficacy of brief dynamic therapy plus conventional medical treatment versus medical treatment plus supportive listening, in out-patients with chronic symptoms of IBS.

The trial

The trial was a randomised, controlled trial of brief dynamic psychotherapy plus conventional medical treatment versus supportive listening plus medical treatment in out-patients with refractory IBS. Patients were recruited from a busy gastrointestinal (GI) clinic in a teaching hospital in the north of England. Consecutive patients fulfilling the following criteria were asked to take part in the study:

(a) abdominal pain, abdominal distension and an abnormal bowel habit associated with normal haematology, serum biochemistry, rectal biopsy and colonoscopy or contrast radiology
(b) continuous symptoms for over one year
(c) attendance at the GI clinic for at least 6 months without improvement
(d) patients below the age of 18 years were excluded, but there was no upper age limit
(e) patients who were actively suicidal were excluded (i.e. expressed clear intentions to kill themselves in the near future).

Patients who agreed to take part were randomly allocated to the treatment or control group. Assessments were conducted at the beginning of the trial, and at the end, 12 weeks later. The gastroenterologist, who remained blind to the trial groups, independently rated the patients' gastrointestinal symptoms at the beginning and end of the trial period. In addition, the patients completed self-report questionnaires of physical symptoms and kept a daily diary chart of bowel symptoms throughout the trial period. They also completed a variety of psychological measures including self-rating scales for depression (Beck *et al*, 1961) and distress (Kellner & Sheffield, 1973).

The treatment group received a long introductory session of three to four hours followed by six sessions of 45 minutes of psychotherapy spread over the next 12 weeks. All the psychotherapy was carried out by one therapist (EG). The approach was exploratory, following the conversational model of Hobson (1985). This model stresses the importance of the developing relationship between therapist and patient, and considers the process of developing this relationship, a fundamental part of the treatment. The model assumes the patient's presenting problems arise from disturbance of significant personal relationships. The development of a healthy therapeutic relationship and the furnishing of links between the therapeutic relationship and other relationships in the patient's life produce insights and new solutions to interpersonal problems. This model was specifically chosen for patients with refractory IBS, because of its emphasis on metaphor and the development of a mutual relationship through conversation. It was felt this approach may be particularly helpful for patients who have difficulty in putting feelings into words. The psychotherapy does not attempt to force a psychological explanation of physical symptoms onto the patient, but merely tries to help the patient to understand and acknowledge any emotional factors that seem relevant to the physical symptoms that he/she is experiencing.

It was necessary to make some modifications to the practice of psychotherapy because of the nature of the trial and the patients involved; these people were not seeking therapy, did not view their symptoms in a psychological way and were not expecting to be referred to a psychiatrist. The principal modifications included:

(a) the therapist being present in the GI clinic when the patient was initially recruited
(b) a very long first session of psychotherapy to maximise the development of a solid therapeutic alliance and encourage the expression of transference material
(c) the explicit use of bowel symptoms as metaphors by the therapist to generate a feeling language between the patient and therapist, e.g. "you're feeling a bit bunged up?", "your guts feel all churned up?".

In addition the patient was given a relaxation tape with brief instructions. If the patient found the tape useful, this was used to emphasise the link between psychological symptoms and bowel symptoms, and if the patient did not use the tape, this was tentatively and gently explored at a psychodynamic level as resistance.

Patients in the control group were seen on five occasions by the same therapist (EG) during the trial period. The therapist appeared warm and empathic during these meetings and discussed and reviewed the patient's symptoms in a sympathetic manner. There was no attempt, however, to try to develop a close relationship with the patient, or make links between psychological and somatic symptoms, or interpret transference material.

Common factors in most psychotherapies include the patient's experience of seeing someone who appears interested in their symptoms, seems warm

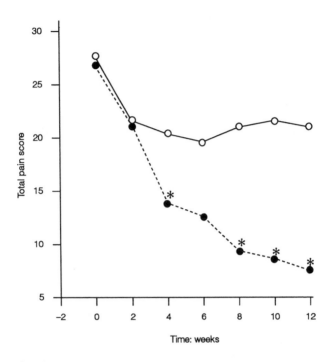

Fig. 6.1. Self-rating of abdominal pain according to daily bowel charts (●----● treatment group, ○—○ control group) (*P<0.05)

and sympathetic, and treats them in a respectful way. It is a mistake to assume these factors are not important, as they can have a powerful therapeutic action. But it is important to control for them to establish whether there is a specific effect as a result of the specialised type of therapy employed.

Results

One hundred and fifteen consecutive patients were approached; four refused, five had pronounced suicidal ideation, two could not speak English, and a further two patients, who were randomised and completed the trial, were withdrawn after they were subsequently found to have underlying organic pathology. This left 102 patients with IBS who entered the trial. The age range was 20–75 years (mean age, 47 years) with 44 patients (40.2%) aged over 50 years or over. Fifty-three patients were allocated to the treatment group and 49 to the control group. Thirteen patients dropped out, seven from the treatment group and six from the control group. All but two of

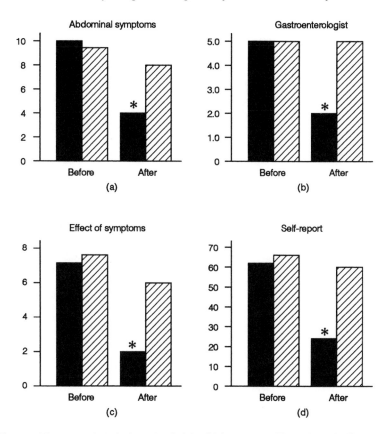

Fig. 6.2. The scores at the beginning and end of the trial for treatment (■) and control (▨) groups: (a) self-rating of abdominal symptoms; (b) gastroenterologist's rating; (c) the limiting effect bowel symptoms had on the patient's life; (d) self-report of abdominal pain on a linear analogue scale (*P = 0.05)

the drop outs were assessed at the end of the trial period. The two patients who were not assessed refused further contact and were actively hostile.

The treatment and control groups did not differ significantly in terms of age distribution, marital status, employment status and social class. However, following the withdrawal of the two patients with organic gastrointestinal disorder, there were significantly more men in the control group (34.7%) compared with the treatment group (15.1%) ($\chi^2 = 4.28$, $P < 0.05$). On account of this, the results were analysed for the group as a whole and then separately for men and women to make sure any differences between the groups were not due to gender.

Baseline measures of both gastroenterological and psychological symptoms were similar. At the end of the trial period, the treatment group showed a significantly greater improvement in gastroenterological and psychological symptoms compared with the control group. Figure 6.1 shows the patients' self-ratings of abdominal pain according to the diary charts for the trial period. Figure 6.2 shows the patients' scores, at the beginning and end of the trial, according to four measures: patients' overall rating of abdominal symptoms, the gastroenterologist's rating, a self-rating of the limiting effect the symptoms had on the patients' life, and a linear analogue scale recording pain. In all cases there was no difference before the study, but a significant difference ($P<0.05$) between treatment and control groups at the end.

When the results were analysed separately for each sex, similar trends emerged for men and women, with greater improvement shown by the patients in the treatment group. However, this improvement was not significantly different for men. Table 6.1 shows the comparison of improvement in scores (baseline score minus 3-month score) between the treatment and control group for the Beck Depression Inventory, and the Symptom Rating Test. When the results were analysed separately for each sex, similar trends emerged for men and women, with greater improvement shown by the patients in the treatment group. However, this was not significantly different for men and there was a slighty greater reduction in anxiety for the men in the control group in comparison to the treatment group.

To discover possible prognostic factors, those patients in the treatment group who improved were compared with those who showed little or no improvement (Table 6.2). Good prognostic factors included the presence of symptoms of depression/anxiety, and the recognition of a causal link between physical symptoms and psychological stress. Patients did poorly if they complained of constant, unremitting pain as opposed to intermittent

TABLE 6.1

Comparison of improvement of psychological scores at the end of the trial: treatment group v. control group

Measures	Treatment median (range)	Control median (range)	
All patients	($n = 50$)	($n = 46$)	
BDI	5 (-8 to 33)	2 (-24 to 32)	$P<0.01$
SRT	8 (-14 to 45)	2 (-13 to 26)	$P<0.01$
Males	($n = 7$)	($n = 15$)	
BDI	5 (-8 to 26)	2 (-8 to 16)	NS
SRT	1 (1 to 12)	2 (-9 to 26)	NS
Females	($n = 43$)	($n = 31$)	
BDI	5 (-5 to 33)	3 (-24 to 32)	$P<0.05$
SRT	8 (-14 to 45)	2 (-13 to 15)	$P<0.01$

Higher scores indicate greater improvement.
BDI = Beck Depression Inventory.
SRT = Sympton Rating Test.

TABLE 6.2
Comparison of baseline characteristics of 'improvers' v 'non-improvers'

Characteristic	Improvers	Non-improvers	χ^2	Significance
Males	3	2		NS
Age over 50	15	6		NS
Psychiatric illness	20	3	4.9	$P<0.05$
Constant pain	7	8	4.7	$P<0.05$
Pain exacerbated by stress	20	2	5.2	$P<0.05$
			M-W U test	
			z	*Significance*
Median number of years for current symptoms	2	4.5	-2.90	$P<0.01$
Median number of weeks off work	2 (0–8)	6.5 (3–8)	-2.87	$P<0.01$

pain, had taken a lot of time off work in the preceding year and had had bowel symptoms for a long time (median 8 years).

Discussion

The patients in this trial represent only a small sample of patients with IBS and should not be regarded as being representative of the group as a whole. They were recruited from a major teaching hospital in the north of England and many were secondary or even tertiary referrals. Only those who did not respond to conventional treatment were included in the study, and thus psychotherapy was being employed as an end of line treatment, after all else had failed. This study clearly demonstrated that approximately two-thirds of patients with refractory symptoms of IBS can be helped by dynamic, explorative psychotherapy. Although there was a trend for male patients to improve, the effectiveness of this treatment in men could not be conclusively established.

Unlike many other trials of psychotherapy, this particular trial is unusual both in terms of employing a large sample size (over 100) and an independent assessor.

The psychological theories of the development of psychosomatic symptoms are complex and confusing. The data collected in the present study are not sophisticated enough to determine the way psychotherapy was able to relieve patients' distress, although the improvement in bowel symptoms appeared to follow improvement in psychological status. Most patients who improved went through a process of psychological change: first, they were able to acknowledge the importance of emotional factors in relation to the bowel symptoms; second, they were able to link emotional feelings towards the therapist with feelings towards important others in their lives; third, they were then able to understand the way difficulties in their relationships resulted in the development or exacerbation of bowel symptoms; and finally they were able to consider making changes to the nature of the relationships that they formed. It is important to point out, however, that some patients improved without undergoing any of the above changes.

The patients who did not respond to dynamic psychotherapy appeared clinically to have somatisation disorders with marked abnormal illness behaviour. They had a firm conviction that their symptoms had a physical cause, had had their symptoms for several years and in many cases had a lot to lose emotionally and financially (because of invalidity benefit) if their condition improved. It is not surprising that such a brief intervention as the therapy described above did not help these patients who are at the very severe end of the IBS spectrum. It is possible that these patients would respond to a different psychological approach such as the behavioural strategies used with patients with chronic pain, although it is difficult to envisage many of them engaging or complying with pain programmes.

In conclusion, the majority of patients with IBS respond to simple measures including an explanation of their symptoms, reassurance and pharmacological agents such as bulking agents and antispasmodic drugs (Harvey *et al*, 1987). It is unlikely that a psychotherapeutic intervention could be justified, at this point, as even brief therapy is relatively time-consuming and therefore costly. The skill of the gastroenterologist in being able to provide adequate counselling is paramount, and it is important that psychiatrists collaborate more closely with gastroenterologists. They should establish a friendly dialogue, and provide guidance and supervision when requested. For the patients with refractory IBS, it is possible that psychological intervention at an earlier stage, before the symptoms become intractable, may mean even more than two-thirds of these patients can be helped by psychotherapy, although this remains to be studied.

There is mounting evidence that psychological factors are important, not only in IBS, but also in many other so-called functional conditions such as chronic back pain, common migraine etc., where an underlying physical cause cannot account for the severity or longevity of symptoms. The vast majority of these patients, of which there are many thousands, are rarely offered psychological help and are often prescribed drug after drug in an attempt to alleviate their symptoms. It is important that greater priority is given to the development of psychological and psychiatric services within the general hospital setting so that these kinds of patients can be offered effective treatments for their symptoms.

Case examples

Two patients who participated in the study are briefly described: the first case describes the therapy of a patient who improved, and the second case describes a patient who was not helped by the therapy. These cases are not meant to be representative of all the patients who participated in the study. No common psychological theme or underlying personality structure or core conflict could be identified. In fact there was a diversity of personalities, psychological problems and relationship difficulties.

Case 1

Pat was a 72-year-old married woman, who had suffered with abdominal pain for 50 years. She had had two episodes of hospital treatment. The first was when she was in her twenties and the second had been 7 years previously, when she had been referred back to the out-patient clinic because of a relapse of her symptoms; she had continued to attend regularly since then. She had been married to the same man for 54 years, and described him as very kind and supportive.

She described an extremely unhappy childhood, with a violent and alcoholic father, who had frequently beaten her with a strap when she was little. She described her mother as kind and loving, but very frail, and having little time for her, as there were seven other children in the house. Her mother died when she was 13 years old, and after that she was brought up by her elder sister.

When she began courting her future husband, her father became very disapproving and on two occasions physically threw him out of the house, and threatened to kill him. Because of this, she eventually eloped with him and never saw her father again.

She described having had troubles with her bowels since she was a teenager. The abdominal pain she experienced was very sharp, "knife like" she said, "like something twisted inside".

In the first session she was keen to understand her bowel symptoms in a psychological way, although she had been initially surprised and rather reluctant to see a psychiatrist, when first approached in the clinic. She said she had felt tense all her life, was never able to relax, and had often wondered whether her bowel trouble was connected to the way she felt. She went on to describe the pain in more detail.

> "It comes on suddenly, I can just be doing something and then it's there. Somehow I know it will never go away, even when I don't feel it, I feel it in a funny kind of way. It's sharp and it sticks inside, and it makes me feel sick. It's spoilt my life, prevented me from doing things I've wanted to do. When it comes I just think oh no."

As the first session progressed the image of the pain became more and more awful, "A big monster that has ruined my life". We used the metaphor "a wound that has never healed"; Pat graphically described feeling she had a bleeding, pustular sore inside her that continually weeped and oozed. The links between this internal wound and the real repeated wounds caused by her father (and the neglect by her mother) became more and more obvious, but when I tentatively suggested a link between the two, she did not take it up and became more distant in the session. I did not push any further but simply commented that although for many years she had thought the pain was perhaps linked to how she felt, it was actually very disturbing to look at it face to face.

In the following sessions, she developed a strong positive transference towards me, and saw me as representing all the potential qualities she could have had, if she had not been 'spoilt'. She finally went on to divulge that she had been sexually abused by her father, when she was a little girl, but never told anyone, not even her husband.

She felt she had only survived as an adult because her husband had been so kind and supportive. They had had two sons and he had taken on more of the child care than most men, and encouraged her to work and develop her own interests and identity. She came to see the pain as a sign that something had been irrevocably damaged inside her and could not be replaced or restored. She went on to realise that the pain had become much worse in recent years, partly because she had retired, but also because her younger sister had died. She confided in me that she thought that her sister had also been abused by their father. When Pat eloped with her husband, she had always felt guilty that she had left her younger sister behind, to be at the mercy of their father. The two of them had never discussed this, and her sister's death meant that they never would.

The positive, idealised transference towards me enabled Pat to look at some of her feelings about her mother. The very last session revolved around her feelings that her mother had ultimately betrayed and abandoned her, and that I was doing the same thing.

Her symptoms gradually improved with the therapy and when she was followed up one year later, she reported that the abdominal pain was much better. She had told her husband about the abuse and had spent a lot more time talking to him about her feelings. He, as a result, had also confided more in her. She was beginning to enjoy her retirement and had joined an art class, specifically so she could express some of her feelings by painting. At the age of 73 years, having never held a paint brush before in her life, she won a prize for the best watercolour. The ending of the therapy had also enabled her to feel angry with her mother for the first time in her life, and subsequently also be able to acknowledge some good things she had got from her mother which previously she had denied. The guilt about her sister remained, although she was able to feel more angry with her father and rationally see that the abuse was his fault, not her own. In her heart, however, she still felt responsible.

Case 2

Dorothy was 49 years old and had had abdominal pain for 20 years. It commenced shortly after she married. She had no children. Her husband worked as a telephone engineer and was a very quiet, passive man. She described him as a saint. He looked after her, brought her cups of tea, did all the shopping for her and took her out for walks in her wheelchair. On some days if she was not too tired and the pain was not too severe she would try to walk a few yards, but would then feel completely exhausted and have to rest.

She had consulted numerous doctors over the years, all of whom, she took great delight in telling me, were baffled by her symptoms. She had been admitted several times for investigation and undergone bowel surgery. One doctor had told her that the pain was due to a 'large pouch of bowel' and another doctor had said the only way to cure her would be to 'take it all out'. If it came to that she thought, she would face it stoically like she had faced all her other admissions and operations. She was very brave, she would endure any treatment, undergo any trial if it would result in her cure. She herself knew it was physical, and thought that there was little point in her seeing me.

Dorothy had been brought up in an unhappy household. Her father had died when she was 4 years old from tuberculosis and her mother had had several admissions to hospital with 'her nerves'. Dorothy had consequently had several absences from her mother, both real and emotional. She had been a good child, well behaved at school and had always helped with the housework. She got married, aged 29 years, to her first boyfriend whom she had met through her church. He had had a very sheltered upbringing and on their marriage he moved into the house Dorothy shared with her mother. Dorothy's trouble began within a few weeks of the marriage, and she rapidly became an invalid. She had no social outlets or close friends and no real enjoyment in life. Her pain had become much worse since the death of her mother 10 years previously, although she herself did not make this connection.

In her sessions with me, she spent most of the time complaining of her pain, but had difficulty in describing its quality.

"It hurts right here, just goes down my leg now like a knife, just down there. Sometimes it's absolutely unbearable – I just have to lie down the pain is so bad. Now it's there like a ball just here" (pointing to her stomach).

When I asked her to describe the quality of the pain, she replied "It's pain, you know what pain is don't you, it hurts, it hurts, it hurts!". Our sessions consisted of long episodes where she would cry and tell me that she was in pain. She felt, however, that her cries were not heard. I did not make her better. It did not help to come and see me.

In the therapy, she invoked powerful countertransference feelings of anger and hatred, and I often had the desire to take her wheelchair away from her and set fire to it and also had fantasies of disembowling her with a long knife. She was highly resistant to any suggestion that her emotional life was in anyway relevant to her physical complaints, and regarded that a failure to improve with therapy would prove that there was no underlying psychological cause.

At the end of the therapy she felt angry and dissatisfied but also triumphant. One year later there had been no change in her symptoms. Dorothy (and her husband) had too much to lose by getting better. Psychodynamic therapy was far too threatening. It is possible that she may have been helped by a more behaviourally orientated approach, although it is doubtful whether she or her husband would have complied.

One of the most important aspects of her future management was to liaise with the gastroenterologist responsible for her care to provide long-term continuity in order to prevent further unnecessary investigations or surgery.

References

BECK, A. T., WARD, C. H., MENDELSON, M., *et al* (1961) An inventory for measuring depression. *Archives of General Psychiatry*, **4**, 561–571.

BENNETT, P. & WILKINSON, S. (1985) A comparison of psychological and medical treatment of the irritable bowel syndrome. *British Journal of Clinical Psychology*, **24**, 215–216.

CREED, F. H. & GUTHRIE, E. (1987) Psychological factors and the irritable bowel syndrome. *Gut*, **28**, 1307–1318.

—— & —— (1989) Psychological treatment in the irritable bowel syndrome: a review. *Gut*, **30**, 1601–1609.

GUTHRIE, E., CREED, F., DAWSON, D., *et al* (1991) A controlled trial of psychological treatment for the irritable bowel syndrome. *Gastroenterology*, **100**, 450–457.

HARVEY, R. F., MAUAD, E. C. & BROWN, A. M. (1987) Prognosis in the irritable bowel syndrome: a 5-year prospective study. *Lancet*, 963–965.

——, HINTON, R. A., GUNARY, R. M., *et al* (1989) Individual and group hypnotherapy in treatment of refractory irritable bowel syndrome. *Lancet*, 424–425.

HOBSON, R. (1985) *Forms of Feeling*. London: Tavistock.

KELLNER, R. & SHEFFIELD, B. F. (1973) A self-rating scale of distress. *Psychological Medicine*, **3**, 88–100.

KINGHAM, J. G. C. & DAWSON, A. M. (1985) Origin of chronic right upper quadrant pain. *Gut*, **26**, 783–788.

KLEIN, K. B. (1988) Controlled treatment trials in the irritable bowel syndrome: a critique. *Gastroenterology*, **95**, 232–241.

SVEDLUND, J. (1983) Psychotherapy in irritable bowel syndrome: A controlled outcome study. *Acta Psychiatrica Scandinavica*, **67** (suppl. 306).

THOMPSON, W. G. (1984) The irritable bowel. *Gut*, **25**, 305–320.

WHORWELL, P. J., PRIOR, A. & FARAGHER, E. B. (1984) Controlled trial of hypnotherapy in the treatment of severe refractory irritable bowel syndrome. *Lancet*, *ii*, 1232–1234.

7 Management of atypical non-cardiac chest pain

RICHARD MAYOU

Non-cardiac chest pain is common in all medical settings (Mayou, 1989). In general practice, it is one of the commonest of all presenting symptoms, and usually has a good prognosis. However, a minority of general practice attenders are not reassured and continue to consult doctors, and to complain of symptoms and disability (Mayou, 1989; Chambers & Bass, 1990). In hospital practice, there is consistent evidence that patients who are admitted for investigation and found to have normal coronary angiograms continue to report symptoms and disability. There is also increasing evidence that chest pain presenting to hospital emergency departments and out-patient clinics also has a poor symptomatic outlook. Overall it would seem that the more specialist the setting and the more intensive the investigation, the less likely it is that patients will have improved at follow-up.

General practitioners and hospital physicians are concerned about the appropriate management of patients presenting with chest pain of unexplained cause and remain uncertain about the advantages and disadvantages of continuing investigations, and the best ways of reassuring patients and minimising iatrogenic disability. Our current debates about management use different terminologies, but in fact are a continuation of over a hundred years of controversy about syndromes such as soldiers' heart, irritable heart, effort syndrome and neuro-circulatory asthenia (Mayou, 1989). Many of the patients who would formerly have been given such diagnoses are now recognised and treated as suffering from anxiety disorder or other psychiatric conditions, but there are still many patients in whom clear medical or psychiatric diagnoses cannot be made.

Controversy about aetiology continues unabated with rival specialists suggesting specific explanations (Chambers & Bass, 1990). These narrow approaches have been largely unhelpful and it is much more likely that the explanation is multi-causal. Such a view was first put forward 50 years ago by Dr Paul Wood in his classic research on effort syndrome, or what he christened Da Costa's syndrome (Wood, 1941; Wood, 1986; Chambers &

TABLE 7.1
Aetiology

Predisposing factors	Precipitating factors	Maintaining factors
Personality	Life events	Persistence of physiological/
Psychiatric disorder	Illness events (others,	pathological factors
Illness (cardiac and other)	media, etc.)	Anxiety, depression, panic
experience	Psychiatric disorder	Response of family and
personal		friends
family		Iatrogenic
neighbours		
media		
Heart disease		
Social circumstances		

Bass, 1990). His work on the lack of a cardiac basis for the syndrome is widely quoted, but his cogent arguments for a multi-causal aetiology and his emphasis on patients' individual understanding of the meaning of symptoms has been neglected. I believe that this model in which there is an interaction between psychological factors and either minor physical pathology or excessive awareness of normal physiological function remains fundamental to understanding non-cardiac chest pain.

An aetiological model

The model used in this chapter combines all the physical and psychiatric factors that have been suggested by other writers. It makes explicit what is often implicit in everyday clinical practice, but has often been ignored by research workers (Chambers & Bass, 1990).

Predisposing factors

A variety of predisposing psychological and social factors (Table 7.1) make it more likely that bodily perceptions of minor medical significance will be misinterpreted as evidence of serious cardiac or other disease (Pearce *et al*, 1990). For some people, concern about possible physical illness is a feature of personality with regular exacerbation at times of stress. Others are inclined to make pessimistic interpretations and to mistrust medical advice because of their personal, family or other experience of illness in this treatment. A number may have had previous heart disease or had previous special knowledge, for example, having a bad family history of heart disease will inevitably cause concern about any symptoms which might be due to heart disease.

It is important to be aware that non-cardiac pains are frequently described by patients who have ischaemic or other heart disease. It is unsurprising that they are very frequent during recovery from myocardial infarction, and especially in those with undoubted angina. Cardiac surgery is particularly likely to cause pains and discomfort because of the problems relating to the incision.

Sometimes, a primary psychiatric disorder (depression or, more frequently, anxiety) may be the cause of the underlying physical perceptions, as well as predisposing to misinterpretation. Panic attacks are very commonly described and may be either a primary cause of the presenting symptoms or part of the secondary emotional reaction to misinterpretation. However, there has been a tendency to over-emphasise the significance of panic in some recent psychiatric literature and chest pain. The management principles described here apply to patients with all forms of psychiatric disorder. Although psychiatric disorder is common, even usual in hospital practice, it is essential to recognise that disabling chest pain with substantially psychological origin can occur without a psychiatric disorder.

Precipitating factors

Symptoms may be precipitated by minor physical problems, by life stresses or psychiatric disorder. Previous illness experience and knowledge of illness in others are important. Patients frequently relate dramatic accounts of similar symptoms in relatives, friends or in other people (Pearce *et al*, 1990). For example, reading in a newspaper about the heart disease of a famous person may be enough to trigger concern and misinterpretation. Concern about symptoms inevitably results in increased attention being focused upon them, thereby enhancing their subjective severity. Concern may also lead to a variety of types of behaviour which may again exacerbate the symptoms. These behaviours include focusing on and checking physical signs, pursuit of medical advice, reading medical literature, and avoidance behaviour.

Maintaining factors

Once established, a variety of factors may perpetuate symptoms. These include persistence of the underlying bodily perception, secondary emotional distress (depression, anxiety, panic) and iatrogenic factors, such as misleading, contradictory or uninformative medical advice.

Doctors' caution and their concern not to miss physical diagnosis is understandable and indeed good practice. However, it is crucial that it is not accompanied by neglect of psychological factors. Investigations and diagnostic difficulties and uncertainties must be clearly explained and patients and relatives must be given the opportunity to ask questions. Many patients can tolerate the uncertainty if they are able to understand the issues and their implications. On occasions when several doctors are necessarily involved, the role of the general practitioner remains important in coordinating care and in ensuring that minor discrepancies and misunderstandings are dealt with. Many of the patients who are at risk of unnecessary caution and anxiety are extremely sensitive to anything they think may indicate a sinister cause.

Implications of the model

The model implies that any physical procedures to modify underlying perceptions (for example, medication for oesophagitis) and specific psychiatric treatments (such as antidepressant medication) have an important role. Table 7.2 lists the main issues in management; most have practical implications for general practitioners and physicians rather than psychiatrists. However, psychiatrists and psychologists must help both by offering specialist care and by formulating and evaluating simple treatment for use by others, treatments which depend upon a clear model of aetiology.

An aetiological model in which patients' misinterpretations (or attribution) result in excessive and inappropriate distress and disability also allows formulation of psychological treatments, which aim to modify beliefs and behaviour. This is a cognitive–behavioural approach and it is appropriate and sensible to apply the specific techniques that have been shown to be effective in the treatment of anxiety and other psychological disorders (Clark, 1986).

Although there is considerable clinical experience of the psychological treatment of non-cardiac chest pain, and one can draw analogies from other areas of psychological treatment, research evidence on the effectiveness of treatments of non-cardiac chest pain is relatively limited. We have shown that cognitive–behavioural intervention can be effective (Klimes *et al*, 1990). There is also evidence that drug treatments can be useful (Beitman *et al*, 1988), especially in patients with depression or anxiety disorders. There is a clear need for further research to evaluate treatments, especially treatments which could be applied in ordinary clinical practice by non-specialists.

TABLE 7.2
Issues in management

(1) Routine physical and psychological examination
(2) *Appropriate* medical investigation
(3) Multicausal explanation *discussed* with patient
(4) Identify those requiring specific medical treatment
(5) Identify those requiring specific psychological treatment
(6) Follow-up review
    (a) if improved, discharge
    (b) if unimproved, offer more intensive treatment

Principles of management

Advice on the management of atypical chest pain has usually been a matter for generalised exhortations by rival specialists. It needs to be much more precise and focused on the practical issues of providing better and appropriate care for large numbers of people, most of whom are seen in primary care rather than in hospital practice. The remainder of this chapter is therefore concerned with the clinical application of our aetiological model in general practice, medical out-patient clinics and in specialist psychiatric or psychological care.

Our clinical experience with patients recently referred to the cardiac clinic shows that successful treatment does not require sophisticated psychological skills or extra time. The evidence about the poor prognosis for non-cardiac chest pain is based on highly selected populations, and should not obscure the better prognosis and more straightforward management that is likely to be effective for many patients newly presenting in general practice.

Better planned routine management could prevent considerable persistent morbidity, but patients who do not respond to routine care are identified as early as possible and offered more intensive individual treatment. Early recognition of the significance of psychological factors would also enable a reduction in medical investigation and reduce the iatrogenic complications.

Table 7.3 lists the main elements of treatment. The non-specific elements are fundamental. They concentrate on establishing a working relationship in which the doctor emphasises the role of physical and psychological factors from the very beginning.

Assessment

Physical factors

There are many medical causes of chest pain, most of minor clinical significance (Chambers & Bass, 1990). Although it is important to be able

TABLE 7.3
Elements of treatment

Non-specific	Specific
Accept symptoms are genuine; avoid argument	Provide re-evaluation of significance of symptoms
Convey that patient has a common and treatable problem	Demonstrate the contribution of attention and situational factors
Provide treatment rationale	Provide methods of symptom control
Offer opportunity to express emotion and feelings about care	Encourage return to normal behaviour
	Treat depressive disorder
Involve relatives	Treat associated social or interpersonal factors

to identify chest wall pain and other causes, the search for such factors should not lead the doctor to exaggerate their aetiological and clinical significance. The single-minded pursuit of particular explanations of non-cardiac chest pain has been unhelpful, diverting the doctor's and the patient's attention from psychological factors.

Cognitive–behavioural assessment

A systematic enquiry should always be made about the patient's beliefs and behaviour. The useful detailed history of the physical symptoms should be accompanied by routine enquiry about the circumstances in which they occur, the patient's response, and about other somatic symptoms.

It is often useful to concentrate on detailed accounts of particular episodes, since this enables an analysis of traits preceding the symptoms, and the nature and development of the symptoms and their consequences. Specific questions about the nature of fears and beliefs are much more useful than general enquiry.

Mental state

Doctors should ask about current symptoms of depression, anxiety and panic, and about previous psychiatric disorder and associated non-specific somatic complaints. Patients may be suspicious of an overly psychiatric approach to a problem that they see in entirely physical terms. It is essential that questioning is in common-sense terms, with full consideration of bodily symptoms before enquiries about psychological symptoms. Most patients find it possible to accept that emotional factors affect the subjective perception of their symptoms (whatever their origins) and that treatment of stress and response to symptoms may be the worthwhile part of an overall management plan.

Diaries

Patients are often asked to complete a diary of their symptoms and activities, a procedure which can be as helpful in managing angina as in non-cardiac pain. These provide valuable information about the circumstances in which symptoms occur and a baseline for treatment. Patients are unobtrusively introduced to the general principles of behavioural treatment and are often able to draw their own unprompted conclusions about predisposing and precipitating factors.

Formulation

At the end of the assessment, the doctor should have a provisional medical and psychosocial formulation and also have established a good working relationship with the patient. The formulation must now be put to the patient, discussed and agreed. It is essential to avoid argument. The suggestion that psychological factors contribute to distress and disability should not be seen as underestimating the possibility of a physical contribution, or that the patient's concern has been inappropriate. It may be appropriate to suggest that psychological treatment should be pursued for the time being, but that if it fails or if there are other indications, it would be possible to consider the role of further physical investigation or treatment. Many patients, whatever their views about underlying causes, will accept that they have had all that physical medicine can offer, and that it would be worth examining other ways of reducing the distress associated with their symptoms.

Organisation of care

Since large numbers of people suffer from non-cardiac chest pains, and since psychosocial prognosis varies from excellent to poor, it is essential that treatment in any medical setting should aim to provide good routine care for everyone, together with selective extra help for all those who need it. Only a minority will require skilled psychological and psychiatric treatment; even so it is doubtful whether at present the resources or skills are available in hospital settings. There is almost certainly a need to train specialist cardiac or other nurses who may be able to take on much of the treatment.

General practice

Although non-cardiac chest pain is one of the commonest reasons for presentation in general practice, we know relatively little about its natural history and how it is currently managed. Most patients are reassured by consultation, but a significant minority continue to be users of medical resources and suffer continuing symptoms, distress and disability.

There is consistent evidence that general practitioners often find it difficult to make precise diagnoses of angina in general practice, but that they refer only a minority of such patients. Many patients are treated symptomatically and regarded as suffering from possible or probable angina or other uncertain diagnoses. Some patients can tolerate this uncertainty, but others, who may not have angina, become stressed and limit their activities.

At the first consultation, the general practitioner should aim to provide appropriate medical care, to identify major psychological problems and give the patient the opportunity to discuss the explanation of the symptoms. All patients should be told to come back if they have any continuing problems (Table 7.4).

TABLE 7.4
General practice

(1) Appropriate simple physical and psychological investigation
(2) Provisional explanation to patient
(3) Follow-up appointment
(4) If persistent – more thorough assessment and discussion to identify physical and psychological factors
(5) Consider referral for specialist medical opinion
(6) If no improvement with full medical assessment, explanation and reassurance, consider referral for psychiatric assessment

Those that return because of persistent problems require rather more prolonged assessment. It may be appropriate to investigate the possibility of angina or other physical causes, but it is essential that from the outset the doctor keeps in mind both physical and psychological factors and conveys this interactive view to the patient.

The precise and practical approach to somatisation symptoms described by Goldberg and his colleagues (Goldberg *et al*, 1989) is valuable and enables the general practitioner to establish a basis for effective management, using explanation and advice, antidepressants, a simple cognitive–behavioural approach or other psychological measures.

Referral for a cardiac or other medical opinion is often indicated to confirm the diagnosis, but should be part of an overall plan, for which the general practitioner retains primary responsibility. If management in general practice is not successful, psychiatric referral should be considered. The general practitioner's emphasis on the importance of psychological factors from the outset should make it easier to explain the reasons for referral and more likely that the outcome of referral will be successful.

Out-patient clinics

More than half of the patients who are referred to cardiac clinics with chest pain are not given a cardiac or other major physical diagnosis. Cardiologists normally discharge such patients back to primary care with general reassurance. Unfortunately, this reassurance is effective with no more than a third of patients (Mayou, 1989).

We have recently assessed 94 patients who were consecutively referred to a cardiac clinic, with presenting complaints of chest pain or palpitations. Over a half were given no major physical diagnosis and were reassured. Two-thirds of these patients described continuing symptoms at follow-up at 6 months and 3 years. Symptoms were associated with significant disability, distress, use of resources and dissatisfaction with medical care. This poor outcome for large numbers of patients means that we need to consider ways in which clinic explanation and reassurance could be made more effective and patients with continuing symptoms can be offered further help.

TABLE 7.5
Out-patient clinic

(1) Appropriate physical and psychological assessment
(2) Discuss provisional explanation with patient; provide written information
(3) Consider further investigation; if ordered, expain fully
(4) If major psychiatric problem, consider immediate referral, otherwise follow-up appointment
(5) If symptoms persist at follow-up: review and more thorough discussion; if indicated, refer psychological assessment, otherwise offer further follow-up
(6) If symptoms still persist, refer

Table 7.5 summarises what might be the aims of treatment for the cardiologist. It is essential to reassure but also to provide an explanation of the symptoms, and also to offer the patient the opportunity to discuss anxieties and fears together. The cardiologist should also identify major psychiatric morbidity which might benefit from immediate psychiatric referral and treatment. Patients who are reassured require an opportunity for further review, either in the out-patient clinic or in general practice. Some patients do not always return to their general practitioners. It will often be most sensible to offer a further out-patient appointment, whilst at the same time sending full information to the general practitioner.

Many patients with persistent symptoms at follow-up may benefit from further and more detailed explanation. At this stage, referral to a psychiatrist or psychologist should be considered, but the best solution might be direct access to help from a specialised nurse or counsellor based within the cardiac clinic.

Referral to a psychiatric clinic often poses problems. These arise from the scepticism of cardiologists and physicians, the unwillingness of patients to see their physical symptoms in psychological terms, and unfortunately, from the past unwillingness of psychiatrists to take on the treatment of patients who do not suffer from traditional forms of psychiatric disorder. Referral is normally successful if the physician gives a clear explanation, the psychiatric clinic is welcoming (especially if it is based within the general hospital), and if the early medical management has emphasised the significance of both physical and psychological factors. Most patients find the interactive aetiological model convincing and are reassured by being told that they have a common problem, and that referral for treatment of nervous and muscular tension does not imply mental illness.

Other medical settings

The procedures described above for out-patient attenders can be adapted for use with other general hospital patients with non-cardiac complaints, for example those who have had normal coronary angiograms and emergency attender admissions with chest pain. In these circumstances, reassurance about not having heart disease is frequently hurried, incomplete, inadequate and ambiguous. Patients who have normal coronary angiograms are often given the encouraging results of investigation in catheter rooms and in busy wards shortly before discharge. This means that the subgroup of patients with non-cardiac chest pain who are known to be the most psychiatrically disabled have the least opportunity to discuss the final outcome of medical assessment. As in the out-patient clinic, it is important to discuss alternative explanations and to suggest an appropriate follow-up at which persisting symptoms can be reviewed.

In the emergency department, non-specific physical symptoms are common (Mayou, 1989). Doctors need to be more aware of the importance of recognising anxiety and panic disorder, and also that the management is as important as treating physical disorder. Patients and their relatives require information about the ways in which such symptoms can contribute to acute physical symptoms.

Specialist referral

In the past, most psychiatric out-patient clinics have been unwilling to manage non-cardiac chest pain and other non-organic physical symptoms. A proportion of patients do require intensive specialist treatment skills and these must be made widely available. It is all to evident that many senior psychiatrists do not have experience in managing such symptoms, and that treatment skills are given insufficient emphasis in psychiatric training. There is encouraging clinical evidence that relatively simple procedures are helpful with many patients (Table 7.6). The identification and treatment of major depression with antidepressant medication is important, although depression is not a common psychiatric cause of chest pain. It is sensible to choose an antidepressant with relatively few side-effects, and to take great care in explaining the treatment, the need for perseverance and ways of coping with the side-effects.

TABLE 7.6
Specialist care

(1) Ensure referring doctor discusses aims of referral with patient
(2) Review all medical notes before seeing patient
(3) Full psychiatric assessment (patient + informant)
(4) Cognitive–behavioural analysis of symptoms
(5) Consider antidepressant medication
(6) Consider cognitive–behavioural treatment
(7) Discuss role of psychological treatment; agree treatment contract
(8) Provide written information
(9) Coordinate psychological care with any on-going medical care
(10) Discuss plans with general practitioner and any others involved in care

TABLE 7.7
Psychiatric treatments

(1) Antidepressant medication
(2) Cognitive
     modify beliefs and related behaviour by discussion
     behavioural experiments
(3) Behavioural
     anxiety management
     breathing exercises
     graded practice
(4) Other
     psychotherapy/counselling
     family problems
     social problems

Standard cognitive–behavioural methods (Table 7.7) are helpful for many patients. Frequently, an explanation of the interactive model of aetiology, of the role of anxiety and panic, and encouraging the patient to monitor symptoms in a detailed diary is all that is required. Other patients require somewhat more elaborate anxiety management, and a small proportion needs skilled cognitive therapy.

Special problems

Patients who fail to engage in treatment

Though the failure to engage in treatment usually indicates lack of appropriately careful preparation by the referring doctor or difficulties in initial meeting, some patients are particularly unwilling to accept any form of psychological help. It is sensible that the offer of this treatment is kept open, and to tell all those involved in care that psychological treatment is both appropriate and available whenever the patient would like to take it up. Sceptical patients will accept another appointment for review.

It is important to try and end the assessment on good terms and to ensure that failure to engage in psychological treatment does not result in a resumption of the research for inappropriate physical remedies.

Problems with multiple somatisation symptoms

This chapter is mainly concerned with patients presenting with the single symptom of chest pain. In a minority of subjects, the chest pain is but one aspect of a chronic syndrome of hypochondriasis or somatisation. Such patients often consult a number of doctors and other therapists. They are frequently given somewhat conflicting advice and their symptoms and disabilities are made worse by the uncoordinated medical input. Close liaison with all those involved in care is fundamental to successful treatment. It is usually possible to simplify treatment and to define the continuing contributions of all those involved. Even so, some patients are adept at obtaining further advice which inevitably involves minor discrepancies. It is essential to avoid criticising colleagues, but to continue to attempt to control medical care. Damage limitation (controlling medical care and preventing further iatrogenic disability) may be a more realistic aim than cure.

Failure to improve

Failure to improve may be due to inadequacies of the psychological formulation, lack of compliance or to the development of significant physical disorder. It is necessary to be alert to all these possibilities.

As in all psychiatric practice, personal, interpersonal and social difficulties may be much more profound than is apparent at initial interview. Regular contact with relatives will make it easier to detect such problems.

Systematic diary keeping must be encouraged as it will enable the therapist to discuss with the patient the ways in which lack of progress is due either to failure to follow agreed plans or to difficulties which mean that aims and plans should be re-evaluated.

Very occasionally, physical causes are eventually found for unexplained symptoms. Occasionally, new physical conditions develop during the course of treatment. The multicausal view of aetiology enables the therapist to take all physical symptoms seriously and to suggest further physical investigation when appropriate. Physical investigation for clear medical indications is a proper part of management of unexplained physical symptoms.

Conclusions

The management of physical symptoms without apparent physical cause has always been a substantial clinical problem for doctors in general practice and hospital practice. Common-sense reassurance and explanation is often effective, but large numbers of patients continue to suffer distress and disability. In the past, psychiatry has had little to offer to such patients and both patients and their doctors have found psychiatric referral both difficult to achieve and eventually unhelpful.

There is now very considerable clinical evidence and an increasing amount of research evidence to support a much greater role for psychological treatments. Some of these are complex, intensive and can only be provided by the specialist. Others can be applied within general practice or general hospital clinics. Even so, it is unrealistic to expect that busy clinicians will always have the time that many of these problems demand. The solution is not just a question of increasing specialist resources, it is also a question of providing expertise within general practice and hospital clinical units. The economic cost of unexplained physical symptoms is very large, and there is overwhelming justification for new clinical and administrative approaches to providing effective treatment.

Chest pain is one of the commonest of such symptoms and it is to be hoped that cardiologists will recognise the importance of extra care for clinic attenders, emergency admissions and patients undergoing investigations for what eventually turns out to be non-cardiac chest pain. We must persuade those who plan and provide psychiatric services to give more attention to providing care for the large numbers of people with non-organic physical symptoms. This will mean changes in training, adequately staffed consultation–liaison services with cognitive–behavioural skills and resources in every health district.

References

BEITMAN, B. D., BASHA, I. M., TROMBKA, L. H., *et al* (1988) Alprazolam in the treatment of cardiology patients with atypical chest pain and panic disorder. *Journal of Clinical Psychopharmacology*, **8**, 127–130.

CHAMBERS, J. B. & BASS, C. (1990) Chest pain and normal coronary anatomy: review of natural history and possible aetiologic factors. *Progress in Cardiovascular Disease*, **33**, 161–184.

CLARK, D. M. (1986) A cognitive approach to panic. *Behaviour Research and Therapy*, **24**, 461–470.

GOLDBERG, D., GASK, L. & O'DAVID, T. (1989) The treatment of somatization: teaching the techniques of reattribution. *Journal of Psychosomatic Research*, **6**, 689–695.

KLIMES, I., MAYOU, R. A., PEARCE, M. J., *et al* (1990) Psychological treatment for atypical non-cardiac chest pain: a controlled evaluation. *Psychological Medicine*, **20**, 605–611.

MAYOU, R. A. (1989) Invited review: atypical chest pain. *Journal of Psychosomatic Research*, **33**, 373–406.

PEARCE, M. J., MAYOU, R. A. & KLIMES, I. (1990) The management of atypical non-cardiac chest pain. *Quarterly Journal of Medicine*, **281**, 991–996.

WOOD, P. (1941) Da Costa's syndrome (or effort syndrome). *British Medical Journal*, 767–772, 805–811, 845–851.

——— (1986) *Diseases of the Heart and Circulation* (3rd edn). London: Eyre and Spottiswoode.

8 In-patient management of chronic pain

AMANDA C. de C. WILLIAMS

Why pain management?

The main aim of an in-patient pain programme is not to relieve pain. It is rather to enable the pain sufferer to improve the quality of his or her life, despite pain. This is achieved by changing the way he or she behaves in relation to the pain. Treatment practices developed from this model are described here, in particular in-patient treatment. This offers the chronic pain patient the opportunity to examine and change long-established habits of activity, inactivity, and the beliefs associated with those habits, and to do so in a setting free of some of the external factors which perpetuate those habits. This is carried out by operant and cognitive techniques. Changes in behaviour and thinking must be sufficiently resilient to persist when the patient returns to his or her old environment. The St Thomas' in-patient pain management programme is described here in detail, and the advantages and disadvantages of in-patient treatment compared with out-patient treatment are elaborated. Finally, assessment and preliminary results are presented in brief.

The problem of chronic pain

All experience of pain has a psychological component, not as a secondary reactive stage, but as an integral part (Bonica, 1977; Melzack & Wall, 1982). Acute pain, however, is most usually dealt with by the sufferer or by others on his or her behalf with reasonable expectation of relief and eventual resolution. Some chronic pain cannot, by definition, be relieved by existing medical procedures and physical techniques. The model of chronic pain on which pain management is based emphasises the role of maladaptive beliefs and behaviours, some of which arise from the attempts by the patient and others to relieve the pain.

Clinical and research data on the personality and psychopathology of the chronic pain patient have yielded little consistent data, with no clear implications for treatment (Fordyce, 1976; Turk *et al*, 1983). Individual case histories may suggest factors which predispose to poor management of chronic problems, but it is much harder to determine common factors in patients' learning histories which contribute to their difficulties in managing chronic pain. In addition, we know all too little about non-patients, who manage their chronic pain and remain outside the orbit of pain clinics and researchers. In a recent British survey, 11% of respondents reported chronic pain, over half stating that it restricted their ability to work and to lead a normal life (Rigge, 1990). The complaint of pain and its interference with lifestyle rises with self-reported stress, anxiety and depressed mood, making measurement of pain-related disability a complex undertaking (Sternbach, 1986; Dworkin *et al*, 1990).

There is no 'objective' measure of pain: there is only the patient's report and behaviour. Pain-related behaviour includes excessive rest and reduced activity; occasions of relative overactivity; overuse of analgesics and of psychotropic drugs; and repeated seeking of medical help even when appropriate modes of treatment have been exhausted. Such strategies, often effective in coping with acute pain, are increasingly unhelpful as pain persists, and tend to vary less with the reported intensity of pain than with situational factors such as the presence or absence of other people, or the satisfactions or dissatisfactions of current activity (Fordyce *et al*, 1984). The chronic pain sufferer often describes the pain as having 'taken over', such that behaviour is governed by the intention of avoiding increased pain. The emotional experience is one of loss of control, loss of pleasant activities and sources of self-esteem, and anxieties about further deterioration and loss. All these experiences contribute to depressed mood (Lewinsohn, 1974; Seligman, 1975; Beck *et al*, 1979), which in turn can worsen the experience of pain. Pain sufferers also complain of isolation despite dependence on others for practical help and support. It is not easy for patients, for their families or for their doctors to accept that there may be no relief available. The difficulty is compounded by the attempt to explain all the behaviours by reference to the original trauma or demonstrable pathology: when this fails, it is all too common for the patient's distress and distorted behavioural patterns to be attributed to psychopathology or personality, for which the equivalent lay model is that it is 'all in the mind'. These explanations risk undermining further the patient's self-esteem and sense of control.

Pain itself and pain-related behaviours have many potentially adverse consequences for the sufferer. Rest leads to the disuse syndrome (Bortz, 1984; Brena & Chapman, 1985), and data on the pathophysiology of inactivity is accumulating. Loss of muscle tissue and strength contributes to postural and movement problems, often worsened by distortion of gait and by guarding; modest activities become arduous and painful for the unfit person. Bones lose calcium; connective tissue shrinks; joints are poorly lubricated. Cardiovascular and respiratory function deteriorate, and patients often gain weight, placing further demands on joints and muscles in poor condition. There may be lasting neural changes resulting from the original injury, at spinal and peripheral levels (Wall, 1985). At a cerebral level, the patient is alert to pain messages, and may have difficulty labelling unusual sensations (stretch, muscle tiredness from activity) in non-pain terms. Not surprisingly, when the unfit pain sufferer is active, he or she often feels distinctly unwell, confirming his or her fears about the dangers of activity, and strengthening suspicions of sinister disease or inevitable degeneration. The task for pain management programmes is to reverse these changes and the beliefs associated with them.

Treatment

Fordyce redirected the focus of treatment from pathology-based models of what the patient *has*, to what he or she *does*, emphasising the role of learned behaviour. Distinguishing acute from chronic pain (Sternbach, 1976; Bonica, 1977) is crucial, for those who treat the patient as much as for the patient. The doctor's response to acute pain is to take responsibility for its management, to investigate, advise, educate and treat, with good expectation of a resolution. But if pain persists for months or years this imbalance in responsibilities may lead both doctor and patient into mutual dissatisfaction and blame. The patient imputes lack of skills or care to the doctor, who in turn may suspect a hidden psychological, social or financial agenda on the part of the patient whose complaints and difficulties are resistant to understanding as signs and symptoms, and which seem unrelieved by attempts at treatment. Both find it hard to look outside the interaction, and to address the central tasks in chronic disease and disability: namely, how the sufferer can best cope, and how he or she can be helped to do so. Unnecessary and inappropriate referral, investigation and intervention can worsen the situation (Pither & Nicholas, 1991).

Research to date suggests that non-medical treatments for chronic pain produce significant improvements in mood and symptoms associated with pain, without notable changes in pain intensity (Keefe, 1982; Linton, 1982, 1986; Malone & Strube, 1988; Benjamin, 1989). Few satisfactory functional measures are available; follow-up assessments rely overmuch on global measures and cover a short period in relation to the chronicity of the pain. No single method of treatment appears superior or inferior to others. The inclusion of satisfactory functional measures, and of follow-up for at least one year after treatment, are still not standard, and the analysis of treatment components is only beginning. It appears that simply increasing activity is not enough for long-term maintenance of improvement in function, even in combination with an explicit rationale (Harkapaa *et al*, 1989). Return to the setting in which the maladaptive behaviours were established presents the same problems of maintenance as in other areas of behavioural change (Rimm & Masters, 1974). The achievement of lasting change remains a challenge in the face of pressures at home and work, and is done by attempting to integrate operant and cognitive techniques as fully as possible within other aspects of the programme.

Cognitive–behavioural treatment addresses the factors currently maintaining the patients' maladaptive behaviours, beliefs, and thought patterns. Fordyce (1976) outlines three main factors.

First is the direct positive reinforcement of pain behaviours. Speech content, tone of voice, gestures, postures, facial expressions, gaits, and physical aids convey pain and suffering to onlookers. The aim is not to judge these behaviours, or to classify them as wrong or maladaptive, but to determine what elicits them, and what their consequences are for the patient. Those consequences may be sympathy, care and offers of help, which may or may not enable the patient to cope better: commonly, patients report feeling pitied, helpless, and indebted as a result of receiving help. In a medical setting, the same behaviours may elicit in attendant staff irritation, avoidance, and unproductive referral for repeat investigation or treatment. At work, pain behaviours are likely to disadvantage the patient whatever his or her work performance.

Second is the indirect positive reinforcement of pain behaviour by avoidance of aversive events or circumstances. Patients in general have, for a variety of reasons, used rest and avoidance of activity both for pain relief, and with the longer-term hope of resolution of the problem. This contributes to lack of fitness and the disuse syndrome described. Consequently, activities which before were not physically very demanding become painful and fatiguing: sitting for the duration of a social engagement or a journey, walking around shops, standing to cook or wash up. Such activities cannot usually be avoided entirely, but are only undertaken when pressures (such as external demands, or the patient's own frustration) become too great. This gives rise to cycles of relative overactivity followed by rest and inactivity, in which pressures towards another burst of activity build up. Over time, the patient achieves less by overactivity, and takes longer intervening rests. Avoidance may be limited to certain types of activity, but here the balance of gains and losses must be carefully assessed: assumptions about the universal aversiveness (to patients) of paid work, or home duties, have led to pejorative labels such as 'compensation neurosis', for which the evidence is poor (Turk *et al*, 1983; Benjamin, 1989).

Third is the lack of reinforcement for 'well behaviour'. This is perhaps the easiest to observe in the interactions of many pain patients with their close family members, and with health care staff, who are trained to attend to problems and difficulties. A patient's pride and pleasure, for example in walking for the first time for years without a walking stick, may be punctured by the anxious reproach of the spouse for the 'unnecessary' risk. Alternatively, the achievement may be met by the spouse's doubting the validity of the previous disability, or by plans for the patient to use the new-found facility to take on arduous and unrewarding duties. Involvement of the spouse or significant other is a core component of treatment (Fordyce, 1976; Rowat & Knafl, 1985; Payne & Norfleet, 1986; Flor *et al*, 1987; Romano *et al*, 1989).

Initially, cognitive techniques were drawn from those used successfully in acute and experimental pain: a focus on schema-directed monitoring and labelling of symptoms, enhancing internal locus of control, and identifying thoughts as cues for muscle tension and increased pain (Weisenberg, 1977; Pennebaker, 1982; Pearce, 1983; Philips, 1988). Pain-related thoughts have been variously classified: Philips (1989), for instance, found factors of rumination about the cause, helplessness, focus on the emotional reaction to pain, desire to withdraw from others, disappointment with oneself, and contemplation of a bleak future. More recently, research and treatment have drawn on well established theories and treatment of anxiety and depression, identifying cognitive distortions and maladaptive schemata which guide the patients' behaviour (Lefebvre, 1981; Turk *et al*, 1983; Philips, 1989), and addressing them with education and cognitive and behavioural techniques. Addition of a cognitive component to operant treatment can improve maintenance of treatment gains (Kerns *et al*, 1986), and there is now a flourishing literature relating the extent of disability to coping strategies (Rosenstiel & Keefe, 1983; Turner & Clancy, 1986), to beliefs about control over pain (Flor & Turk, 1988), and to self-efficacy in relation to pain (Dolce, 1987). Increased pain tends to be associated with an increased frequency of negative thoughts (Gil *et al*, 1990), and poor compliance with physical treatment may be related to the patient's dissatisfaction with the explanation for his or her pain (Williams & Thorn, 1989).

In-patient pain management

Aims

The opportunities of in-patient treatment allow the possibility of intervention in a range of problem areas. Treatment aims can be summarised as follows.

(a) To increase patients' activity level. Exercise is incompatible with pain behaviour, and is necessary to develop fitness, flexibility and range of movement to work towards desired goals.

(b) To improve patients' function, by enabling patients to work towards specific and realistic goals, long and short term, in their chosen activities.

(c) To reduce patients' intake of analgesic and psychotropic drugs, insofar as their action is not consistent with the aims of the programme and with goal attainment. This is achieved by changing pain-contingent (p.r.n.) drug regimens to time-contingent drug use, and reducing the dose gradually.

(d) To reduce patients' pain behaviour by not reinforcing it, and teaching more direct methods of communication.

(e) To increase patients' 'well behaviour', by reinforcing efforts towards increased activity and goal attainment, or towards following the agreed programme.

(f) To teach patients the skills of monitoring thoughts and feelings, and of challenging and changing of dysfunctional thoughts and distorted beliefs.

As far as possible, the methods used to pursue these aims are the integrated application of the behavioural and cognitive principles above. This requires that all staff, of whatever discipline, are trained in both behavioural and cognitive techniques, and that these techniques are used to enhance the contribution of each discipline to the programme.

Potential advantages and disadvantages of in-patient treatment

Given the potential difficulties in generalisation and maintenance of the patients' newly acquired skills in pain management, is in-patient pain management worth the costs involved in a hospital stay? Data on the relative advantages of in-patient and out-patient psychologically based pain management are still largely lacking, since in the countries where both treatments are established, the choice is dominated by funding arrangements. Only one randomised controlled trial of in-patient and out-patient treatment has been published to date (Peters & Large, 1990): both treated groups improved in comparison with untreated controls, but little difference emerged between in-patients and out-patients. Unfortunately, despite randomisation, there were pre-treatment differences between groups; in combination with other methodological problems discussed by Peters & Large, this made firm conclusions impossible. Two other recent comparisons of unrandomised in-patients with out-patients gave conflicting results. Jarvikoski *et al* (1986) found that in-patients made greater improvement in physical condition and activity level at follow-up, despite pain and distress ratings returning to baseline. Cairns *et al* (1984) found that in-patients maintained improvement less well, and were less likely to return to work, unrelated to the degree of change in pain: however, they entered treatment considerably more disabled than the out-patients. The experience to date in our in-patient programme at St Thomas' suggests a number of reasons for making in-patient treatment available.

(a) The main practical reason is that most chronic pain patients have considerable problems travelling even a short distance, so that for many, in-patient treatment is the only form available.

(b) The time available within an in-patient stay allows for repetition and integration of components, and for their application on an individual basis. These appear to be of considerable value for patients who are slow to learn, and to the more hopeless, since any change brought about during the programme challenges beliefs in the inevitability of decline.

(c) A major psychological advantage of in-patient treatment is removal of the patient from the factors in his or her environment which maintain the increasing disability and preoccupation with pain. The programme must however maximise transfer of skills from in-patient environment to home, and involve the spouse or significant other in supporting new adaptive behaviours.

(d) Group cohesion, with encouragement, selective reinforcement (although not reliably in the right direction), modelling, and 'team spirit' which seems to discourage drop out, is most commonly mentioned by patients as an advantage of in-patient treatment.

(e) A further possible advantage of in-patient treatment is a 'coming into hospital factor': a combination for the patient of being taken seriously enough for admission, and of expecting change in his or her own behaviour in proportion to the effort and cost expended in treatment on his or her behalf.

(f) In addition, a full-time programme has a full-time staff, with specialisation and experience of considerable potential for research and for training.

Set against these advantages are two major issues. The first concerns generalisation of changes in behaviour to the home, work and social environments of the patient; long-established reinforcement contingencies in those settings played a part in shaping and maintaining the pain behaviour. Involvement of the patient's family, and liaison with his or her general practitioner, employers, and local support services, are all much more difficult when patients are treated far from their homes. The second is the cost of in-patient treatment: even hostel-type accommodation is far more expensive than out-patient treatment. Cost effectiveness is not yet demonstrated, but the cost of an in-patient stay must be set against the cost of longer-term inappropriate use of health care (further hospital admissions, investigation and treatment; lifetime prescription of a variety of drugs) and social and welfare costs. The important question to address will be not only whether in-patient treatment has overall advantages, but for whom it is more effective (and more cost effective) than out-patient treatment.

The INPUT programme

In 1987, the King's Fund awarded a major grant to two anaesthetists, a psychologist, and a physician, who had worked together in the Pain Clinic at St Thomas' Hospital, to enable them to carry out a large-scale randomised controlled trial of in-patient versus out-patient treatment. Patients who agree to be randomised are treated within the main in-patient and out-patient cohorts. Referrals come from the entire UK, and all patients are subject to the same research assessments. The in-patient programme at St Thomas', known as INPUT (In-patient Pain Management Unit), will be described in this chapter. The programme is based on the experience of major in-patient programmes in America and on the results of previous research and clinical experience.

The team

At INPUT, the team consists of two clinical psychologists (one of whom directs the programme overall); a part-time anaesthetist with considerable experience in pain (who is also the medical director of the project); a senior physiotherapist; a charge nurse; an occupational therapist; and a secretary/administrator. An additional assistant psychologist and half-time physiotherapy aide are required to collect, manage and help with analysis of data. Psychology and physiotherapy trainees and visitors on placement, blind assessors, and ex-patient volunteers, all add to the team, treating about 100 in-patients (and 30–40 out-patients) per year.

All non-psychologist staff have chosen to enhance the efficacy of their existing skills by learning cognitive and behavioural techniques. Staff are trained on a continuing basis by means of case discussion, reading, and role play. As far as possible, all staff, including secretarial, administrative and ancillary staff who have contact with patients, such as cleaners, are educated in treatment practices, so that they respond to patients in the same way as the therapeutic team.

Patients

Patients are referred from various sources, including other pain clinics. As the service has become more widely known, more referrals have come directly from general practitioners, sometimes at the request of the patient who has read or heard about INPUT. The inclusion criteria, shown in Table 8.1, are broad, since little is known of factors which predict response to this type of treatment. Clinical details of patients accepted onto the INPUT programme are given in Table 8.2.

The first contact with the patient, screening for inclusion on the in-patient or out-patient programme, is at a joint clinic run by anaesthetists and

TABLE 8.1
Selection criteria for entry to INPUT

	% of sample scoring
Inclusion – any *two* of the following:	n = 212
Widespread disruption in activity (except work) owing to pain.	94.7%
Habitual overactivity leading to increased pain.	34.5%
Use of excess medication related to pain problems (regular use of analgesics and/or sedatives for more than 6 months without adequate relief).	71.3%
High affective distress score on assessment; clear signs or reports of emotional distress attributed by the patient to pain.	62.6%
Use of unnecessary aids (e.g. crutches, corset), assessed during medical examination.	7.0%
High levels of reported or observed pain behaviour.	53.2%
Work reduced, impaired or ceased owing to pain.	70.2%
Exclusion – any *one* of the following:	n = 134
Cannot use English, written or spoken.	5.2%
Cannot climb stairs.	9.7%
Current major psychiatric illness.	3.7%
Unavailability for four weeks.	8.2%
Suitable for further physical treatment, assessed during medical examination.	39.6%
Pain for less than one year.	3.0%
Under 18 years old.	0.7%
Currently using opiates prescribed as treatment for drug dependence, or not prescribed for patient.	0.7%
Met less than two inclusion criteria	32.0%

TABLE 8.2
INPUT patients (n = 134)

Mean age   51 years (range 20–84 years)
Sex   35% male, 65% female
Chronicity of pain   Mean 10 years, median 7 years
Pain site
   49% low back
   11% lower limb
   10% shoulder and upper limb
   7% neck
   5% each head/face, thorax, abdomen, pelvis
   3% perineal/genital
Employment
   7% employed full time
   7% employed but restricted by pain
   32% unemployed because of pain
   19% retired early because of pain
   10% housewife/homemaker
   23% retired by age

psychologists. The patient has completed details of personal and medical history, and a summary of his or her medical history is used to establish that all reasonable attempts to relieve the pain have been offered to the patient.

Patient selection is performed through semi-structured interviews of the patient by psychologist and anaesthetist, separately and together, and completion of several standardised self-report measures (see Table 8.3). It is important at this stage that fundamental principles are agreed, primarily that there is no doubt about the reality of the pain. In addition, it is made clear that since no appropriate treatment has relieved the pain sufficiently, the task is now one of learning to manage it better. The focus for this task is the array of difficulties which the patient experiences; the ways in which he or she tries to combat these difficulties; and the patient's beliefs about the meaning of the pain, the course of treatments undergone, and what needs to be changed. Explicit acceptance that the patient has chronic pain, and that the suffering this causes is of concern, is a great relief to patients who have come to fear that the pain might, somehow, be 'all in the mind'. Once this common ground is established, patients are willing to discuss the difficult issues of how their beliefs and feelings might affect the pain, and the ways in which their attempts to cope may worsen their situations.

Before entry to the programme, the patient is assessed further. Functional, psychological, and physical measures provide a baseline both for research and for treatment. The patient is asked to bring someone who knows him or her well, and this 'significant other', usually the patient's spouse, completes a measure of the patient's function. Interaction between patient and significant other can also be observed, and the latter can be encouraged to attend parts of the programme and to recognise his or her important role in maintaining improvements.

Setting

INPUT aims to provide a setting which is less that of a hospital, more that of a residential course. In a free-standing building in the hospital grounds, patients have their own rooms, and keys to the entrance of the unit. They organise their own time in the evenings, including making an evening meal. At weekends, they are encouraged to go home, to practise their new skills in the old environment, with a view to improving generalisation and engaging those around them in their new ways of coping. For some patients, the discomfort and expense of travelling long distances may prevent this, and when this arises, the spouse is accommodated at the unit over the weekend. The unit is staffed only during the daytime, and on weekdays therefore the patients admitted have to be able to manage self-care with the minimum of help.

Programme

Patients are admitted in groups of five, at fortnightly intervals, and stay for four weeks. The timetable runs for two weeks, starting at 8.30 a.m. each day, and finishing between 4.30 and 6 p.m., with a shorter Friday. It is a mixture of education and practical sessions: exercise, stretch, relaxation, and practising chosen activities, all run on cognitive and behavioural principles. Some teaching and exercise classes are carried out with the whole group of ten, others with new and old groups separately. The first 2 days of the first week serve as a baseline for exercises and for the staff to observe and get to know the patients; on the third day all patients are reviewed, and those in their first week are seen by the entire staff team to agree goals of treatment. In the last week, each patient meets the staff team to review progress and plans for return home. Patients are seen once or twice a week individually, at the end of the day, mainly in order to help to construe the day's activities in psychological terms, rather than looking towards exercise and paced activity as a 'cure'. Patients also have a chance to raise issues which they prefer not to discuss in a group.

The practice of behavioural techniques by all staff is crucial, and important psychological work is carried out by all staff in the course of their sessions. There are also considerable opportunities for contingent attention and reinforcement within casual interactions between staff and in-patients during the working day. Teaching sessions are interactive, using patients' own experience to develop the model and principles of the programme. Written material, containing the main points, is given to the patient as back-up. Patients can sit, stand, or lie down during teaching sessions, and the active participation of those who are lying is sought, breaking the association between lying down and passivity or empty time. The staff break the session with a brief relaxation, thereby modelling its use within a work routine. Relaxation may be a quiet moment sitting still, gentle movement and stretch, or a walk in the garden.

Behavioural techniques of reducing pain behaviour and increasing healthy behaviour are shared with patients, who often report that once they understand that their pain is believed, they are able to find better ways to communicate their needs and feelings. Education sessions may be interrupted by pain behaviour, groaning, or potentially distracting writhing and movement, from new patients. Staff are trained to continue with the agenda, modelling for the other patients that the behaviour does not signify a medical emergency, and encouraging the suffering patient nevertheless to join in with the content of the session, reinforcing this when it occurs. Such behaviour almost always reduces very rapidly within the first few days.

In the evenings, patients have free time, in which they may have visitors; make their own meals; spend time practising goals; complete assignments and reading from the sessions; and share their experience with one another. Although staff have never 'forbidden' talk about pain, the belief that such talk is banned is handed from one group to the next. Patients tend to return to the subject of pain, but when reminded appreciate opportunities to discover other common ground. Staff intervene as little as possible in the relationships within the group; they try instead to enable patients to find acceptable ways to express their dissatisfactions to one another, and to negotiate solutions.

Content of the programme

Understanding chronic pain

Two teaching sessions are led by the anaesthetist. The first covers the nature of chronic pain sensation and transmission, including discussion of the gate control model (Melzack & Wall, 1965) and endorphins, and the second involves discussion of past treatment options. Patients report finding both sessions important, not only for their informational content and answers to their questions, but because of the opportunity to hear a coherent account of the nature of chronic pain from a medical practitioner. Whatever patients retain of the content, it is at least a chance to challenge oversimplified models of pain and pain transmission, and the questions which arise from them, such as "If it's the nerve that's hurting, why can't it be cut?". Patients' comments also suggest a non-specific benefit of being credited with the capacity to understand and use the information.

Fitness

Exercise sessions directly challenge most patients' avoidance patterns. Many report that physiotherapy has made them worse in the past, and a pattern of forced exercise with the expectation of pain relief, followed by symptom-contingent rest and a sense of failure, has confirmed for them the dangers of unaccustomed movement and effort. The rationale for becoming fitter is given on each occasion from the screening interview onwards. In addition, the physiotherapist teaches patients about the effects of disuse, healing, healthy functioning of joints and the spine, body mechanics, and posture.

None of the exercises requires any more elaborate equipment than an exercise bicycle, and most require none. Individual baselines set in the first two days of the programme are reduced by 20% to provide a realistic starting point, even on a 'bad day'. Patients are instructed not to overdo exercise, since it is always possible to increase the rate of change, but discouraging to slow down or cut back from an over-ambitious start. This is in direct contrast to more usual instructions to "do as much as you can"; even "no pain, no gain". The basic fitness programme, and stretch, is repeated daily, including at weekends at home. Patients are also given individual exercises addressing their particular difficulties, and the physiotherapist is closely involved in setting tolerances for sitting, standing, etc., and goals of gradually reducing the use of aids such as sticks, collars, and corsets, as muscle strength increases. Exercise and its benefits provide important evidence against the beliefs that all somatic sensations are unpleasant or signal danger. The new-found self-esteem in becoming fitter may be manifest in the patient arriving in the second or third week wearing a new tracksuit or trainers, rather than everyday loose clothes and slippers in which many begin the programme.

Activities

Goals for activity can be 'building blocks' such as sitting, standing and walking, or part of work and home duties, leisure and social activity. Patients who have become virtually homebound and isolated may need help in choosing enjoyable activities as goals, and patients are encouraged to share their experience and enterprise in specifying achievable goals. Information from the pre-treatment assessment and screening interviews, concerning the activities which patients feel unable to perform because of the pain, or which they perform but without enjoyment, may be of considerable help at this stage. It may be easier to specify what has been lost through pain than to anticipate gains through using pain management techniques. Sexual activity is also placed on the agenda by means of a handout and the offer of individual advice.

Long-term goals, precisely specified (e.g. cleaning the windows once a fortnight; going out for a meal with the whole family once a month; returning to work), are used as a basis for setting short-term goals. The activities required to perform the long-term goal – in the case of cleaning windows, carrying the equipment, stretching, bending, standing, and so on – are all considered, and the area of greatest limitation determines the starting level. The unit provides opportunities to try many household tasks in the patient's living area and in the small garden, with advice from staff on posture, technique and ergonomics. Some long-term goals, such as return to work, and holidays, regularly challenge patients' and staff's ingenuity in devising successive approximations as short-term goals.

The cognitive component of building goal-directed activity is twofold: first to overcome fears that increasing activity will lead to unmanageably increased pain; and second to learn flexibility in approaching practical tasks. The gradual increase of goal-directed activity is in effect a graded exposure programme, and during it much useful cognitive work is carried out on beliefs and worries which patients express. Fears of increasing activity may have been maintained by a variety of factors. Direct advice to rest may have been given by professionals or others whose opinion is valued. The patient may recall occasions on which overactivity led to increased pain and a sense of not being able to cope. The avoidance of activity removes the opportunity to accumulate disconfirming evidence for the beliefs that increased pain implies irreparable damage and strains the patient's capacity to cope. To a lesser extent, certain rules of behaviour may require modification in order for low levels of activity to be seen as worthwhile goals. Common examples are: "If you start a job, you must finish it"; "You can't have people home if you haven't done all the housework first"; "No employer will let me lie down during the day". As far as possible, the occupational therapist responds to such expressions by talking through with the patient the evidence for and against this belief: again, other patients may be involved in this process. At the least, the patient is encouraged to record the thought on a form used in conjunction with psychology sessions, for reconsideration in those sessions.

Pacing

Many patients with back pain (over half the chronic pain population treated at INPUT) have a limited tolerance for sitting. Many patients report being unable to stand or to walk for long. Their usual pattern is to avoid the activity altogether, or to try to force themselves to manage it for as long as possible. Some patients, for instance, rarely sit at home, but will attempt to sit for over an hour for a necessary journey, usually finding the experience so painful and distressing that they are unwilling to repeat it. Pacing makes activity time-contingent, rather than pain-contingent, using a modest baseline and gradual increases in time or difficulty of activity, and is linked to the patient's increasing fitness, strength and mobility. Again, it approximates to a graded exposure programme, with consistent (if not invariable) success, and reinforcement in recognition of the progress.

The baseline is explicitly not the maximum length of time for which the patient can tolerate the pain, but 80% of a manageable mean over several assessments. For instance, a patient with an initial five minutes sitting tolerance may start from four minutes sitting every half hour (with the rest of the time spent in more comfortable positions, or on other tolerances), and increasing every two days by half a minute. By the end of the course, the patient will be sitting reliably for 15 minutes, and continuing to build up at an adjusted rate. This is called 'pacing', and is a key concept in pain management. Instructing patients to use relaxation techniques before or during practice sessions, and to be aware of negative predictions ("I'll never be able to sit for six minutes") and to challenge them, can increase the tolerance time.

Teaching and problem-solving sessions, from the second week onward, are directed towards developing specific plans to deal with setbacks, adapting the relapse prevention model used in other areas of behaviour change (Marlatt & Gordon, 1985). Patients develop written plans of reduced exercise and paced return to previous levels within a week or so, with attention to negative self-statements about having failed, or "gone back to square one".

Medication withdrawal

The framework of goal setting is applied to the pattern and dose of both prescribed and non-prescribed medication. Almost all drugs taken by pain patients fall into the categories of analgesics, antidepressants, and hypnotics/tranquillisers. Approximately 60% of referred patients take opiate analgesics, over half in combination with benzodiazepines (prescribed as hypnotics, anxiolytics, or as an attempt to relieve muscle spasm, but with no evidence of long-term benefit). Commonly, patients report that the drugs are of little help to them, but complain of side-effects. Most patients use analgesics on demand, rather than regularly as prescribed, and around 20% of patients take more than the equivalent of 40 mg morphine daily. Analgesic prescription may serve as validation of the patient's complaint of pain, and any prescription can perpetuate a sense of receiving health care. Demonstrable oversedation occurs particularly in elderly patients, from high doses and interactions between drugs. Practice in relation to changes in medication use is guided by the same cognitive and behavioural principles as other treatment practices, rather than by a dogmatic anti-drug stance. There are several major reasons for reducing and stopping intake of analgesics, benzodiazepines, and antidepressants. Firstly, there is little evidence of their utility in patients still complaining of constant pain and major dysfunction. Secondly, their use may militate against change, particularly where patients use them to sustain other maladaptive behaviour such as overactivity or underactivity. Thirdly, they contribute to (reversible) cognitive impairment. Finally, many patients express a preference for not relying on medication. In summary, benefits previously brought about by the medication may be better achieved by alternative management strategies.

A reduction in drug intake is attained by both education and pharmacological means. Education about drug intake is used to enable patients to develop a more complex and multifactorial explanation of their pain and other symptoms. If patients have taken analgesics or tranquillisers "when the pain is at its worst", pain relief within the subsequent few hours tends to be credited to the drug, at the expense of attention to other adjustments made simultaneously, such as improved pacing or posture. When pain relief has not followed drug intake, many patients report increased anxiety: "My pain is so bad that even strong painkillers can't help me". Additionally, during treatment, patients are discouraged from attributing all unpleasant somatic sensations, such as shakiness or fatigue, to drug withdrawal when there are other possible physical and psychological explanations to consider.

Pharmacological methods are either a 'pain cocktail' (Fordyce, 1976), in which the active dose is reduced by staff, or steady reduction under the patient's control: both methods make drug intake time-contingent, not pain-contingent. With the cocktail, patients begin withdrawal at the morphine or diazepam dose equivalent to the opiates or benzodiazepines they were taking, mixed into a masking linctus, with the active ingredient reduced steadily over three weeks within the same volume of linctus. When 'extra' doses are requested to help with 'extra' pain, the nurse reviews with the patient's alternative strategies for managing, and reminds the patient of recent successes in coping with increased pain without increased medication. Rationalisation of drug dose, closer control preventing excess dosage, and actual reduction in the total amount of medication taken, may all play a part in changes in patients' cognitive state and physical activity within the first 10 days of treatment.

Relaxation

Relaxation skills are taught to enable the patient to cope better with the pain, and with pain-related problems (Linton, 1986). Simple techniques focus on breathing and overall reduction of muscle tension (Benson *et al*, 1977), with the patient moving from more to less comfortable positions, and to walking. Patients are encouraged to practise regularly throughout the day; relaxation breaks of a few minutes relieve long teaching and exercise sessions, and winding down and relaxing are a central part of the sleep management techniques taught. Imaginal strategies (Pearce & Erskine, 1989), mainly distraction and focusing techniques, are used to enhance the benefits of relaxation, and to extend the patient's range of skills and their application. Although most patients find relaxation difficult, some because their attention is directed towards somatic sensations and worrying interpretations, they may be surprised by the sense of control they gain by focusing deliberately on the pain, or visualising it, and finding that the experience is not intolerable. Over the longer term, about a quarter of patients report that it offers partial control of pain intensity.

Sleep management

Very few patients report satisfactory sleep, with or without the help of drugs. Cue control and cognitive techniques are used to address the common problems: lying awake worrying at night in the same place where patients lie and worry during the day; getting up in the night and drinking tea and coffee; excess rest and daytime sleep; difficulty in not attending to the pain and associated worries in the absence of distraction; anxieties about inadequate sleep and its effects on the subsequent day (Lacks, 1987; Morin *et al*, 1989).

Cognitive change

The cognitive sessions, six 40-minute sessions each fortnight, have a simple agenda, adapting widely used cognitive techniques (Beck *et al*, 1979; Blackburn & Davidson, 1990) to a group with mixed problems of anxiety and depression. The first task is to establish that thoughts are valid material for examination, and that patients are not expected to produce major insights, but to report on what goes through their minds at times of increased pain, when they avoid or escape from a difficult event, or are disappointed with their performance. Monitoring forms are used daily to record these situations, and the associated thoughts and feelings (plus a rating of pain). Reference may be made to the basic model elaborated in the first behavioural session, and patients are asked to supply the self-statements which accompany feelings such as fear, depression, and frustration.

The cognitive model of anxiety and panic (Clark, 1986; Blackburn & Davidson, 1990), particularly in relation to health-related fears (Warwick & Salkovskis, 1989), is developed. Starting from the less difficult area of fears unrelated to pain, it is then extended to incorporate patients' pain-related fears, with a focus on worst fears, and 'catastrophising' (Rosenstiel & Keefe, 1983). Frequently reported fears include: that increased pain must signal further damage, and that exercise will worsen disability; becoming bedbound or wheelchair-bound; becoming dependent on family or on strangers (''put in a home''); and ''not coping'', that is, becoming insane. Patients examine the evidence for these predictions, and challenge the certainty with which they have anticipated them. The concept of confidence is introduced, in relation to overcoming fears, working from patients' experience of managing fears unrelated to pain towards those associated with pain.

The following session focuses more on depressive thinking, using examples recorded by patients. In each example, patients generate a negative spiral of thoughts, and associated feelings, from a starting point such as ''The pain is worse after exercise: I must be failing''. The end point tends towards negative predictions about the self, the world and the future. Thoughts of suicide and of ''just not wanting to wake up in the morning'' are usually reported. Patients practise challenging the evidence for each thought, and talking it through internally to prevent progression down the spiral. Emphasis is placed on the importance of recognising and intervening early in such trains of thought.

Certain specific themes are raised often enough by patients to justify their inclusion on a regular basis. The first is the concept of 'positive thinking', which patients often construe as trying to fool themselves with some anodyne statement which they rate as barely credible, such as ''If I don't think about the pain, it will go away'', or ''It will probably be better tomorrow''. Patients attempt to use such self-statements often, although they report feeling angry and misunderstood when others advise them to do so. For this reason, the term 'positive' is rarely used in relation to thoughts: reference is made to realistic and helpful thinking. A second theme is the notion of 'fighting the pain', which usually refers to setting unrealistic goals and overdoing activity, resulting in increased pain and a sense of defeat. Patients are encouraged to challenge the all-or-nothing thinking implicit in the concepts of fighting, winning or losing, and to try to use the notion of negotiating with the pain, by practices such as paced activity. Third, many patients are preoccupied by the question "Why me?", also expressed as "What have I done to deserve this?". Both forms of the question lead to review of unsatisfactory events, self-reproach and self-accusation, and a sense of worthlessness. If patients' own religious or philosophical beliefs have not provided a satisfactory answer, it is suggested that the question may be shelved, in favour of more productive self-questioning. Basic belief systems often emerge in which chronic illness or disability constitutes a personal failing. These can be challenged by asking patients to consider the range of applicability: few claim that they make the same judgement of their fellow patients, for example. Lastly, patients are invited to imagine themselves in the position of their spouse or significant other, and to report what thoughts and feelings they might have, and how their actions towards the patient might be related to those thoughts and feelings. These ideas are developed in a more practical way in a session on communication and assertiveness techniques, and provide material for the meeting between patient, spouse and staff.

Spouses and significant others

The first meeting with the patient's spouse or significant other is at pre-treatment assessment; less than 20% have nobody who knows them well enough to provide useful information. At this appointment, the significant other is given an explanation of the programme and invited to attend the unit on certain days when they may join in the programme, in particular, planning for the weekend. The changes and achievements of the patient are pointed out to them, the behavioural framework explained, and re-inforcement discussed and modelled. Although travel, expense, work demands, or care of children or elderly relatives may make attendance difficult, some spouses manage to overcome these obstacles and to attend the course, often joining in exercise sessions, and showing considerable enterprise in providing novel reinforcers. On some occasions, an entire family has arrived to celebrate the improvements the patient is making.

Clinical experience suggests that more usually, the spouse finds it difficult to enter wholeheartedly into supporting the changes planned. Some are anxious, and continually advise caution, reminding the patient of particularly bad patches of pain they have suffered, and of their debt of gratitude to the caring spouse. A high degree of solicitousness on the part of the spouse is associated with problems in making changes and in maintaining them (Fordyce, 1976; Benjamin, 1989). Others are disbelieving about the reality of the pain, and may fail to grasp the importance of paced activity, leading to unreasonable demands on the patient, once home, to perform as if without pain or limitations. A milder version of this is based on the spouse's observation that the patient is happier when busy and occupied: he or she arranges a remorseless schedule of activity, so that the patient's only escape is into more explicit disability. Occasionally, the patient's family has found a manageable balance of needs around the patient's limited mobility and consequent availability. Family members may be unwilling to support the patient's moves towards greater independence, and fail to help solve practical problems or to reinforce well behaviours. It is more often these spouses who find it difficult to attend the unit when staff are present, or to read the information the patient takes home. Staff search continually for ways to engage spouses better in the patients' changes.

Assessment

Adequate discussion of the measures available would require a chapter of its own. Useful accounts can be found in Karoly & Jensen (1987), Keefe *et al* (1982), and Kaplan (1985). The choice of assessment measures

TABLE 8.3
Assessment

Functional assessment	Coping strategies
(i) Sickness Impact Profile, interview-administered (Bergner *et al*, 1981) to assess function. This is also given to the significant other in a parallel version. (ii) MPI from the Multiaxial Assessment of Pain (Kerns *et al*, 1985) to assess psychosocial factors and activity in relation to pain.	(i) Coping Strategies Questionnaire (CSQ; Rosenstiel & Keefe, 1983), developed and widely used in chronic pain populations. **Cognitive assessment** Pain Cognitions Questionnaire (Boston *et al*, 1990) to assess pain intensity, pain distress, and pain-related beliefs. Pain Self-Efficacy Questionnaire (Nicholas, unpublished), to assess patients' confidence in activity despite pain. The patient's significant other is given a parallel version. Pain Locus of Control Questionnaire (Main, unpublished), to assess control and responsibility.
Mood assessment	
(i) Beck Depression Inventory (BDI; Beck *et al*, 1961), widely used in the chronic pain field to assess depressed mood. (ii) State-Trait Anxiety Inventory (STAI; Spielberger *et al*, 1970), State version.	

In addition, assessment of physical function, designed and under reliability testing by the physiotherapist, includes distance and speed walks, stairs, sit-ups, and arm endurance tests.

depends on several factors, most importantly, the population sampled, the questions addressed, and practical issues.

Measures standardised on pain patients may apply only to a specific diagnostic group, such as low back pain (e.g. the Low Back Pain Questionnaire; Leavitt & Garron, 1978). Clinical populations are always preselected by the health care and funding system, which may account for major differences between samples (cf. Chapman *et al*, 1979). Measures developed for populations with other physical or mental health problems may be insensitive to specific difficulties of chronic pain patients, and are not standardised on an appropriate population (Karoly, 1985). Measures of mood, for instance, were developed in psychiatric populations from which those with long-term illness or disability have been excluded, so that somatic items count towards a total score of psychological disturbance (e.g. the Beck Depression Inventory; Beck *et al*, 1961). Pain patients can be very wary of reporting distress, psychosocial and marital problems, and work dissatisfaction, when they suspect that the agenda is to identify 'secondary gain' in these areas: their responses may be biased (Anastasi, 1988). Assessment for treatment may encourage patients to overstate functional problems in order to 'earn' admission. Finally, there may be a payoff between greater comprehensiveness and diminishing accuracy of responses, particularly

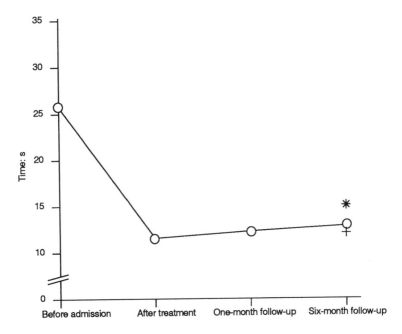

Fig. 8.1. Timed walk: time taken to walk 20 metres (n = 61). Confidence intervals: + 5%, *95%. Change in time taken, by six-month follow-up, F = 16.21, P < 0.001.

in patients who find it hard to concentrate or who may be distressed, and when using postal or telephone follow-up.

The patient, and his or her significant other, is assessed one to two weeks before admission, and at one month, six months, and one year after discharge. The assessment includes functional physical measures (such as walking), an overall measure of functional impairment, and assessments of mood, self-efficacy, and cognitive strategies. The list of assessments currently used at INPUT is given in Table 8.3. A shorter version is carried out at the screening interview and on the final day of the programme. Additional measures of expectation, satisfaction, and maintenance of exercise, stretch, relaxation and cognitive techniques are included at appropriate points, and patients report on their use of medication and medical consultation and treatment. At follow-up assessment, patients also have the opportunity of joining a problem-solving session with one or two staff members and their peer-patient group. Their performance at follow-up is fed back to them by letter shortly afterwards, with emphasis on gains, achievements, and areas for revision.

Preliminary results

Results for the first 18 months of the programme show that patients who completed the course (90 % of admissions) make major improvements,

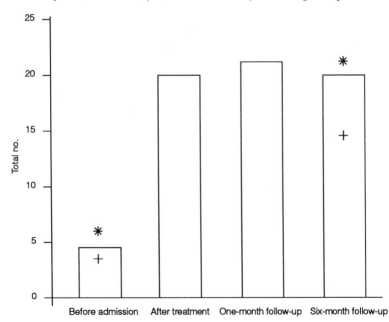

Fig. 8.2. Number of sit-ups to tolerance (n = 61). Confidence intervals: +5%, *95%. Change in total, by six-month follow-up, F = 33.69; d.f. = 3,180; P<0.001

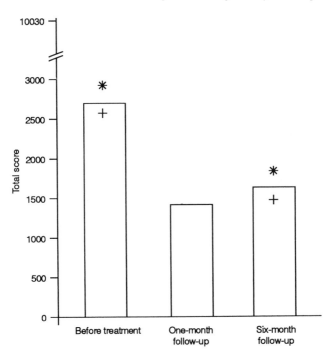

*Fig. 8.3. Total scores on the Sickness Impact Profile (n = 85). Confidence intervals: +5%, *95%. Change in score by six-month follow-up, F = 63.49; d.f. = 2,168; P< 0.001*

sustained at six-month and one-year follow-up, in physical performance; on self-report measures of function, mood, and self-efficacy; and in drug reduction. Some of these are shown in Figs 8.1 to 8.4

There is little change in ratings of pain intensity (rated as average pain over the last week), but a reduction of about a third in ratings of distress due to pain (Fig. 8.5). This is consistent with the approach of the programme, that of achieving a change in behaviour, rather than in pain intensity, to bring about functional improvement.

Conclusion

Chronic pain patients who learn the skills of pain management in an in-patient setting are able to make important and lasting changes in their physical performance and in coping with pain and the limitations imposed by pain. Problems remain in applying and maintaining these skills when the patient returns to home, family, and friends. Further problems are raised by the criteria by which people are judged fit for

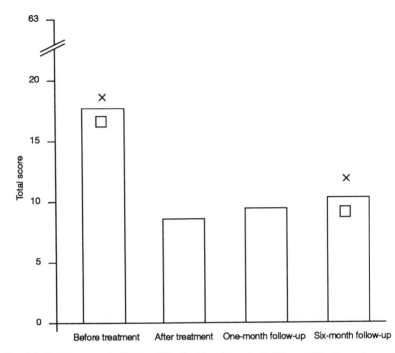

Fig. 8.4. Total scores on the BDI (n = 77). Confidence intervals: □ 5%, × 95%. Change in score by six-month follow-up, F = 38.15, d.f. = 3,228, P< 0.001

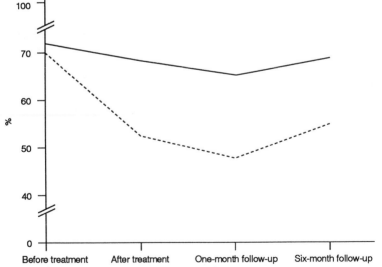

Fig. 8.5. Pain intensity and distress rated 0–100 on a numerical rating scale (n = 78) (—— average intensity; ---- average distress: respective changes by six-month follow-up, F = 2.93, d.f. = 3,231, P< 0.003; and F = 14.59, d.f. = 3,231, P< 0.001)

employment or sufficiently disabled to qualify for sickness-related welfare payments. The randomised controlled trial at INPUT, comparing in-patient with out-patient programmes, will help to determine cost effectiveness, address difficulties for patients in generalisation and maintenance of clear gains from the programme, and indicate for which patients the advantages of the in-patient setting are essential.

Acknowledgements

INPUT is funded by a major grant from the King Edward's Hospital Fund for London, with generous help from the Special Trustees of St Thomas' Hospital and SE Regional Health Authority. Recognition is due to the four grant holders and to all team members, particularly Dr Michael Nicholas, the first programme director, for turning the grant into a treatment and research programme. The author is grateful to Dr Phil Richardson and to Dr Michael Sharpe for most helpful comments on drafts of this paper.

References

ANASTASI, A. (1988) *Psychological Testing* (6th edn), pp. 549–555. New York: Macmillan.

BECK, A. T., RUSH, A. J., SHAW, B. F., *et al* (1979) *Cognitive Therapy of Depression*. New York: Guilford Press.

——, WARD, C. H., MENDELSON, M., *et al* (1961) An inventory for measuring depression. *Archives of General Psychiatry*, **4**, 561–571.

BENJAMIN, S. (1989) Psychological treatment of chronic pain: a selective review. *Journal of Psychosomatic Research*, **33**, 121–131.

BENSON, H., GREENWOOD, M. M. & KLEMCHUK, H. (1977) The relaxation response: psychophysiologic aspects and clinical applications. In *Psychosomatic Medicine: Current Trends and Clinical Application* (eds Z. L. Lipowski, D. R. Lipsitt & P. C. Whybrow), pp. 377–388. New York: Oxford University Press.

BERGNER, M., BOBBITT, R. A., CARTER, W. B., *et al* (1981) The Sickness Impact Profile: development and final revision of a health status measure. *Medical Care*, **19**, 787.

BLACKBURN, I.-M. & DAVIDSON, K. (1990) *Cognitive Therapy for Depression and Anxiety*. Oxford: Blackwell.

BONICA, J. J. (1977) Neurophysiologic and pathophysiologic aspects of acute and chronic pain. *Archives of Surgery*, **112**, 750–761.

BORTZ, W. M. (1984) The disuse syndrome. *Western Journal of Medicine*, **141**, 691–694.

BOSTON, K., PEARCE, S. & RICHARDSON, P. H. (1990) The Pain Cognitions Questionnaire. *Journal of Psychosomatic Research*, **34**, 103–109.

BRENA, S. F. & CHAPMAN, S. L. (1985) Acute versus chronic pain states: the 'learned pain syndrome'. *Clinics in Anaesthesiology*, **3**, 41–55.

CAIRNS, D., MOONEY, V. & CRANE, P. (1984) Spinal pain rehabilitation: inpatient and outpatient treatment results and development of predictors for outcome. *Spine*, **9**, 91–95.

CHAPMAN, C. R., SOLA, A. E. & BONICA, J. J. (1979) Illness behaviour and depression compared in pain center and private practice patients. *Pain*, **6**, 1–7.

CLARK, D. M. (1986) A cognitive approach to panic. *Behaviour Research and Therapy*, **24**, 461–470.

DOLCE, J. J. (1987) Self-efficacy and disability beliefs in behavioral treatment of pain. *Behaviour Research and Therapy*, **25**, 289–299.

DWORKIN, S. F., VON KORFF, M. & LE RESCHE, L. (1990) Multiple pains and psychiatric disturbance: an epidemiologic investigation. *Archives of General Psychiatry*, **47**, 239–244.

FLOR, H. & TURK, D. C. (1988) Chronic back pain and rheumatoid arthritis: predicting pain and disability from cognitive variables. *Journal of Behavioral Medicine*, **11**, 251–265.

——, —— & SCHOLZ, O. B. (1987) Impact of chronic pain on the spouse: marital, emotional and physical consequences. *Journal of Psychosomatic Research*, **31**, 63–71.

FORDYCE, W. E. (1976) *Behavioural Methods for Chronic Pain and Illness*. St Louis: The CV Mosby Co.

——, LANSKY, D., CALSYN, D. A., *et al* (1984) Pain measurement and pain behaviour. *Pain*, **18**, 53–69.

GIL, K. M., WILLIAMS, D. A., KEEFE, F. J., *et al* (1990) The relationship of negative thoughts to pain and psychological distress. *Behaviour Therapy*, **21**, 349–362.

HARKAPAA, K., JARVIKOSKI, A., MELLIN, G., *et al* (1989) A controlled study on the outcome of inpatient and outpatient treatment of low back pain. *Scandinavian Journal of Rehabilitation Medicine*, **21**, 81–89.

JARVIKOSKI, A., HARKAPAA, K. & MELLIN, G. (1986) Symptoms of psychological distress and treatment effects with low back pain patients. *Pain*, **25**, 345–355.

KAPLAN, R. M. (1985) Quality-of-life measurement. In *Measurement Strategies in Health Psychology* (ed P. Karoly), pp. 115–146. New York: John Wiley & Sons.

KAROLY, P. (1985) The logic and character of assessment in health psychology: perspectives and possibilities. In *Measurement Strategies in Health Psychology* (ed. P. Karoly), pp. 3–45. New York: Wiley.

—— & JENSEN, M. P. (1987) *Multimethod Assessment of Chronic Pain*. Oxford: Pergamon Press.

KEEFE, F. J. (1982) Behavioural assessment and treatment of chronic pain: current status and future directions. *Journal of Consulting and Clinical Psychology*, **50**, 869–911.

——, BROWN, C., SCOTT, D. S., *et al* (1982) Behavioural assessment of chronic pain. In *Assessment Strategies in Behavioural Medicine* (eds F. J. Keefe & J. A. Blumenthal), pp. 321–350. New York: Grune & Stratton.

KERNS, R. D., TURK, D. C. & RUDY, T. E. (1985) The West-Haven-Yale Multi-Dimensional Pain Inventory (WHYMPI). *Pain*, **23**, 345.

——, ——, HOLZMAN, A. D., *et al* (1986) Comparison of cognitive–behavioral and behavioral approaches to the outpatient treatment of chronic pain. *Clinical Journal of Pain*, **1**, 199–203.

LACKS, P. (1987) *Behavioural Treatment for Persistent Insomnia*. New York: Pergamon Press.

LEAVITT, F. & GARRON, D. C. (1979) Validity of a back pain classification scale among patients with low back pain not associated with demonstrable organic disease. *Journal of Psychosomatic Research*, **23**, 301–306.

LEFEBVRE, M. F. (1981) Cognitive distortion and cognitive errors in depressed psychiatric and low back pain patients. *Journal of Consulting and Clinical Psychology*, **49**, 517–525.

LEWINSOHN, P. (1974) Clinical and theoretical aspects of depression. In *Innovative Treatment Methods in Psychopathology* (eds K. Calhoun, H. Adams & K. Mitchell), pp. 63–120. Chichester: John Wiley & Sons.

LINTON, S. J. (1982) A critical review of behavioural treatments for chronic benign pain other than headache. *British Journal of Clinical Psychology*, **21**, 321–337.

—— (1986) Behavioural remediation of chronic pain: a status report. *Pain*, **24**, 125–141.

MALONE, M. D. & STRUBE, M. J. (1988) Meta-analysis of non-medical treatments for chronic pain. *Pain*, **34**, 231–244.

MARLATT, G. A. & GORDON, J. R. (1985) *Relapse Prevention: Maintenance Strategies in the Treatment of Addictive Behaviours*. New York: Guilford Press.

MELZACK, R. & WALL, P. D. (1965) Pain mechanisms: a new theory. *Science*, **150**, 971–979.

—— & —— (1982) *The Challenge of Pain*. Harmondsworth: Penguin Books.

MORIN, C. M., KOWATCH, R. A. & WADE, J. B. (1989) Behavioral management of sleep disturbances secondary to chronic pain. *Journal of Behaviour Therapy and Experimental Psychiatry*, **20**, 295–302.

PAYNE, B. & NORFLEET, M. A. (1986) Chronic pain and the family: a review. *Pain*, **26**, 1–22.

PEARCE, S. (1983) A review of cognitive–behavioural methods for the treatment of chronic pain. *Journal of Psychosomatic Research*, **27**, 431–440.

—— & ERSKINE, A. (1989) Chronic pain. In *The Practice of Behavioural Medicine* (eds S. Pearce & J. Wardle), pp. 83–111. Oxford: BPS Books/OUP.

PENNEBAKER, J. W. (1982) *The Psychology of Physical Symptoms*. New York: Springer-Verlag.

PETERS, J. L. & LARGE, R. G. (1990) A randomized control trial evaluating in- and out-patient pain management programs. *Pain*, **41**, 283–293.

PHILIPS, H. C. (1988) *The Psychological Management of Chronic Pain: A Treatment Manual*. New York: Springer.

—— (1989) Thoughts provoked by pain. *Behaviour Research and Therapy*, **27**, 469–473.

PITHER, C. E. & NICHOLAS, M. K. (1991) The identification of iatrogenic factors in the development of chronic pain syndromes: abnormal treatment behaviour? In *Proceedings of the VIth World Congress on Pain* (eds M. R. Bond, J. E. Charlton, C. J. Woolf), pp. 429–434. Amsterdam: Elsevier.

RIGGE, M. (1990) Pain. *Which? Way to Health*, April, 66–68.

RIMM, D. C. & MASTERS, J. C. (1974) *Behavior Therapy: Techniques and Empirical Findings*. New York: Academic Press.

ROMANO, J. M., TURNER, J. A. & CLANCY, S. L. (1989) Sex differences in the relationship of pain patient dysfunction to spouse adjustment. *Pain*, **39**, 289–295.

ROSENSTIEL, A. K. & KEEFE, F. J. (1983) The use of coping strategies in chronic low back pain patients: relationship to patient characteristics and current adjustment. *Pain*, **17**, 33–44.

ROWAT, K. M. & KNAFL, K. A. (1985) Living with chronic pain: the spouse's perspective. *Pain*, **23**, 259–271.

SELIGMAN, M. E. P. (1975) *Helplessness*. San Francisco: Freeman.

SPIELBERGER, C. D., GORSUCH, R. L. & LUSHENE, R. E. (1970) *The State–Trait Anxiety Inventory*. Palo Alto, CA: Consulting Psychologists Press.

STERNBACH, R. A. (1976) Psychological factors in pain. In *Advances in Pain Research and Therapy, Vol. 1* (eds J. J. Bonica & D. Albe-Fessard), pp. 293–299. New York: Raven Press.

—— (1986) Pain and 'hassles' in the United States: findings of the Nuprin Pain Report. *Pain*, **27**, 69–80.

TURK, D. C., MEICHENBAUM, D. & GENEST, M. (1983) *Pain and Behavioral Medicine: A Cognitive–Behavioral Perspective*. New York: Guilford Press.

TURNER, J. A. & CLANCY, S. (1986) Strategies for coping with chronic low back pain: relationship to pain and disability. *Pain*, **24**, 355–364.

WALL, P. D. (1985) Future trends in pain research. *Philosophical Transactions of the Royal Society of London*, **B 308**, 393–401.

WARWICK, H. M. C. & SALKOVSKIS, P. M. (1989) Hypochondriasis. In *Cognitive Therapy: A Clinical Casebook* (eds J. Scott, J. M. G. Williams & A. T. Beck), pp. 78–102. London: Routledge.

WEISENBERG, M. (1977) Pain and pain control. *Psychological Bulletin*, **5**, 1008–1044.

WILLIAMS, D. A. & THORN, B. E. (1989) An empirical assessment of pain beliefs. *Pain*, **36**, 351–358.

9 Evaluation of the long-term benefits of a cognitive–behavioural out-patient programme for chronic pain

SHIRLEY PEARCE and ALEDA ERSKINE

Chronic pain presents a major practical and theoretical problem. Epidemiological studies indicate that up to 85% of the population in the industrialised world will suffer from back pain (Wells, 1985) and the majority of those suffering a first attack will have recurrences (Biering-Sorensson, 1984). In 1982 in the UK, back pain alone resulted in the loss of 33.3 million working days with an estimated £1 billion lost output. In addition, it cost £193 million in sickness benefit (Wells, 1985). Recurrent and long-term patients account for the bulk of this cost with 10% of cases consuming 50–75% of the costs.

The 'human cost' is less easy to evaluate. Pain sufferers may experience depression and feelings of helplessness, financial worries, feelings of anger and frustration, relationship difficulties and social isolation, all of which may make adjustment to their pain condition extremely difficult.

Such intractable pain sufferers present a major social, medical and economic problem and the largely unpredictable success of medical and surgical interventions has led to interest in treatment approaches based on psychological principles.

These principles are largely based on more sophisticated models of pain, some of which not only acknowledge the ability of psychological factors to influence the perception of pain intensity (e.g. Melzack & Wall, 1965) but go on to describe pain as a multi-dimensional experience causing impact at various levels, including the sufferer's belief system and their lifestyle (e.g. Karoly, 1985). These models have been developed in response to the limitations of the direct line transmission theory of pain, which assumes that the intensity of pain experienced is directly linked to the amount of tissue damage that exists. Whilst it is necessary to investigate and treat the physical component of pain, intervention at an exclusively physical level is inappropriate in many chronic pain conditions and may even encourage the development of behaviour patterns which can exacerbate the impact the pain has on the sufferer's life. For example, sending patients for numerous unsuccessful treatments with the hope that someone will take their pain away for them may induce in the patient feelings of lack of control over their pain, which may lead to feelings of helplessness. Such mood difficulties may eventually come to be a major component of the sufferer's 'pain problem'.

Many in-patient pain management programmes, employing psychological techniques, have been established in the USA and one such programme now exists in the UK at St Thomas' Hospital, London. This is described in detail in this volume (Williams). These aim to increase patient's ability to live normal lives despite the pain. They involve developing individual graded exercise programmes teaching relaxation and cognitive coping strategies, and reducing medication consumption. There is little doubt that in-patient programmes run along these lines can produce significant improvements, at least in the short term, on a range of outcome measures (Linton, 1986). Despite the considerable research on in-patient treatments little attention has been directed towards the development and evaluation of out-patient therapies. This is surprising since not only are in-patient programmes very expensive and probably impractical in most UK health settings but there are also sound theoretical reasons for predicting that out-patient treatments may be more effective in the long term than in-patient treatment. There is evidence that improvements in activity only occur while they are actively reinforced/rewarded (Cairns & Pasino, 1977). On discharge from hospital, patients enter another world. They no longer have the constant attention from staff. Their relatives may still treat them as they did before admission and without the encouragement and reminders to use positive coping strategies provided by the hospital staff, patients may soon lapse back into old behaviour patterns. For this reason, generalising progress from hospital to home is a major problem for in-patient programmes. Out-patient treatments have the advantage of teaching new coping skills and increasing activity levels in the patient's own environment. Alternatively, it could be argued that patients on an out-patient programme may not acquire the necessary skills in the first place due to the relatively small amount of contact therapists are able to have in an out-patient setting.

Although no direct comparison of out-patient and in-patient programmes has yet been published, out-patient programmes have been shown to be constructive in helping people cope more effectively with their pain. Kerns *et al* (1986) randomised 29 chronic pain sufferers to one of three groups; a cognitive–behavioural programme, an operant pain programme and a waiting list control. Treatment took place on an individual out-patient basis and while there was no change in the waiting list control group, the two treatment groups both significantly improved in terms of health care usage and goal attainment.

Philips (1987*b*) randomly allocated 40 chronic pain patients to either a cognitive–behavioural group programme or a waiting list control. The programme took place over a 9-week period for 90 minutes a week. The control group showed no significant changes but the treatment group significantly improved over a wide range of measures, including depression, analgesic intake, pain intensity, self-efficacy and avoidance and complaint behaviour. Most of these improvements were not only maintained at 2-month follow-up but improved upon.

The research described in this chapter is a pilot study for a larger comparison of group versus individual approaches to out-patient pain management. It describes the development of an initial evaluation of an out-patient group in the UK.

Pilot study staff

At the Whittington Hospital, London, our team included an anaesthetist, a physiotherapist, a general practitioner skilled in hypnosis, two clinical psychologists and an occupational therapist. Each staff member contributed about one session a week to the project. Although the anaesthetist acted as coordinator and had medical responsibility for the patients, the team worked democratically, with all decisions taken at staff meetings. We met each week before the patients arrived and spent half an hour sharing information, monitoring patients' progress, and equally important, giving mutual support. In this way, the different therapeutic modalities were pulled together so that patients were offered an integrated approach which constantly reaffirmed a self-help ethos.

Selection and preparation of patients

All patients were first seen in the Pain Clinic by the anaesthetist and one clinical psychologist. They were selected from successive referrals to the pain relief clinic. They were heterogeneous with respect to the site and aetiology of pain, cultural background and age. Since so little is known about outcome predictors we kept our inclusion criteria, which are as follows, as wide as possible: age 18–70 years, continuing disability from chronic non-malignant pain despite all appropriate physical investigations and treatments having being tried. Patients also had to be without marked learning difficulties, without past history of serious mental illness, fluent in English, and able to make their own way to the hospital.

A minority of patients wished to exclude themselves for various reasons, of which the commonest were difficulty in accepting that conventional medicine has failed, and suspicion of a psychologically based approach. The latter may involve two worries which are often indirectly communicated: ''Do you think my pain is real?'' and ''Does your recommendation of this course mean that you think I am mentally unstable?'' With careful discussion it was sometimes possible to resolve these concerns.

The anaesthetist explained to each patient that he had studied their files carefully and reassured them that all appropriate medical investigations and treatments had been tried. It was suggested to the patient that in the past this may have been the end of the story but now new ways of understanding pain opened up new possibilities, even if cure remained elusive. The outline of the multi-component model of pain was then introduced as the basis for the course rationale. The two essential points stressed to patients were (a) that the course was designed for people with real pain problems (we do not believe in non-organic pain) and (b) that research suggested that pain patients could learn to mobilise new physical and psychological resources, develop greater physical and mental relaxation, improve their mood, gain an increased sense of control over the pain and improve the quality of their life. No promise of total pain relief was ever made. A history was also taken and, provided the patient met all the criteria, some preliminary goals were worked out. One or two weeks before the start of the course, each patient was seen by the physiotherapist to assess their joint range and exercise tolerance, and to note any particular physical difficulties. Booklets summarising the course content were distributed.

Group organisation

Each group took place on one afternoon per week for 7 successive weeks. It consisted of 8–10 men and women with widely varying diagnoses, attitudes and expectations. Our task was to help them cohere into a working group which could itself become an agent of positive change. Regular attendance and punctuality were stressed and absentees were telephoned on the afternoon of absence. We encouraged the sharing of personal experiences, advice and goals, albeit within a highly structured programme. We discouraged any individual from monopolising group time. Positive problem-solving talk was reinforced, but talk about pain was passed over with little or no comment.

The afternoon started with the group education and cognitive pain control training session conducted by two clinical psychologists. This lasted for one hour and was followed by a 30-minute relaxation/stress-management session and a 45 minute physical therapy session. There was then a 20 minute coffee break which provided a valuable opportunity for patients to socialise and discuss the course informally on their own. The afternoon ended with a one-hour lifestyle and general goal-setting session.

The different components of the treatment package will now be described in turn and clinical examples provided for each component.

Group education and cognitive pain control training

During the screening phase of the course, a rationale for a cognitive–behavioural approach was outlined. Another more detailed explanation provided the starting point for this component of the course. This achieves two things: it gives face validity to the various course components and it begins to shift the patient away from passive helplessness towards a position of active responsibility. We have found a presentation which includes a three-systems approach (Pearce & Erskine, 1989) to pain and an outline of the gate control theory to be helpful.

We asked patients to make free associations with the word 'pain', and adjectives were then written up on a flip chart in three sections. These are related to the physiological, subjective and behavioural systems of pain respectively, and labelled accordingly. In this way, a multi-dimensional view of pain is reintroduced and then reinforced by a theoretical model. The gate control theory needed to be simplified, explained with the help of a diagram and its shortcomings admitted. We put the emphasis on the higher cortical descending influences as this underlined the link between changing attitudes and thoughts and pain management. At the same time, we stressed that there could be no permanent closure of the 'gate', so that pain control rather than pain cessation was reaffirmed as the major goal.

Most chronic pain patients have tried their hand at "thinking of other things", and they are likely to be unimpressed by cognitive strategies unless their relevance and validity is first carefully explained. In teaching pain control strategies we begin by stressing the notion that attention is like a limited capacity channel and that it is possible to learn how to 'tune out' painful stimuli and 'tune in' pleasant ones. This idea was related back to the gate control theory, which links the diversion of attention with the closing of the 'gate'. Finally, borrowing a suggestion from Turk *et al* (1983), we asked the group to relax and one of the authors read out a graphic description of a lemon being cut and sucked. The group was then invited to talk about their reactions. Most patients experienced some physiological responses, for example, salivation, mouth puckering, etc. and some experienced temporary pain reduction or cessation during the reading: all this provided an excellent demonstration of the power imagery has to affect the mind and divert the attention from painful stimuli.

After this introduction, we spent the rest of the session and the next two sessions teaching four main types of cognitive strategies: 'imaginative inattention'; 'imaginative transformation'; 'attention diversion', and 'somatisation'. To date we have had little success with 'transformation of content' and no longer include it in our programme. To illustrate each technique, we worked out an individualised strategy with one of the patients, and asked all the group to experiment with the technique, in their own way. It was emphasised that each patient must try out all techniques before being sure which of the four would be most suitable.

Patients were told to practise the chosen technique or techniques daily for some time until they could be conjured up easily and with maximum concentration and vividness. We advised patients to begin using the techniques at the first sign that pain intensity was on the increase and discouraged them from practising at first when the pain was severe. The techniques must be individualised to be successful, and it is worth giving plenty of individual attention, perhaps by subdividing the group, in order to achieve this and to check subsequent 'homework' assignments.

> Cilla, a 35-year-old secretary with chronic pelvic pain, hit upon her own amalgamation of relaxation and imaginative transformation. She had an image of her pain as a serpent eating her organs. She would relax and breathe deeply and imagine the oxygen from her lungs strengthening the healing white cells attacking the serpent which gradually dwindled into nothing and, with it, her pain. Cilla discovered this strategy was very effective at reducing both pain intensity and distress.
>
> Ranee, a 40-year-old school teacher with back pain, practised an imaginative inattention technique based on a childhood memory. She imagined herself standing on a bridge overlooking a wide river in a rural part of India. She saw herself gazing down, almost mesmerised, at the graceful, slow-moving barges gliding over the shining water. The technique did not affect the intensity of her pain but it did provide a quick means of removing the high levels of anxiety and distress associated with it.

Relaxation

Progressive relaxation and autogenic relaxation can both be successfully practised with chronic pain patients. The fact that one of our team had special training in hypnosis enabled us to explore the use of self-hypnotic relaxation. As with other forms of relaxation, this course component was designed to teach patients a means of reducing physical and mental tension, which promoted a greater sense of control over all kinds of stress, including that produced by pain. It was divided into three stages:

(a) The 'basic' stage, when patients were encouraged to produce deep relaxation by initial induction techniques, and the subsequent use of relaxation instructions. Although different muscle groups were named, relaxation was promoted by verbal suggestion and patients did not tense muscles before relaxing them.

(b) The 'intermediate' stage, when patients were taught to apply the procedure to themselves by listening to a tape at home which recorded the trainer's instructions; in the session, patients were encouraged to achieve deeper levels of relaxation.

(c) The 'advanced' stage, when patients learnt to hypnotise themselves both in the sessions without cues from the trainer and at home without the use of the tape.

The group was also introduced to methods of hypnotic pain control such as group anaesthesia and disassociation (Barber, 1986). At each stage of the course patients were given ego-strengthening post-hypnotic suggestions which prompted them to feel more confident in the acquisition of all of the different skills taught on the course and more motivated to practise them.

We found this method of relaxation had considerable advantages. Through hypnosis, patients attained deep levels of relaxation very quickly and this became a spur to learning the method for themselves. Although the primary aim was relaxation, the more susceptible patients also learnt direct pain-control strategies as well. Finally, the ego-strengthening suggestions were designed to complement the work of other members of staff.

Some provisos need to be made. There are a lot of myths about hypnosis which can deter some patients. It is important to allow time initially to discuss the course fully; also helpful is a practical, confident approach to the subject which stresses the patient's control over compliance at all times. Second, although a group of patients will obviously differ in their levels of susceptibility, this need not present practical problems. With a sensitive therapist, patients can benefit from relaxation instructions and deepening suggestions even if they are only minimally responsive to the hypnotic suggestions themselves.

> Dora, a 65-year-old divorced office worker, suffered from oral pain and chest pain and showed much anxiety. Initially, she insisted on "sitting out and watching" the relaxation class, and seemed highly nervous of joining in. The therapist gave her permission to do this and told her to do however many of the exercises she felt comfortable with. Gradually Dora increased her participation and, much to her surprise, found herself adept at self-hypnosis and practised hard. By the end of the course she was able to relax at will when the pain worsened and her general anxiety level showed a significant drop.

Stress management

As an introduction to cognitive stress control strategies, a simple galvanic skin response (GSR) biofeedback machine can provide a dramatic demonstration of the interrelationship between thoughts and physiology in the stress response. We invited each patient, duly attached to the machine, to imagine himself or herself in a stress situation. We encouraged the patient to use prepared coping thoughts and the biofeedback itself to reduce stress. The next step was to outline the theory of stress, focusing on the fight or flight response and the important role of appraisal in its production. We then used a modified stress inoculation procedure (Meichenbaum & Turk, 1976). The patients were asked to monitor their stress responses in terms of thoughts and physiological change over a week. At the following session, this 'homework' became the basis for a discussion in which individual stressors, characteristic automatic thoughts and physiological response specificity were identified. The linked 'homework' task was to tackle one or two identified stressors by using prepared cognitive coping statements in the anticipatory and confronting stages of stress response. Patients then reported back to the group about their experiences and we encouraged them to continue practising these techniques for the remainder of the course.

> Colleen, a 50-year-old housewife with multiple pains, found her new plans to get a part-time job were held back by interview anxiety. In the group she learned how to use prepared coping statements to repeat to herself while she dressed for an interview and sat in the waiting room. She combined these strategies with some slow breathing. The following week she returned, delighted to tell the group she had been accepted for a secretarial post.

Graded exercise therapy

The aims of this group were:

(a) to decrease the level of fear surrounding movement and activity
(b) to increase the level of physical fitness
(c) to increase the level of physical activity
(d) to alert patients to unhelpful postures and the benefits of good posture
(e) to improve the patient's body image.

The course was structured around a core of exercises involving all the major muscle groups which were designed to promote increased flexibility and stamina. Every patient was given a booklet in which he or she set down the individualised weekly 'homework' goals in terms of choice and number of exercises, and recorded the progress made. The physiotherapist stressed that the patient was in control of the rate of progress and that a certain amount of experimentation would be necessary. She told them some initial increase in discomfort was normal and predictable. Any competition between patients was firmly discouraged and the importance of a paced, graded approach was underlined. This 'core' was supplemented each week by a discussion, by group games, for example with balls or hoops, and by exercise to music.

Joe, an unemployed 60-year-old man, had Paget's disease, a left-kidney malfunction and multiple pain. At assessment, Joe could only walk 300 yards and sit for 20 minutes and he spent most of the day lying down. At week one he was very anxious about exercise and reluctant to join in the group. The physiotherapist modified some of the core exercises for him; for example, the sit-up exercise was changed to head raising from a lying down position, and the step-up exercises were done with a four-inch block. By following a graded exercise progressive programme at home and in the hospital, by week seven, Joe was doing 16 full sit-ups, 20 full step-ups and 16 elbow push-ups. His walking and sitting tolerance had also improved significantly. Joe gained little from the rest of the course, but his new fitness and activity level enhanced his self-esteem and mood.

Analgesic reduction and positive goal setting

This group used goal setting as its principal tool in tackling both analgesic intake and avoidance behaviour over a wide range of activities: self-care, homemaking and work activity, social interaction and leisure pursuits. The case for cutting out analgesics was set out carefully with attention paid to the dangers of addiction and the potential advantages of alternative methods of pain control. Patients also needed to be reassured that a gradual planned reduction rather than an immediate withdrawal was the aim. Long-term goals to change medication intake and lifestyle were then negotiated individually. This could be a demanding process since patients who were demoralised were often reluctant to consider steps which may seem frightening and impractical. What was needed was a dialogue between therapist and patient in which these fears were addressed sympathetically but in a questioning way. Once formulated, goals must be operationalised in clear and specific language. In the group, each patient's goals were shared and written up on a large sheet of paper; in subsequent sessions the chart was referred to so that individual progress was constantly monitored. Each week individual 'homework' tasks related to the goals were set and then checked the following week.

Many patients had a tendency to swing between inaction and all out activity which resulted in unnecessary additional pain and further demoralisation. They needed to be steered towards taking realistic, moderate steps which guarantee continuous progress. When this was done, the effect on patients' self-esteem and self-confidence was soon apparent. It seems likely that in many chronic pain patients, vicious circles are set up between avoidance behaviour and certain cognitions: expectations of pain increase on exposure to feared stimuli, beliefs about incapacity to control pain and memories of past painful experiences (Philips, 1987a). Exposure to the feared stimuli through graded tasks provides an invaluable way of testing and challenging these cognitions and so improving self-efficacy. The patient is also brought into contact with new environmental sources of reinforcement which help to maintain the desired behaviour. Furthermore, the group itself acts as a powerful reinforcer once norms affirming task completion are established.

Difficulties in goal attainment often arise and depression can be a key factor. To tackle this two sessions were allocated in which depression was the major topic. Peck (1985) made useful suggestions for work on increasing pleasant experiences and the awareness of positive attributes in pain patients. A second source of difficulty is secondary gain within the family. From the outset, patients were encouraged to involve a significant other in their treatment and at least one session focused on the possible problems for themselves and their relatives raised by personal change.

> Tom, an unemployed, 59-year-old widower, had once been sociable and a keen gardener. However, since giving up his portering job a year before because of dorsal osteoarthritis he had taken to sitting at home, and his allotment was overgrown with weeds. At the beginning of the course, Tom set two goals: to return to the allotment and to resume his previous pattern of meeting friends in cafés or pubs four times a week. Week by week he gradually increased the time spent on his goals until by week seven he was working one hour a day gardening and had fulfilled his social goal. His new goal is to look for a part-time job.

Design of the study

This was a one-group repeated-measures study. Measurements were taken on five occasions: on selection (time 1); 4 weeks later just before starting the treatment programme (time 2); at the end of treatment (time 3); at follow-up 4 weeks later (time 4). To establish the stability of these changes patients were reassessed at one year (time 5). Full details of the study and treatment content are presented by Skinner *et al* (1990).

A wide range of outcome measures was chosen to represent sensory, affective and behavioural aspects of pain. These were the Zung Self Rating Depression Scale (Zung, 1965), the Spielberger 'State' Anxiety Scale (Spielberger *et al*, 1970), the McGill Pain Questionnaire (Melzack, 1975), the Oswestry Low Back Pain & Disability Questionnaire (Fairbank, 1980), which asks about limits to physical activity, e.g. walking, sitting, self-care, and the Pain Responses Questionnaire (Pearce & Mathews, 1986). This last questionnaire contains three scales: the negative cognitions scale records the use of negative strategies reflecting hopelessness and helplessness in response to pain, the positive cognitions scale reflects the use of distraction and anxiety-reducing strategies and the avoidance/disruption scale reflects the extent to which behaviour and lifestyle are interrupted by pain. The Pain Locus of Control Questionnaire (Main *et al*, personal communication) was used with a cognitive control scale in which a high score indicates optimism about the possibility of controlling pain, and the pain responsibility scale which indicates acceptance of personal responsibility for controlling pain. Visual linear analogue scales of pain intensity and distress were also used and the number of analgesic tablets consumed per week was also recorded. All questionnaires were completed by the patients in the presence of a member of staff.

Patients were then assigned to four successive groups of approximately nine in each group. Each programme took place on one afternoon a week for 7 consecutive weeks and the content was as described above.

Results

Thirty-four patients completed all parts of the treatment programme and the first follow-up assessment. The means and standards errors of each of the outcome variables on these four occasions of measurement are given in Table 9.1 and in Figs 9.1 and 9.2.

Separate univariate repeated-measures analysis of variance (ANOVAs) for each variable over time were conducted. In the first instance repeated-measures ANOVAs between pre-selection (time 1) and treatment (time 2) were conducted to investigate the stability of the measures for these patients prior to the intervention. None of the dependent variables showed significant changes prior to treatment. A further series of repeated-measures ANOVAs were conducted to assess changes over time between pre-treatment (time 2) and post-treatment (time 3) and follow-up (time 4). The linear F ratios for this change during treatment and the follow-up period are also shown in Table 9.1. The degrees of freedom vary slightly according to the variable measured since some patients did not complete all the questionnaires on each occasion.

There were significant changes after treatment for measures of analgesic consumption, anxiety, depression, physical disability, and coping skills. The improvement in coping skills means that after treatment when patients got pain they were more likely to "think of something pleasant rather than concentrate on the pain", or "think of things to do to distract me from the pain". They were less likely to "think it's never going to end" or "find my attention focuses on the pain". It therefore seems reasonable to suggest patients develop a more positive attitude to their pain problem, taking less medication and increasing their activity levels.

The pattern of changes described above was not observed for all the dependent variables. Measures of pain intensity failed to show a clear pattern of significant changes. There were no changes for the affective scales of the McGill Pain Questionnaire and the visual analogue scale ratings of pain intensity on average over the previous week. Visual analogue scale ratings of pain intensity at worst and the sensory scale of the McGill Pain Questionnaire do, however, show a significant change although the clinical significance of these changes is questionable since the absolute levels at

TABLE 9.1

Means and standard errors of outcome variables on each occasion of measurement

	Time 1: selection mean (s.e.)	Time 2: baseline mean (s.e.)	Time 3: treatment mean (s.e.)	Time 4: follow-up mean (s.e.)	Linear F time 2, 3 and 4	Degrees of freedom
Analgesic tablets consumed	23.7 (5.25)	22.0 (4.3)	10.4 (3.2)	6.6 (2.8)	14.44	1,17***
McGill Pain Questionnaire						
sensory	10.8 (1.2)	12.3 (1.2)	13.1 (1.2)	10.3 (1.4)	5.20	1,21*
affective	3.4 (0.5)	3.6 (0.5)	4.8 (1.6)	3.9 (0.8)	0.02	1,21 NS
Visual analogue rating scales						
Pain intensity						
on average	59.2 (4.4)	61.2 (5.0)	51.3 (6.7)	51.2 (5.22)	2.00	1,21 NS
at worst	68.2 (6.7)	78.8 (5.4)	69.2 (5.4)	68.8 (5.4)	4.48	1,21*
Distress						
on average	57.1 (5.6)	58.1 (4.9)	31.4 (6.0)	44.8 (6.9)	8.12	1,21**
at worst	82.6 (4.3)	78.9 (3.3)	47.7 (7.6)	61.6 (6.2)	8.50	1,21**
Mood						
Spielberger 'State' anxiety	44.9 (3.1)	42.4 (2.5)	34.7 (3.1)	37.5 (2.5)	5.51	1,22*
Zung depression rating	29.4 (2.3)	28.0 (1.87)	23.6 (1.9)	21.0 (1.9)	20.73	1,26***
Physical disability						
Oswestry Low Back Pain and Disability Questionnaire	39.0 (3.3)	37.6 (3.8)	32.2 (4.0)	30.8 (4.2)	9.49	1,22***
Coping questionnaires						
Pain locus of control						
cognitive control	6.8 (1.1)	6.7 (0.8)	12.4 (0.8)	11.3 (1.0)	22.38	1,22***
pain responsibility	8.2 (0.6)	9.7 (0.7)	12.2 (0.6)	11.3 (0.6)	4.25	1,22*
Pain Responses Questionnaire						
negative cognitions	2.8 (0.3)	3.0 (0.4)	2.3 (0.4)	1.8 (0.4)	6.49	1,27**
avoidance disruption	3.3 (0.3)	3.1 (0.3)	1.7 (0.3)	1.7 (0.3)	12.36	1,27***
positive responses	2.1 (0.2)	1.8 (0.3)	2.8 (0.4)	3.0 (0.4)	7.60	1,27**

*$P<0.05$; **$P<0.01$; ***$P<0.001$

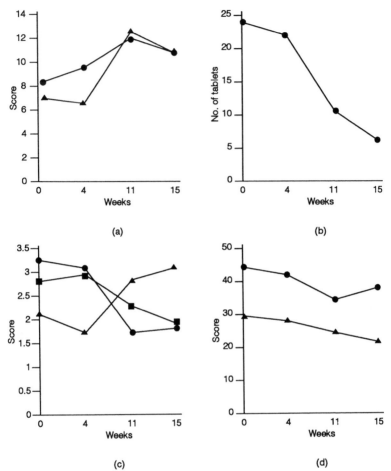

(a)

(b)

(c)

(d)

(Figs 9.1 and 9.2 are reproduced from the Journal of Psychosomatic Research, vol. 34, J.B. Skinner et al, "The evaluation of a cognitive behavioural treatment programme in outpatients with chronic pain", pp. 13–19, © 1990, with kind permission from Pergamon Press Ltd, Headington Hill Hall, Oxford OX3 0BW, UK)

Fig. 9.1. Results at week 0 (selection), 4 and 11 (treatment) and 15 (follow-up). (a) ▲ Pain locus of control: cognitive control, ● Pain locus of control: pain responsibility; (b) ● Analgesia consumption (tablets per week); (c) ■ Pain Responses Questionnaire: negative cognitions scale, ● Pain responses questionnaire: avoidance/disruption scale, ▲ Pain Responses Questionnaire: positive responses scale; (d) ● Spielberger 'state' anxiety, ▲ Zung self-rating depression scale

follow-up are little different from those at time 1. Hence we cannot confidently say that patients were reporting lower levels of pain intensity at short-term follow-up. Ratings of how distressing the pain is showed significant reductions during the treatment period which is in keeping with the observed improvements in mood and coping abilities.

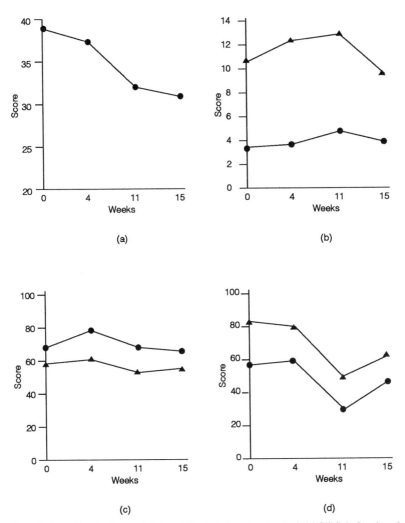

Fig. 9.2. (a) ● *Oswestry Low Back Pain and Disability Questionnaire; (b)* ● *McGill Pain Questionnaire (affective),* ▲ *McGill Pain Questionnaire (sensory); (c)* ▲ *VAS pain intensity (on average),* ● *VAS pain intensity (at worst); (d)* ● *VAS pain distress (on average),* ▲ *VAS pain distress (at worst)*

Durability of change

Twenty-six patients (66%) were available for reassessment at one-year follow-up. Significant reductions in pain intensity and disability as measured by the Oswestry Scale were observed between the short-term follow-up and this one-year follow-up. No further reductions occurred for mood, coping strategy use or analgesic consumption.

Discussion

It is clearly feasible to set up a multidisciplinary pain programme of this sort within a pain relief clinic of a district general hospital, and we have shown that it can have a powerful effect on certain aspects of chronic pain.

The question, however, arises as to whether it is the treatment programme itself that has effected these changes or whether they represent spontaneous changes that would have occurred anyway. Support for the specific effect of the treatment comes from the repeated-measures ANOVAs which indicated that none of the variables showed significant changes during the pre-treatment period.

It has been suggested that the type of patients who are referred to pain management programmes constitute a population in which psychopathology is unusually predominant (Turk & Rudy, 1990). In a review, they compare reports of the prevalence of depression, for example in patients in pain clinics and those involved in surveys conducted in the community and not referred to pain clinics. Crook *et al* (1984) directly compared those pain sufferers referred to pain clinics with those suffering persistent pain in the community not attending these specialist clinics and found those attending the specialist clinics to be more emotionally distressed. This clearly suggests caution when trying to generalise the results of such pain programmes to the general population. However, the fact that pain management techniques are helpful to patients with increased levels of distress provides support for their efficacy.

The lack of an effective control procedure is acknowledged and further studies should be conducted with appropriate no-treatment control procedures. It should be remembered, however, that all patients have failed to respond to standard conventional treatments given over a number of years and showed no significant change during the baseline period of observation. Apparently, therefore, as a result of treatment patients are less depressed, less anxious, more active and more likely to report they can cope with life and their pain.

Measures of pain intensity are largely unchanged in the short term but at one-year follow-up those patients available for assessment show significant reductions in pain. It must be remembered that this is a selected sample at one-year follow-up and hence generality about longer-term changes must be treated with some caution. However, it is clear that those patients who have maintained increases in activity appear to show associated reductions in pain.

At present it is unclear how each of the programme components contribute to the eventual outcome, and we can only speculate about the mode of action. Further research is needed to answer such questions; however, there is some evidence that different approaches produce different changes, as would be predicted if specific treatment effects were producing change. For example, Linton & Gotestam (1984) compared two out-patient groups, one receiving relaxation training plus an operant programme and the other receiving relaxation training alone. Their follow-up data show that whilst the relaxation-only group experienced reductions in pain intensity, the relaxation-plus-operant group experienced similar reductions in pain intensity plus improvements in activity and medication reduction. This provides tentative evidence that the changes brought about are not the result of non-specific factors such as attention. Indeed there is some evidence to suggest that non-directive attention may have adverse effects on some scores. For example, White & Sanders (1986) found that positive verbal reinforcement for talking about pain influenced subsequent ratings of pain intensity higher than when they were verbally reinforced for discussing 'well behaviours'. Although the numbers used in the study were small ($n = 4$) it does provide some support for the efficacy of specific treatment factors in pain management.

This study suggests that results comparable to those reported from residential programmes in the USA can be achieved in Britain on an outpatient basis, at lower cost to the health service and suggests that further research will be practically as well as theoretically rewarding.

Acknowledgements

We are grateful to Julia Curl and Anne Miles for their help in the preparation of this manuscript. We are also grateful to the other members of the multidisciplinary team who made the project possible and to the patients who collaborated in this venture.

We are also grateful to the Medical Research Council for the financial support they have provided to extend this research.

References

BARBER, J. (1986) Hypnotic analgesia. In *Pain Management: A Handbook of Psychological Treatment Approaches* (eds A. D. Holzman & D. C. Turk). New York: Pergamon.

BIERING-SORENSSON, F. (1984) A one year prospective study of low back trouble in a general population. *Largeporenihgens Vorlag Copenhagen.*

CAIRNS, D. & PASINO, J. A. (1977) Comparison of verbal reinforcement and feedback in the operant treatment of disability due to chronic low back pain. *Behaviour Therapy,* **8,** 621–630.

CROOK, J., RIDEOUT, E. & BROWNE, G. (1984) The prevalence of pain complaints in a general population. *Pain,* **18,** 299–314.

FAIRBANK, J. C. T. (1980) The Oswestry Low Back Pain and Disability Questionnaire. *Physiotherapy,* **66,** 271–273.

KAROLY, P. (ed.) (1985) *The Assessment of Pain: Concepts and Procedures in Measurement Strategies in Health Psychology.* New York: Wiley.

KERNS, R. D., TURK, D. C., HOLZMAN, A. D., *et al* (1986) Comparison of cognitive-behavioral and behavioral approaches to the out-patient treatment of chronic pain. *Clinical Journal of Pain,* **1,** 199–203.

LINTON, S. J. (1986) Behavioural remediation of chronic pain: a status report. *Pain,* **24,** 125–141.

—— & GOTESTAM, K. G. (1984) A controlled study of the effects of applied relaxation and applied relaxation plus operant procedures in the regulation of chronic pain. *British Journal of Clinical Psychology*, **23**, 291–299.

MEICHENBAUM, D. H. & TURK, D. C. (1976) The cognitive behavioural management of anxiety, anger and pain. In *The Behavioural Management of Anxiety, Depression and Pain* (ed. P. O. Davidson). New York: Brunner/Mazel.

MELZACK, R. (1975) The McGill Pain Questionnaire: major properties and scoring methods. *Pain*, **1**, 277–299.

—— & WALL, P. D. (1965) Pain mechanisms: a new theory. *Science*, **150**, 971–979.

PEARCE, S. & ERSKINE, A. (1989) Chronic pain. In *The Practice of Behavioural Medicine* (eds S. Pearce & J. Wardle). The British Psychological Society and Oxford University Press.

PECK, C. (1985) *Controlling Chronic Pain: A Self-help Guide*. London: Collins.

PHILIPS, H. C. (1987a) Avoidance behaviour and its role in sustaining chronic pain. *Behaviour Research and Therapy*, **25**, 273–279.

—— (1987b) The effects of behavioural treatment on chronic pain. *Behaviour Research and Therapy*, **25**, 365–377.

SKINNER, J. B., ERSKINE, A., PEARCE, S., *et al* (1990) The evaluation of a cognitive behavioural treatment programme in outpatients with chronic pain. *Journal of Psychosomatic Research*, **34**, 13–19.

SPIELBERGER, C. D., GORSUCH, R. L. & LUSHENE, R. (1970) *Manual for the State Trait Anxiety Inventory*. Palo Alto, CA: Consulting Psychologists Press.

TURK, D. C., MEICHENBAUM, D. & GENEST, M. (1983) *Pain and Behavioural Medicine: A Cognitive Behavioural Perspective*. New York: Guilford Press.

—— & RUDY (1990) Review Article: Neglected treatment factors in chronic pain treatment outcome studies – referral patterns, failure to enter treatment and attrition. *Pain*, **43**, 7–26.

WELLS, N. (1985) *Back Pain*. London: Office of Health Economics.

WHITE, B. & SANDERS, S. H. (1986) The influence on patients' pain intensity ratings of antecedent reinforcement of pain talk or well talk. *Journal of Behavioural Therapy and Experimental Psychiatry*, **17**, 155–159.

ZUNG, W. W. K. (1965) A self rating depression scale. *Psychiatry*, **12**, 63–70.

10 Identifying the causes of poor self-management in insulin dependent diabetics: the use of cognitive–analytic therapy techniques

ANTHONY RYLE, CHERRY BOA and JACKIE FOSBURY

The greater precision of methods now available for measuring the physiological effects of psychosocial factors and of 'stress' need to be matched by the development of more precise descriptions of associated psychological processes. Common stresses of everyday life are frequently generated or maintained by the individual's particular life strategies but even when one considers the impact of independent events and disasters the individual's mode of construing and coping with the situation is of central importance in determining the long-term outcome. In this chapter we present a method of describing psychological processes and of carrying out psychotherapy which we believe goes some way towards the goal of identifying precisely and modifying the specific mechanisms associated with poor control in insulin dependent diabetic subjects.

While there is no evidence for a psychological factor in the aetiology of diabetes, associated psychological symptoms and difficulties, some emotionally and some organically determined, are common. There is some evidence that psychosocial factors are associated with poor diabetic control; thus Bradley (1979) demonstrated that poor control was associated with life events, Cohen et al (1960) and MacGillivray et al (1987) demonstrated stress-induced keto-acidosis in children and Barglow et al (1983) reported a combined effect of life events and 'poor ego development'. However, in recent years it has become evident that by far the most frequent immediate cause of poor control is non-compliance with aspects of management, that is to say, it is derived from patients' failure to adhere to diets, to test blood sugar levels regularly, and to administer the correct insulin dosage (Tattersall, 1985).

Background

The Diabetic Unit at St Thomas' Hospital offers a full programme of education to diabetic patients, seeking to maximise the patient's capacity for effective and autonomous control. Despite this, a substantial proportion of attending patients fail to maintain satisfactory levels of blood sugar and are hence at risk of developing serious and eventually life-threatening complications. This led to the setting up of a research enquiry in conjunction with Professor Sonksen. The enquiry was initiated by Dr Jane Milton (see Milton, 1989) and is being continued by J. Fosbury. The clinical material reported here was gathered in the course of this latter study. The patients concerned are seriously non-compliant as indicated by a sustained rise in the percentage of glycosylated haemoglobin (HbA_{1c}) above 11.5% for one year or longer. This measure is a reliable indication of the average level of blood sugar over the preceding three months. The study is a controlled intervention study, patients being randomly assigned to either specialist nurse education or to time-limited cognitive analytic–therapy. In addition, we are investigating how well non-compliance can be predicted in newly diagnosed subjects, with a view to introducing early intervention.

Cognitive–analytic therapy

Cognitive–analytic therapy (CAT) is a focused, time-limited therapy combining techniques and understandings from psychoanalytic and cognitive–behavioural therapy (CBT). It has been developed and reported by Ryle (1990). A central feature of the approach is the emphasis on the reformulation of the patient's problems. Over the first three sessions the patient and the therapist work together to achieve the clearest possible description of the patient's harmful or ineffective procedures. The term 'procedure' refers to an individual's way of organising some aspect of his or her life, in particular the pursuit of his or her aims and relationships. A full account of a procedure is of a circular, usually self-maintaining process; it will describe a regular sequence of mental processes (perception, appraisal, aim formation, prediction of efficacy and outcome, choice of means), an account of the action or role played, a description of the consequences of the action, an evaluation of the efficacy of the action, and the meaning of the consequences and the confirmation and revision of both the aim and the means used. A 'neurotic' procedure is one which produces harmful or restricting results and which does not get revised. Three main patterns account for this failure to revise; they are called traps, dilemmas and snags (Ryle, 1979). In the case of traps, a negative assumption generates a form of action which produces consequences leading to the apparent confirmation of the negative assumption. In the case of dilemmas, possible actions or roles are seen to be limited to polar, dichotomised alternatives. In the case of snags, appropriate aims are abandoned because of the experience or prediction of negative outcomes, either from the responses of others or from internal processes such as guilt or the fear of envy. The reformulation of an individual's problem in these terms is normally presented in writing at the fourth session and is modified and finalised with the patient's participation. This reformulation is given in the form of a letter which recounts the patient's history, demonstrates the means developed to cope with past adversity and shows how this has led to the current ineffective procedures. These procedures are described in summary (as 'traps', 'dilemmas' and 'snags'). In most cases, to underline the self-maintaining, sequential nature of these harmful procedures, diagrams will also be developed; examples of these are given in the case histories below.

The relation of CAT to other psychotherapy models

Many of the techniques used in CAT are drawn from CBT, notably the use of self-monitoring and the explicit sharing of the ideas with the patient, but the underlying theory and the emphasis placed on the therapy relationship are derived more from psychoanalysis. In nearly all cases, the neurotic procedures responsible for damaging or restricting an individual's life will not only be the topic of therapeutic conversations, they will be enacted in the relationship of the patient to the therapist and to the tasks of therapy. An approach which demands the rational cooperation of the patient, such as CBT, will often fail, especially in more disturbed patients, because the patient is uncooperative, that is to say, the patient behaves in a way typical of his or her problem. Such problems are particularly prominent in the non-compliant patients considered in this chapter, for the people who persist in seriously damaging behaviours in respect of diabetic control will in nearly all cases show similarly unhelpful responses to psychotherapeutic treatments. The understanding of this tendency, derived from psychoanalysis, is central to the practice of CAT. Negative attitudes and behaviours identified in the reformulation of the patient's presenting story and drawing on the life history, current behaviour and attitudes in many situations, will, when they reappear in the treatment context, provide the therapist with an immediate opportunity to demonstrate to the patient what is happening. The reformulation serves in this way as a basis for recognition of damaging procedures both in the session and, through self-monitoring, in daily life.

Cognitive–analytic therapy is based on a theoretical model related to the object relations school of psychoanalysis, but little emphasis is given to concepts of instinctual drives and defence compared with psychodynamic practice. In common with psychoanalysis, however, the basic model emphasises the origin of both personality and patterns of relationship in early childhood. These are understood in terms of the elaboration of 'reciprocal role procedures' which are expressed in the patterns of self-management and of relationships to others, or which may be replaced by defensive or symptomatic procedures. In CAT, resistance to change is not seen as motivated, but rather as due to the stability and self-reinforcing nature of neurotic procedures.

Our experience shows that a wide range of problem procedures may underlie failure to manage diabetes satisfactorily. In the majority of cases the patients are not in any sense psychiatrically ill and most would not think of seeking help for their emotional problems. However, difficulties of a degree which might pass unnoticed in those who are physically well can have serious consequences with a diabetic subject. Thus, depressed individuals may act out their self-destructive or self-neglecting attitudes through poor diabetic control. Adolescents may use diabetic management as a vehicle for rebellion against the authority of parents and doctors and will, in any case, have to deal with the impact of a chronic restricting condition in addition to the normal doubts and confusions about their changing bodies. Eating disorders are common in young women and interfere with dietary control and omitting insulin is an all too easy and dangerous way of achieving weight loss (Fairburn *et al*, 1991). A few individuals may be phobic about self-injection or blood testing and others may be so frightened of the symptoms of hypoglycaemia that they may maintain themselves with too high a level of blood sugar. In many instances denial and projection are used as ways of avoiding the anger and anxiety associated with illness and this leads to failure to fully recognise the implications of bad control. While the choice of non-compliance as an expression of a neurotic problem could represent a half-concealed suicidal impulse it is more often just part of a relatively more trivial neurotic problem but one which leads, unfortunately, to a serious, non-trivial medical outcome.

Treatment

In understanding how therapy can change people, CAT draws on many sources, but the underlying assumption is that all therapies involve, in varying proportions, the patient's exposure to new experience, new behaviour and new understanding. The change sought in CAT is procedural change and the procedural sequence described above includes the full range of perception, memory, judgement, planning, action and evaluation and may be modified by changes at any point in the sequence. The modification of particular neurotic procedures may need to go hand-in-hand with the development of better higher-order integrating procedures. In both these, the main focus in CAT is on the therapeutic relationship and on insight. The relationship is one in which the role of the therapist is to offer respecting care and in which, with the help of the reformulation, responses serving to reinforce the patient's damaging procedures are avoided. The kind of insight sought is not so much the understanding of hitherto forgotten memories and desires (in the way once characteristic of psychoanalysis) as on the ability to describe accurately the currently damaging procedures and the capacity to recognise them reliably. The success of short-term therapy depends on the patient learning to know himself or herself accurately, in respect of the main destructive tendencies, so that conscious thought can intervene to block and in due course to replace the damaging procedures.

Cognitive–analytic therapy differs from other psychodynamic therapies in the cooperative way in which reformulation is arrived at, in the use of written material and diagrams and in the explicitly didactic use made of these materials. In the case of long-term non-compliance, patients who are 'known to the clinic' and who elicit groans or shrugged shoulders from frustrated staff, the written and diagramatic reformulation can also help doctors and nurses to avoid responses which feed into the patients' problematic procedures.

These points are illustrated with brief accounts of three treated patients.

Case examples

Case 1 (treated by Cherry Boa)

Janet, a 22-year-old English woman, had been diagnosed as diabetic while on a year's study abroad. At the time of her diagnosis she had become confused and unable to communicate clearly with local medical staff, or with an unfamiliar social and work network. She telephoned home but her parents had not, it seemed, realised how she was feeling and it was some time before they had come out to help her. Eventually they did bring her home but there followed a further period of confusion while her treatment regimen was determined.

When Janet was first offered therapy her HbA_{1c} was 14.8% and she was a very angry young woman. For example, when asked who her consultant was she responded with an outburst, saying that she would like to know, as she had been attending the clinic for nearly 2 years and had never seen the same person twice.

Janet's biography suggested that her early experience could be encapsulated in the words "everyone is too busy to look after me, I am not important". When she was 2 years old a brother was born and seems to have demanded a lot of attention. Two years later Janet started school and her mother, who had resented being trapped at home, returned to study and later to work. Taking on more and more outside activities, her mother was so busy that she was often late, or would even forget to collect Janet from her after-school minder. Janet remembered how she used to sit and rock by the front door, waiting for her mother to come. However, Janet did not acknowledge any painful and angry feelings around this story; she was protective of her mother and blamed herself for her needy, unhappy feelings.

In understanding the effects of this childhood, it seemed that Janet had learned to expect rejection from others and, while usually coping, would also feel painfully needy and angry. She had two main procedures for avoiding these negative feelings. On the one hand she sought independence and, putting on a "brave face", she attempted to care for herself. This meant that whenever she needed a little help, she was unable to ask for it and this often resulted in her getting into a worse mess. An example

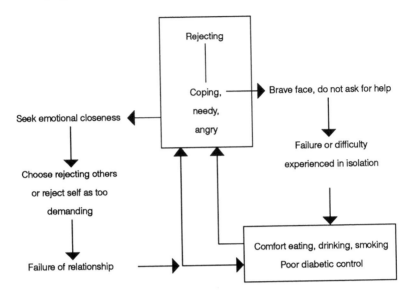

Fig. 10.1. Sequential diagram: Janet

of this was the period in France when her diabetes was diagnosed. Often, as a result of this pattern, she would end up in a lonely and helpless state, and would then resort to self-comforting activities such as drinking too much, smoking heavily or overeating.

Her other procedure was equally ineffective. In the search for emotional closeness she was repeatedly attracted to partners who (predictably) did not reciprocate her feelings. When these relationships ended she would blame herself, feel resentful and once again, feeling lonely and isolated, she would drink, smoke and overeat.

Her inner assumptions about relationships are summarised in the core of the diagram (Fig. 10.1) and the two procedures described above indicate how the core state was maintained and how her non-compliance was fuelled. The 'core state' ['internal parent to inner child'] relationship is seen to be derived from her early childhood experiences. The needy aspect of her 'inner child' was seen to generate an over-demanding involvement with others, leading to rejection and disappointment, while her 'coping' (historically prematurely autonomous) side led to her rejecting help and then reacting badly to failures. Poor self-management of her diabetes therefore reflected both an angry rejection of others and damaging self-comforting.

The course of Janet's 12 sessions of therapy was summarised by the 'goodbye letter' written at termination.

> "When we first met, you were feeling quite angry with all the doctors and staff in the clinic for being so busy that you never had any continuity of contact with any one of them. You felt they were all too full of their own importance and that you were not of sufficient interest to warrant their care.
>
> We came to see how this is a repeated pattern in your life – others whose help or attention you need seem otherwise preoccupied, leaving you feeling alternately guilty (for your need) and resentful that they do not see it. We also learned how this reflected your formative family experience when

your active, disorganized mother was often too busy to give you the love and care you yearned for.

You react to your neediness, which you see as guilty demandingness to be despised, with hurt, resentment and despair. This in turn leads to your cutting off, so you fail to get your real needs met and often leads directly to failed diabetic management and self-care. In our work together we had similar problems when, having got yourself into a 'mess', in the shape of the unwanted, unplanned pregnancy, you felt unable to attend for your appointments because you felt 'guilty' and 'stupid', and assumed that I was too 'busy' and 'important' to want to know or to help.

I hope our work together will have helped you to know that it *is* possible to ask for help when you need it, and for others to respond appropriately, if you will give them half a chance. I would ask you to refer to the diagram we have devised, over the new few months, to monitor your progress – the successes and the usefulness of possible occasional failures – and I will look forward to our further review.''

At the 12-month follow-up she reported continued change in how she managed her life and her HbA_{1c} percentage, although not ideal at 10.7%, showed a worthwhile reduction from the level at intake.

Cases 2 and 3 are presented by J. Fosbury as illustrations of the use of sequential diagrams to locate poor diabetic self-management; the treatment history is not given.

Case 2

Samantha, aged 23 years, had developed diabetes in infancy. For the past 8 years her control had been poor with a mean HbA_{1c} level of 14%.

The underlying issues were concerned with her relation with her parents; it was as if she had to choose between the safety of being their dependent and compliant child or the pain of their rejection. Her resentment at the former state was expressed through difficulties with self-injection and overeating (see Fig. 10.2).

Case 3

Craig was a 38-year-old salesman with developing complications (background retinopathy and nephropathy), and a mean HbA_{1c} level of 11%. He recalled a childhood dominated by his father, who was critical and undermining, and his mother who was cold and often beat him. His self-description was of a "laid-back fool with an attitude problem"; in effect he replayed the childhood themes, either critical and contemptuous of himself and others or resentfully resisting their demands and using alcohol as a substitute comfort (see Fig. 10.3).

Conclusion

The three cases presented were all seriously neglectful or self-sabotaging in their diabetic management. The causes and mechanisms of their

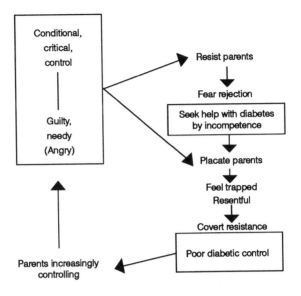

Fig. 10.2. Sequential diagram: Samantha

failures were different, however. In case 1, a pattern of self-isolating coping was combined with emotional neediness and disallowed dependency; damaging oral gratifications were the source of her poor control. In case 2, the patient had developed diabetes in infancy and her problems stemmed from incompletely achieved separation from her parents.

The patient in case 3 was still locked in battles with himself and others in ways engendering defiance and passive resistance to all demands, whether from others or himself; he was also, as in case 1, dealing with unhappiness by drinking. These case histories demonstrate the need for an individual approach to treatment and suggest that such treatment needs to address wide-ranging aspects of the person's life, as opposed to aiming for specific behavioural change in respect of detailed management techniques.

We believe that the needs of this group are well served by an initial psychiatric assessment, to identify the (rare) cases of treatable illness, followed by time-limited intervention of the kind described here, which offers both a specific identification of the roots of non-compliance and a wide consideration of their relation to the individual's life. There are not any contraindications to this approach, the worst outcome of which might be the need for further therapy. In our experience to date we have not encountered patients in whom severe symptoms, such as uncontrolled bulimia or needle phobias, required behavioural interventions, but such

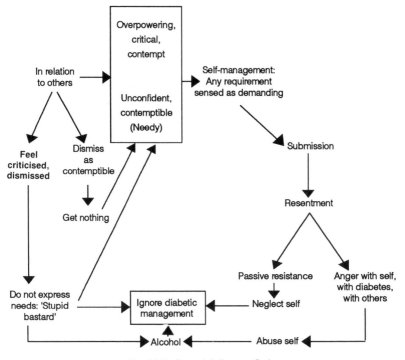

Fig. 10.3. Sequential diagram: Craig

might occur. The overall efficacy of this approach and the possible benefits of prediction and early intervention will be clearer when the current research is completed.

References

BARGLOW, P., EDIDIN, D. V., BUDLONG-SPRINGER, A. S., *et al* (1983) Diabetic control in children and adolescents: psychosocial factors and therapeutic efficacy. *Journal of Youth and Adolescence*, **12**, 77–94.

BRADLEY, C. (1979) Life events and the control of diabetes mellitus. *Journal of Psychosomatic Research*, **23**, 159–162.

COHEN, A. S., VANCE, V. K., RUNYAN, J. W., *et al* (1960) Diabetic acidosis: an evaluation of the cause, course and therapy of 73 cases. *Annals of Internal Medicine*, **55**, 55–86.

FAIRBURN, C. G., PEVELER, R. C., DAVIES, B., *et al* (1991) Eating disorders in young adults with insulin-dependent diabetes mellitus: a controlled study. *British Medical Journal*, **303**, 17–20.

MACGILLIVRAY, M. H., BRUCK, E. & VOORHESS, M. L. (1981) Acute diabetic ketosis in children: role of the stress hormones. *Paediatric Research*, **15**, 99–106.

MILTON, J. (1989) Brief psychotherapy with poorly controlled diabetics. *British Journal of Psychotherapy*, **5**, 532–543.

RYLE, A. (1979) The focus of brief psychotherapy; dilemmas, traps and snags and target problems. *British Journal of Psychiatry*, **134**, 46–64.

——— (1990) *Cognitive Analytic Therapy: Active Participation in Change.* Chichester: John Wiley and Sons.

TATTERSALL, R. B. (1985) Brittle diabetes. *British Medical Journal*, **291**, 55–56.

11 A psychoanalytic approach to the treatment of brittle diabetes in children and adolescents

PETER FONAGY and GEORGE S. MORAN

This chapter describes the psychoanalytic treatment of patients with so-called 'brittle diabetes', a form of insulin dependent diabetes mellitus (IDDM) characterised by extreme and chronic failure to maintain blood glucose control. A small group of young patients with IDDM experience long-term and severe problems in maintaining blood glucose levels near to the range for non-diabetics. The observed prevalence of such difficulties is greatly affected by clinical practice and thus varies between centres but it has been estimated at 1% of the juvenile IDDM population (White & Santiago, 1985a; Gill et al, 1985a; Tattersall & Walford, 1985).

The cause of brittle diabetes is not known (Gill et al, 1985b). As its prevalence appears to be extremely low in patients above 30 years of age, it has been suggested that the disorder is either fatal or it resolves spontaneously (Williams & Pickup, 1985a). More recently, however, community-based studies have identified a similar clinical picture in elderly patients (Griffith & Yudkin, 1989). Certain organic factors which may play a part in bringing about brittle diabetes are well recognised. Impaired subcutaneous insulin absorption (Dandona, 1978; Home et al, 1982; Williams, 1985), frank insulin resistance (Gill et al, 1985b), exaggerated response to insulin withdrawal (Madsbad et al, 1979) and hyperlactataemia have all been demonstrated to be more prevalent in these patients. But even when all known organic causes have been eliminated, there remain numerous cases whose inability to manage their diabetes is unexplained (see Pickup, 1985). The proportion of patients whose aetiology is unequivocally psychological has been variously estimated as one-third (Gill et al, 1985b), two-thirds (Williams & Pickup, 1985b) and over three-quarters (Schade et al, 1985; Tattersall et al, 1991) of individuals with hyperglycaemia. They are most likely to be female, adolescent, and slightly above average in their body weight and insulin intake. They are unlikely to be helped by pumps or pens for stabilising or improving control (Brink & Stewart, 1986; Hardy et al, 1991). Nor are they likely to be helped by closely supervised subcutaneous infusion of insulin (Williams & Pickup, 1985*a*). It seems likely that patients with a tendency to hypoglycaemia are in graver physical danger than those whose diabetic imbalance manifests mainly in terms of keto-acidosis (Tattersall *et al*, 1991). We have now treated psychotherapeutically more than 20 of the latter type of young patients (Moran, 1987; Fonagy & Moran, 1990; Moran *et al*, 1991) and we feel able to offer a preliminary formulation in respect of our hypotheses about the common unconscious determinants of this syndrome and the usefulness of psychoanalytic formulations in clinical practice. This chapter is intended primarily to be a summary of our clinical and empirical work. We will precede the description with a brief review of other psychological approaches to the treatment of brittle diabetes.

Psychosocial context of brittle diabetes

The role of psychosocial factors in diabetes mellitus has long been an intensively researched topic in psychosomatics and health psychology. There exists a number of comprehensive reviews of this literature and here we will only touch on some of the most salient issues (Johnson, 1980; Shillitoe, 1988; Fonagy *et al*, 1989; Helz & Templeton, 1990).

Children at risk of problems in blood glucose regulation

There exists a large body of empirical investigations which link psychosocial factors and metabolic control in diabetes. Studies correlating emotional factors with diabetic control, as indicated by glycosylated haemoglobin (HbA_{1c}), have demonstrated higher HbA_{1c} (poorer control) in patients who had a history or current indications of psychiatric diagnosis (e.g. Peyrot & McMurray, 1985; Lustman *et al*, 1986). In children, however, mild psychiatric disorder appears to be associated with good rather than poor control (Close *et al*, 1986; Fonagy *et al*, 1987). This pattern of findings is consistent with a view that extremely poor diabetic control is linked to overt behavioural and emotional disturbance (see Orr *et al*, 1983, 1986; Mazze *et al*, 1984; Tattersall, 1985), but psychiatric disorder *per se* does not necessarily lead to poor control.

There seems to be a specificity in the relationship of certain types of psychiatric disturbance and diabetic control. For example, there may be a relationship between eating disorder (primarily bulimia) and chronic poor control (Powers *et al*, 1983; Robin *et al*, 1985; Wing *et al*, 1986; Steele *et al*, 1987, 1989; Nielsen *et al*, 1987; Fairburn *et al*, 1991). Consistent with the view that poor control may be, in part, linked to a subclinical or clinical eating disorder is the predominance of young women (12–18 years) amongst those with poor control (Hamburg & Inoff, 1982; Anderson *et al*, 1983; Kaar *et al*, 1984; Peyrot & McMurry, 1985). There also appears to be a striking similarity between the characteristics of families of eating disordered and chronically poorly controlled diabetic children. Survey data reveal such families more likely to contain parental conflict, to be low in cohesion and lacking in support for the child (Cederblad *et al*, 1982; Anderson *et al*, 1983; Bobrow *et al*, 1985; Wallander *et al*, 1989). Minuchin and his colleagues (1978) observe the same dysfunctional family transactional patterns (overprotectiveness, enmeshment, rigidity and lack of conflict resolution) in both eating disordered and psychosomatic diabetic families. Not all family studies, however, find such an association (e.g. Stevenson *et al*, 1991).

Researchers have also identified specific beliefs, ideas and attitudes which appear to place a child at risk of poor diabetic control. On the whole, the more positively diabetes is viewed by both child and parent the better the control of the child (Johnson, 1984). External locus of control appears on the whole to protect children from poor control (e.g. Connell, 1986; Grey *et al*, 1991). The causal significance of both cognitive and emotional predictors of diabetic control has been hard to establish. Psychiatric complications, dysfunctional family patterns and negative cognitions may be the result rather than the cause of poor control.

Psychosocial interventions

There are several case reports suggesting that individual psychotherapy with diabetic patients has a favourable effect on control (e.g. Templeton, 1967; Moran, 1984). Group therapy has been shown to be particularly important in providing peer support in adolescents (see Warren-Boulton *et al*, 1981; Groen & Peltzer, 1982). Minuchin *et al* (1975, 1978) used family therapy with families of children who were recurrently hospitalised with keto-acidosis. The therapy, along systemic lines, was successful in reducing the need for repeated hospitalisation.

Work with adults offers some evidence for the effectiveness of progressive relaxation training and biofeedback (Bradley, 1982; Rose *et al*, 1983; Lammers *et al*, 1984; Landis *et al*, 1985). A number of other studies, however, have not confirmed that relaxation therapy in itself can bring about positive changes in groups who are chosen for their poor control and a history of emotional disorder (Seeburg & deBoer, 1980; Feingloss *et al*, 1987).

Other workers have suggested that children with diabetes may be able to learn to discriminate changes in their blood glucose levels in the absence of chemical assessment. Outcome studies, however, tend to provide no support for such a claim (Gross *et al*, 1985). Contingency management techniques have also been widely used to improve diabetic control (e.g. Lowe & Lutzker, 1979; Epstein *et al*, 1981; Carney *et al*, 1983). Failure of generalisation of rapidly acquired contingencies and poor outcome after contract termination (Gross, 1982; Schafer *et al*, 1982) suggest caution about the clinical relevance of some of these findings.

In summary, it would appear that behavioural cognitive and family therapy approaches have all been tried with diabetic patients with chronic poor control, but no study has thus far been able to demonstrate radical improvement in diabetic control associated with limited treatment programmes. A single case study reported by Snyder (1987) describes behavioural treatment of a 14-year-old boy with diabetes. The exemplary behavioural programme involved several hospital admissions and 150 days of treatment. The meticulous identification of the contingencies between parental behaviour with child, the child's antisocial behaviour and inappropriate diabetic self-care eventually led to an effective formulation of the problem and a successful intervention. The complexity of the programme illustrates that it is unlikely that serious problems of diabetic imbalance can be tackled without careful attention to the precise circumstances in which the problems emerged in each case. Perhaps it matters less than we might anticipate whether the ultimate formulation is inspired by a behavioural or a psychodynamic approach.

Psychodynamic formulations of brittle diabetes

As part of our study of a series of brittle diabetic patients, we carried out formal assessments of the dynamic nature of the psychopathology of these individuals. In this process we delineated two major pathways of psychological causation of the brittle diabetic state, the first relating to pathological biochemical functioning and the second to psychopathological functioning.

First, it is known that the *metabolic imbalance* found in diabetic patients weakens the homeostatic capacity of the *neuroendocrine system* of some patients who then respond to even mild psychosocial stress by excessive release of cortisol and other stress hormones (Gilbert *et al*, 1989). These, in turn, serve to counteract the normoglycaemic influence of insulin and bring about a further intensification of the stress responses. Anxiety, consequent upon continued psychosocial stress (parental psychopathology, broken homes, unhappiness at school), may thus be expected to cause chronic diabetic imbalance through its interference with the insulin regimen. This aspect of the problem has been intensively studied, but by no means conclusively resolved, in several laboratories in North America (e.g. Baker & Barcai, 1970; Barglow *et al*, 1986; Cox *et al*, 1988). We can present no data to cast light upon this controversial issue, although our findings suggest that neuroticism and anxiety, at least in mild form, are not inconsistent with maintaining good diabetic control (Fonagy *et al*, 1987).

The second pathway concerns the *conscious or unconscious acts of transgression* of the prescribed treatment regimen. In all the cases of brittle diabetes we have treated psychotherapeutically we have found significant instances of non-adherence to the regimen which could have, in and of themselves, accounted for the child's volatile blood glucose level. Non-adherence may well be associated with high levels of anxiety and stress (Fonagy *et al*, 1989). This formulation is consistent with the findings of a number of other specialist centres (Farberow, 1970; Schade *et al*, 1985; Stancin *et al*, 1989; Tattersall *et al*, 1991).

We recognise, however, that the mere observation of poor adherence does not provide a compelling explanation for the aetiology of brittle diabetes, as major transgressions of the diabetic regimen are the rule rather than the exception in both paediatric and adult diabetic clinics (Wilson & Endes, 1986; McNally *et al*, 1987). Nonetheless, it is our view that such transgressions are both more frequent and more serious in brittle diabetic patients and self-destructive deviations from the prescribed routine are the most important path to poor diabetic control.

While non-adherence to the regimen is a plausible, as well as a clinically verifiable, explanation for chronic metabolic imbalance, diabetologists sometimes balk at the idea, probably because it conflicts with the common-sense model of human motivation to which they subscribe. Such a model does not readily accommodate the irrational, profoundly self-destructive nature of the behaviour of brittle diabetic youngsters. The idea that children and adolescents regularly go to extreme lengths 'deliberately' to bring about pain and ill-health is, naturally, seen as implausible if not absurd. The threat such clinical observations pose to those with an optimistic view of human nature is probably in itself sufficiently compelling to cause endocrinologists to redouble their effort to identify the biological bases of brittle diabetes in general, as well as in each individual case (Keen, 1985).

From a psychoanalytic perspective there is less difficulty with the concept of self-destructiveness, inexplicable though it may seem to those who are unfamiliar with the nature of unconscious mental functioning. In our psychoanalytic assessment and treatment of a significant number of such patients we were able to identify three patterns present in those who go on to develop brittle diabetes, and which may serve to explain their self-injurious behaviour pattern.

These were: (a) the regulation of the distance between the mental representation of self and the object (the mental representation of a significant other); (b) the unconscious use of diabetes for the manipulation by the child of an aspect of his reality situation that avoids a significant source of unpleasure; (c) the presence of irrational anxieties rooted in the unconscious symbolic significance of some aspect of the diabetic regimen which creates the wish for avoidance and in this way leads to non-adherence. We realise that, although presented as discrete, these categories are not independent of one another either conceptually or clinically, and we put them forward solely as an heuristic device that may help focus clinical interventions.

The mental proximity of the object

In the first, by far the most common, and potentially the most severely disturbed group of patients, the brittle diabetic state serves what may be metaphorically referred to as a *distance-regulating function*. We maintain that the patient may be motivated by powerful feelings associated with the unconscious psychological experience of proximity (closeness or distance) *vis-à-vis* an internal object. Feelings of *wellbeing* and *safety* may be achieved through mentally distancing oneself from or achieving internal proximity to a particular representation of an important figure from the past. What we metaphorically refer to as 'proximity' may also be seen as the individual's readiness to undertake mental action, to think of, fantasise about, or experience feelings in connection to the mental image of the other. The quality of such mental proximity may take the form of identification (to feel at one with – and this is most common), or it may involve conflict and sadomasochistic interchange (to fight, to rebel against, to be punished by some mental representation of the other).

> A patient was chronically embattled with the medical establishment in a bitter conflict over blood glucose levels which both patient and consultant independently likened to the trench warfare of World War I. In the course of treatment it transpired that these bloody struggles were comforting to the patient because they actualised her sense of self-criticism and self-hatred. Her mother was an ever-nagging woman, quite unable to tolerate aggression in her daughter. She put her child to bed each evening with the caution that she should apologise to anyone she felt angry with in case they died during the night. Her behaviour ensured that the medical team would provide a close resemblance to the caring figure, struggling with powerfully repudiated rage, ending up as endless nagging.

In other patients, temporary lapses in control may have losing and recapturing as their theme (to feel abandoned in hyperglycaemia and be rescued by insulin). Indeed, probably any active mental representation of the self in *affect-laden transaction with the object* can be enacted in the 'theatre' of the diabetic body.

Many of the most seriously brittle diabetic patients appear to unconsciously experience the physical condition of chronic metabolic imbalance, as the psychic equivalent of achieving some kind of intrapsychic proximity to, or distance from, the internal mental representation of an important figure. The experiences which serve this unconscious psychological function are, however, highly variable, frequently over-determined and include symptoms such as the hyperventilation of keto-acidosis, the faintness of hypoglycaemia, the general experience of physical illness or hospitalisation, intense physical pain, infections such as boils or cystitis.

> For example, a diabetic adolescent we treated deliberately omitted taking her insulin in order to control her weight and maintained herself in a constant

perilous state of near keto-acidosis. She would give herself just enough insulin to survive. In the course of treatment it emerged that through maintaining herself constantly near death, she felt comforted by the feeling of being close to her mother, who died tragically of cancer when she was 7 years old. The feeling was strengthened by the unconscious link she made between the ulceration in her mouth (that she became prone to) and her memory of mother's operation on her neck to which she was exposed as a child. Another patient experienced hyperglycaemia as a sense of unreality in being in a world apart, separate from the real world. Both her parents were psychotic. She felt the brittle state to be an island of mental tranquility, distanced from the chaos of relationships that memories of her parents evoked.

In understanding brittle diabetes in this group of patients, it is not the explication of particular symbolic links between physical state and mental representation that is of primary relevance. There is no magical cure even when such links are identified and accepted by the patient. Rather the analyst seeks to identify and interpret the source of the patient's feeling of internal danger from which the experience of diabetic imbalance, through the regulation of the closeness of the threat, affords temporary respite. The internal danger is invariably associated with the patients' representation of themselves in relation with the primary object. What is feared and anticipated feels far more immediate than the remote possibility of complications or even death through diabetic mismanagement; the danger is the immediate destruction of the self in the creation of an aspect of the dreaded intolerable relationship with the object. Through the medium of the poorly controlled diabetes, paradoxically, the diabetic individual achieves a reassurance that he/she (the self) is safe. The object may be experienced as invading the self or abandoning it. The wish to achieve separation or closeness will always be part of a profound conflict and therefore the self-destructive acts of diabetic mismanagement will represent a compromise in both cases. Where the basic aim is the creation of a mental gap between dangerous objects and the self, some aspect of the physical symptoms of poor blood-glucose regulation will serve to ensure closeness to the object. Alternatively, where proximity to the object is achieved mentally by chronic metabolic derangement, the patient will also seek to repudiate this closeness through the brittle diabetic state.

These patients frequently, but not invariably, fall into the category of severely disturbed malignantly narcissistic individuals which has often been the subject of psychoanalytic interest. Of particular relevance is Joseph's (1982) paper describing patients who appear addicted to a mental state of being close to death. We strongly differ from this author in the general model of development we employ and diverge from her most explicitly in our speculations concerning the genesis of a mental self. Our approach utilises the developmental epistemological framework championed by Anna Freud (Freud, 1965) and attempts to integrate this with the perspective of modern developmental psychology and the model of psychological disturbance based upon the inter-relationship of mental representations and affects (Sandler & Sandler, 1978).

The unconscious precipitant of the self-destructive behaviour patterns in patients such as these is to be found in dysfunctional self- and object-representations. The mental representation of both self and object is incomplete as a consequence of a developmental disturbance in the establishment of the mental representation of psychological functioning. This is the result of the defensive inhibition of the capacity to conceive (create a mental representation) of the mental states of others. The inhibition of mental processes that underlie an enduring representation of the self in affective interaction with the object serves to protect against the painful awareness of violence, irrationality, or vacuousness in the mind of the primary caretaker (Fonagy, 1991; Fonagy & Moran, 1991). Children with such backgrounds, in our experience, frequently defensively inhibit their capacity to think about the mental states of the other. This is most likely to occur between the ages of 2 and 4 years when the child's ideas concerning the mental world undergo rapid development (Perner *et al*, 1987; Harris, 1989) although there is no reason why such defensive inhibition should not take place at a later developmental stage.

While in extreme cases this developmental disturbance can lead to a widespread reluctance to think about one's own, or others', mental worlds, in the cases we are concerned with here the patient's difficulties are much more limited and specific. The patients' relative incapacity to conceive of an object at a mental or psychological level causes them to seek identifications or create mental separations via bodily experiences. If the object is not represented as a thinking and feeling figure, imbued with intentionality, they may become psychically accessible only through physical experiences. This was the case for the patient described above, whose sole route to her dead mother was via the creation of a state of constant near-death within her own body. Similarly, if the representation of the self as a thinking, feeling and experiencing figure cannot be created, an essential component of self-cohesion is absent and the child's self-structure will be vulnerable to fragmentation. Thus, if the patient seeks a refuge from an overpowering internal figure, in the absence of the psychic capacity to integrate the unintegrated parts of the self into a cohesive internal picture, bodily experiences may be called upon to create an experience of psychic distance. This is evident in cases where the recourse to diabetic mismanagement creates a poverty of internal object and self-representations through the dynamic inhibition of the psychic processes which underlie them.

We recognise that, in many respects, our model of the nature of this disturbance echoes the observations of McDougall (1974) and Marty & de M'Uzan (1963) of the Ecole Psychosomatique. Their concept of 'pensées operatoires' emphasises the same characteristic lack of expected mental activity which we identify but account for differently.

The incomplete structuralisation of the self enables patients to disavow ownership of their body. This is of primary importance since the pain and discomfort they inflict upon themselves are probably only bearable because of the separation of their self-representation from their representation of their physical state. As their bodily states are, to a certain extent, represented outside of their self structure, the former is available as a stage upon which the nature and functioning of the mental world can be actualised or enacted. In such cases we observe a self that is not yet integrated into a bodily representation. The careless disregard of the body that characterises patients with chronic self-injurious behaviour may be rooted in a disturbed inter-subjective sense of self when the infant's identity extends beyond his as yet poorly organised bodily experience.

Using diabetes to reduce exposure to unpleasurable aspects of the external world

Patients who manifest the second category of precipitants are those who, through the manipulation of diabetes, were able to achieve a degree of control over an intolerable aspect of family interaction or some other aspect of the external environment. Tattersall & Walford (1985) contend that ''brittle diabetics engage in dangerous behaviour . . . often because it 'pays' in the sense of fulfilling other needs whether for love, shelter, approval or escape from an otherwise insoluble conflict'' (p. 76). From a psychoanalytic standpoint, we construe such extreme transgressions of the regimen as neurotic adaptations to anxiety and guilt. Unlike patients in the previous group, unconscious conflict does not arise out of pathology of the self but represents a neurotic solution to interpersonal or intrapsychic problems.

For example, an 8-year-old may show her sense of being unloved and uncared for in the course of parental conflict and divorce by deliberately bringing about repeated hypoglycaemic coma which she knows will unite her parents in ensuring her survival. Psychotherapy in this context is sought to help brittle diabetic patients arrive at an understanding of the preconscious antecedents of transgressions via the provision of insight into their conflicts, anxieties and maladaptive defences. In our experience such pathological manipulations are most common in a pre-adolescent group.

Symbolic significance of diabetes

We have also had to treat cases from our third category, where the un-conscious significance of some aspect of diabetic management, manifested, for example, in a phobic reaction to injections, appeared to be sufficient explana-tion of the child's apparently intractable medical condition (Moran, 1984).

An 11-year-old girl feared and phobically avoided injections. Although the therapist suspected that this anxiety concerned her worries about her weight, subsequent work revealed that her fear of injections was closely linked to her concern about sexuality and her terrifying infantile fantasies about penetration during intercourse. Such worries are most common with the youngest age group (oedipal and latency). They appear to respond relatively readily to psychological treatment focused on fantasies and anxieties concerning the nature of diabetes and dangers perceived in connection with aspects of its management.

Here we will present data from three investigations which lend limited support to the formulations of brittle diabetes presented here.

Time series analysis

First of all, we will summarise some recent process record-based individual case studies carried out at the Anna Freud Centre. Initially, our work aimed to develop a technique with which to test our understanding of the psychopathology of brittle diabetes and the manner in which psychoanalysis was helpful in restoring metabolic equilibrium in youngsters with this condition. We assume that, if our hypotheses were substantiated, the clinical material over the course of a child's treatment would be found to bear a systematic relationship to the day-to-day fluctuations in blood glucose regulation.

We employed time series analysis to study the interaction between clinical material and diabetic control during the 184 weeks of the five-times weekly psychoanalysis of a diabetic teenager (Moran & Fonagy, 1982).

> Although she had numerous psychiatric problems, Sally was referred for treatment in connection with her brittle diabetes which had proved intractable to other medical and psychological treatments. Her life was disrupted by recurrent, self-induced, episodes of keto-acidosis and occasional hypoglycaemia. Her diabetic control was monitored daily and was extremely poor for at least 2 years before her referral and during the initial phase of her psychoanalysis. Her control varied during her treatment, but showed a strong trend to improvement throughout the latter half of the analysis.

Dramatic improvement associated with the analysis was also evidenced by other criteria, for example, by her improved school attendance and reduced hospital admissions (see Table 11.1).

Weekly estimates of the quality of Sally's blood glucose regulation were obtained by averaging the daily records over six years (see Moran & Fonagy, 1987). The weekly, approximately three-page, narrative accounts of the progress of the psychoanalysis could be used as the basis for the rating of clinical material. The reports detailed major analytical themes with vignettes of therapeutic interaction focusing on Sally's current anxieties, the therapist's psychoanalytic understanding of these and reports of interpretations offered to the patient together with her responses.

TABLE 11.1
Sally's improvement during the course of her psychoanalysis

	Two years prior to analysis	During analysis (4 years)	Three years after analysis
Mean (range) number of hospital admissions per year	3.5 (2–5)	0.25 (0–1)	0 0
Mean (range) number of days absent from school per year	24.5 (17–34)	18.3 (6–31)	8.3 (6–10)
Diabetic control (HbA$_{1c}$)	Not available	13.4 (16–10.5)	8.5 (7.3–9.4)

An end-of-treatment summary condensed weekly clinical material into a single narrative account from which the major themes of the analysis were extracted. Operational definitions were drawn up of those themes monitored in the weekly reports that appeared to recur throughout the analysis. We succeeded in devising operational definitions for 10 out of 18 clinical dimensions thus identified. Limitations on information available in the reports meant that crucial aspects of Sally's psychopathology and the analytic process defied our initial attempts at operationalisation. Five principal analytic themes were identified as part of Sally's pathological mental processes (intra-psychic conflicts) which we assumed to be crucial to her consistent diabetic mismanagement. These concerned:

(a) Sally's feeling of having been *unappreciated and ignored by her father*, frustrated in her femininity and angry with him for his lack of responsiveness and worried and guilty in case her hostile wishes further jeopardise her longing to be loved, admired and valued by him

(b) *intense oedipal rivalry* with her mother for the sparse indications of father's love and attention and anxiety of losing her mother's love as a consequence of her feelings

(c) anger, confusion and concern around an image of her mother as withdrawing, probably deriving from her memory of *mother's serious depression* when Sally was 6 years old

(d) anxiety and guilt feelings over *destructive, murderous and sadistic wishes* towards her parents and other family members who let her down and of whose relative happiness she deeply resented

(e) conflicts concerning the *threats associated with diabetes*, both reality-based (complications, restrictions of lifestyle) and as distorted by defensive processes (sexual anxieties, concern about body shape).

A second set of themes of comparable prominence in the analysis related to Sally's psychological symptoms. These included:

(a) Sally's *imitation of boys* (wearing boys' clothes, uniquely playing boys' games) and related fantasies (of being a male)

(b) *phobic anxiety* associated with episodes of separation, particularly around school attendance

(c) acting out of unconscious guilt through *self-punitive acts* (accidental injury) or fantasies of being punished

(d) poor self-esteem, particularly a fantasy that *her body is inadequate or damaged*

(e) guilt and aggression directed against the self, manifesting as *resistance against the analysis* (lateness, silence, failure of free association).

We formulated operational definitions with examples for each of the conflict-based and symptom-based thematic categories in order to examine each of the 184 weekly reports with these themes in mind. The weekly reports were rated on all 10 themes by two child analysts unfamiliar with the case on five-point scales from 'definitely present' to 'definitely not present'. The correlations between the independent raters were greater than 0.60 for all but three of the analytic themes (conflicts over murderous wishes, and the symptoms of a damaged self-representation and resistance to the analysis), which were discarded. The inter-rater correlations for the remaining themes ranged from 0.78 to 0.62 (mean 0.70).

There were strong associations between diabetic control and the therapist's ratings of the seven reliable psychoanalytic themes due to a confound in the data. Sally showed a gradual improvement in diabetic control, increasingly clear-cut manifestations of psychic conflict, and a decrease in psychological symptoms as analysis progressed. All associations due to common trends were systematically removed by differencing the series (i.e. subtracting the previous week's value from that of the current week, so the data were transformed into week-to-week change). We computed the correlation coefficients between the week-to-week changes in diabetic control and the ratings made on the basis of the weekly reports. To strengthen our causal arguments, 'cross-lagged correlations' were also computed to give an indication of the extent to which changes in analytic themes may be predicted by, or indeed may predict, changes in diabetic control. In order to examine this issue, we averaged the normalised cross-correlation coefficients for individual symptom and conflict themes (see Table 11.2) over two-week periods.

Table 11.2 illustrates that the presence of themes of conflict in the analytic material for two of the four themes foreshadowed improvements in diabetic control for one to two weeks. However, improved diabetic control appeared to increase the likelihood of manifest psychological symptomatology two to four weeks later. This weak but statistically significant pattern of co-variation is consistent with our psychoanalytic account of brittle diabetes. Poor diabetic control, brought about by transgressions of the diabetic regimen, serve as adaptations to the anxiety and guilt aroused by unconscious conflict. In Sally's case, interpretation of her conflicts may have brought about short-term

TABLE 11.2
Average cross-lag correlation coefficients between themes of symptoms and conflict and diabetic control

| | Lag: weeks | | | | |
| | Predicting diabetic control | | | Predicted by diabetic control | |
	3–4	1–2	0	1–2	3–4
Conflicts					
Unappreciated by father	0.02	0.15*	0.19*	0.06	0.09
Oedipal rivalry with mother	0.21*	0.20*	0.13	0.01	− 0.08
Mother's depression	0.03	− 0.02	− 0.12	− 0.07	0.015
Threat of diabetes	0.06	0.07	0.07	0.10	0.06
Symptoms					
Imitation of boys	− 0.02	0.05	0.13	− 0.05	− 0.04
Phobic anxiety	0.05	0.02	− 0.05	0.11	0.24*
Self-punitive acts	0.08	0.10	0.10	0.19*	0.24*

*$P < 0.05$.

improvements in her diabetic control, by reducing the need for such transgressions. The consequent improvement in her condition was noted by Sally and at times this perhaps led to temporary increases in anxiety and guilt manifested in displacement as phobic anxiety and deliberate acts of self-punishment.

We pursued the statistical analysis of Sally's treatment further with the help of transfer functions. Time series analysis using cross-lag correlations may yield false positive results, as it is sensitive to associations between variables present, because of common frequencies of temporal fluctuation due to a third variable which exerts control over both the series. Thus, the oestrous cycle could, for example, have caused coincidental changes in both diabetic control and analytic material. This, and other similar sources of bias may be controlled for using transfer functions with auto-regressive integrated moving average (ARIMA) modelling (Box & Jenkins, 1976). A transfer function is a linear equation which relates the past of one time series to the present and future of another. By first mathematically modelling regularities and filtering these from the effector series, such functions can estimate the proportion of the *random* variability in the dependent variable and can be accounted for by the predictor measure.

We created several transfer functions (see Moran & Fonagy, 1987, for a full account). There were no significant transfer functions in which psychological symptoms could be used as lead (predictor) variables. Three out of the four series of conflict ratings however produced transfer functions which accounted for a statistically significant proportion of the variance in accounting for diabetic control. Ratings related to the theme of mother's depression failed to contribute significantly to the model. The most robust model was for diabetic control and oedipal conflict where ratings of oedipal conflict in the psychoanalytic material was shown independently to predict diabetic control over the 3 weeks following its ratings in the analysis ($P < 0.005$). The contribution of conflicts related to the threat of diabetes and the experience of paternal rejection were both significant at the 1% and 5% levels respectively (Table 11.2).

Time series analysis supports causal inference based on temporal order, i.e. that the cause is usually observable prior to the consequence. This is undoubtedly a simplistic model of causality. Nevertheless, establishing a temporal sequence provides indirect evidence of a potential causal link, even if it does not remove the need for a more direct experimental test. The suggestion of causality is strengthened if the measurements taken can in no way be expected to be biased by the rater's expectation of a causal link. To this end, we asked our raters to estimate diabetic control from the weekly reports of analytic material. None of the raters, not even the clinician treating the case, was able to obtain a statistically significant correlation with diabetic control. Thus the study showed a relationship between two sets of variables across time which were conceivably linked by psychological forces at work within the patient during her analysis. This is of itself, however, of little interest. Concomitant variation cannot imply causation. To be of interest, such a demonstration has to be part of a broader causal story.

An outcome study

In our second study, reported in more detail by Moran *et al* (1991), we evaluated our in-patient programme for brittle diabetic youngsters by comparing it with routine medical care offered to comparable groups of patients. Our in-patient treatment combined psychoanalytic psychotherapy and ward management which was informed by knowledge and understanding gained in the process of psychotherapy. Our sample was relatively small. It consisted of 22 child and adolescent patients referred to two London hospitals serving distinct but comparable catchment areas. The treatment group consisted of 11 patients admitted to one of the hospitals who were offered psychotherapy in conjunction with medical supervision. They were consecutive admissions over a 3-year period.

Children in the comparison group were admitted with the same diagnosis during the same time period in two other paediatric wards in the same hospital group. Allocation to the wards was on the basis of residence as the wards served adjacent but distinct catchment areas. There were no statistically significant differences between the groups in any of the critical determinants of outcome including age, sex, severity of illness, etc. They were seen routinely for psychiatric or psychological assessment but psychotherapy was not offered to this group. No routine medical treatment was withheld but duration of hospitalisation and ward milieu differed considerably.

The criteria for selection were: age between 6 and 18 years, IDDM of at least 2 years' duration, diagnosis of brittle diabetes according to specific criteria, and the absence of psychotic disorder or severe learning difficulties. The operational criteria for the diagnosis of brittle diabetes were: (a) at least two episodes of severe hypoglycaemia and/or hyperglycaemia in the previous 3 months, (b) clear indication of significant interruption to the child's life at home and/or at school, (c) the brittle condition was chronic, retrospectively identifiable at least 6 months prior to referral, and (d) at least two diabetes-related admissions to hospital in the preceding year.

Children were treated by two analysts with at least 5 years' experience, who were trained in the child psychoanalytic tradition of the Anna Freud Centre (the Hampstead Child Therapy Course and Clinic). The treatment programme began with a detailed description of the child's condition from an endocrinological and social and developmental perspective. Based on this information, dynamic hypotheses were formulated for each child as to the probable cause of their psychological difficulties and occasional disregard of the diabetic regimen. These involved both intrapsychic (conflicts over aggressive, destructive wishes, fear of retaliation, unconscious guilt etc.) and interpersonal (parents' sexual interest in, or hostility toward child, sibling rivalry etc.) constructs.

The treatment recommendation of psychotherapy three to five times a week for 15–20 weeks (actual range 5–28 weeks) was made to all parents. Parental involvement with the treatment varied from occasional joint ('family') sessions to complete non-participation by parents who appeared at the time to be unable to take a role exploring the underlying reasons for their child's condition. Parents were normally seen by a professional worker other than the child's therapist who would help them to understand and to cope with their child's problem. Frequently, the child's therapy revealed ways in which the parents inadvertently made a contribution to their child's condition, which they were given an opportunity to explore.

The interviews with the child were initially unstructured and focused on the child's interests and emotional concerns. Therapists aimed specifically to help the child to feel that he or she had an ally in the person of the therapist. To this end, the therapist, for example, would avoid direct questioning of the child concerning the causes for episodes of metabolic derangement.

As treatment progressed, information from interviews gradually accumulated, enabling the team involved with the child's treatment (the therapist, the professional working with the parents, and the medical and nursing staff) to further refine its hypotheses concerning the factors underlying non-adherence to the diabetic regimen. We identified a number of common patterns which related diabetic control and the child's psychological difficulties. The illness or aspects of its treatment could

(a) express forbidden aggressive or sexual thoughts or desires
(b) express guilt or punishment for repudiated wishes
(c) provide ways of avoiding difficult or stressful situations
(d) concretely represent anxieties about bodily damage
(e) deal with issues of separation or dependency
(f) serve a defensive function of distracting the child from mental representations of him/herself as profoundly inadequate or even empty.

The therapists' aim was the verbalisation of the child's conflicts and the clarification of the ways in which diabetic imbalance was *used* by the child for the purposes of adaptation to situations perceived as impossible (internal as well as external). Therapeutically derived understanding was reinforced to enable the child to identify and practise less self-destructive ways of coping. More generally, therapeutic attention was focused on loosening the links between the nature of psychological disturbance and diabetes and diabetic mismanagement.

The team met regularly to discuss strategies for the management of the child on the ward. Such strategies sometimes include quasi-behavioural measures such as the nursing and medical staff confronting the patients with their transgressions of the diabetic regimen. Staff were also trained to communicate to the child that they recognised the need for the child to be in hospital to safeguard him or her from their own destructive behaviour. Ward meetings also took into account the emotional reactions of staff in the face of what at times appeared profoundly provocative behaviour on the part of certain patients.

Children in the comparison group also received considerable psychological input, including a somewhat less intensive systematic assessment, diabetic education and frequent consultations on the part of ward staff about transgressions. The medical care was equivalent to that provided for the treatment group, although criteria for discharge were somewhat less strict. In five of the 11 cases, routine medical treatment included the involvement of a psychologist or psychiatrist and a certain amount of cognitive–behavioural or supportive therapy. None of the children in this group was offered or received psychotherapeutic help.

One of the outcome indicators was glycosylated haemoglobin (HbA_{1c}) concentration. HbA_{1c} is derived from a single assay and reflects average blood glucose levels over the preceding 4 weeks. All subjects were assayed at approximately 3-month intervals for HbA_{1c}. Diabetic control was assessed in the period 6 months prior to admission ('admission'), upon terminating hospital treatment and for the subsequent 4 months ('short follow-up'), and for the subsequent 8–10 months of up to six measures ('one-year follow-up'). Values were aggregated where more than one for a period was available.

For the psychotherapy treatment group mean HbA_{1c} values decreased significantly between the time of admission ($x = 14.3$) and short follow-up ($x = 11.1$). Levels remained at this level one year from the end of treatment ($x = 11.5$) for the children in this group. Blood glucose levels were essentially unchanged for the comparison group relative to levels on initial admission (admission: $x = 13.6$, 'short follow-ups': $x = 13.5$) and there were no indications of spontaneous remission at the one-year follow-up ($x = 13.7$). The analysis of variance yielded a significant group by time of assessment interaction ($F = 5.08$, d.f. $= 2,15$, $P < 0.01$). In order to equate the groups for mean HbA_{1c} levels at admission two analyses of covariance were also performed for the short and one-year follow-ups ($F = 5.11$, d.f. $= 1,19$, $P < 0.04$ and $F = 4.47$, d.f. $= 1,19$, $P < 0.05$ respectively).

A clinically oriented examination of changes in HbA_{1c} revealed that all but one of the psychotherapeutically treated ex-patients showed a consistent reduction in HbA_{1c} over the course of the treatment, yet only four out of the 11 youngsters in the comparison group showed a similar trend during this period (Fisher's exact $P < 0.01$). Nine of the 11 psychotherapeutically treated patients remained below their pre-admission average HbA_{1c} levels for the year subsequent to their treatment, compared to only three of the second group ($P < 0.025$). The 'acceptable' range for diabetes ($< 10\%$) was achieved in six of the psychotherapeutically treated subjects but none of the untreated group showed the same degree of improvement ($P < 0.025$).

The second major indicator of diabetic balance are M-values. M-values measure how far a given glucose level deviates above or below a given standard derived from an individual patient (Schlichtkrull *et al*, 1965). Thus high M-values were computed for this group of patients. The results indicated a substantial reduction in the variability of blood glucose levels as measured before treatment and following its conclusion, and showed significant improvement between admission ($x = 85.1$) and discharge ($x = 29.5$) for the psychotherapeutically treated group but not for the comparison group ($x = 66.2$ v. $x = 58/8$, $P < 0.05$). When hospital admissions for reasons other than diabetic imbalance were excluded, there was also a statistically ($P < 0.05$) significant reduction in requirement for in-patient care for psychotherapeutically treated patients.

Improvement in diabetic control did not necessarily go hand-in-hand with improvements in the child's psychological problems. The treatment goal of this brief intervention was the breaking of the link between psychological difficulties and diabetic mismanagement rather than the resolution of these difficulties. Nevertheless, the improvements in the psychotherapeutically treated group extended beyond the diabetes although these were not systematically measured. For example, eight of the 11 children were able substantially to improve their family relationships and two resolved significant educational problems. The success of our intervention was measured in terms of the quality of blood glucose control. Improvements in this measure, following primarily psychotherapeutic intervention, are consistent with the view that brittle diabetes is at least exacerbated by the investment of the disease and/or its treatment regimen with unconscious emotional significance and this can lead to a life-threatening disregard for normal diabetic care.

We do not wish to exaggerate the theoretical implications of the study, particularly in the light of several methodological shortcomings. The patients in the comparison group, though matched for severity of illness and medical management, were not at all comparable in terms of the amount of professional attention they received, expectancy and therapist skill and time. The present study cannot show us which components of this complex treatment programme may have been effective. The groups were not matched for length of stay in hospital, nor for the provision of psychoanalytically informed ward management or therapeutic milieu. Particularly, the ward milieu was far more psychologically oriented for the experimental group than for the comparison. It is possible that any, or all, of these aspects, rather than the psychotherapeutic components, was critical in achieving the clinical gains. This is a pilot study which calls for further work to confirm that psychotherapeutic help rather than some other component of this multi-modal approach or even 'attention placebo' was the effective therapeutic component. The severity and refractory character of the group of patients studied, combined with the observation that brittle diabetic patients receive a great deal of attention from both physicians and nurses, all argue against the notion that our patients improved as a consequence of simple attention placebo.

Together with the systematic single-case investigation reported above, which demonstrated a temporal relationship between the fluctuations of diabetic control and insight gained during the course of treatment, we feel on stronger grounds to pursue such a programme of work.

Physical growth and diabetic control

The psychotherapeutic application of single-case designs developed in the behavioural field (Barlow & Hersen, 1984; Peck, 1985; Morley, 1987, 1989) is just beginning (Fonagy & Moran, 1992). Traditional psychoanalysis represents a so-called 'B design', where observations and the start of treatment coincide. The 'A–B design' is somewhat more sophisticated. This includes a 'baseline', a period of time set aside for monitoring the individual's problem prior to beginning the treatment. The value of a baseline lies in enabling researchers to contrast treatment-related changes with changes which are independent of the treatment (e.g. the course of the disorder, life events, maturation, carry-over effects from previous treatment). The influence of non-treatment factors will be apparent if baseline observations of the patient are made.

By taking a baseline of sufficient duration and frequency and repeating the observations throughout the treatment we can strengthen our claim that factors associated with the treatment rather than factors unrelated to it were causal in bringing about improvements in the patients' status. Not all measures of therapy outcome are equally susceptible to confounding by non-treatment factors. Psychiatric measures of change, frequently used in psychotherapy research, are particularly vulnerable. Most instruments which are sensitive enough to register change are relatively unstable; change has to be large to achieve statistical significance or a large sample of subjects will be required to show an effect. In fields of psychology where measurement is more exact (e.g. psychophysics, physiological psychology) large sample sizes have always been regarded as unnecessary. Most psychometric instruments with the exception of some cognitive (e.g. WAIS) and personality (e.g. EPQ) measures which are far too robust to be helpful in measuring therapeutic change, lack the normative data to provide researchers with a basis for individual comparison with expected change in the measure in the absence of therapeutic intervention. There are but a handful of developmental processes where adequate normative data are available to enable researchers to assess the statistical significance of changes associated with psychotherapy in the individual case. Physical growth is an exception to this generalisation.

Familial, social and organic factors all play a part in the aetiology of growth retardation (Smail, 1984). The short stature of children with brittle diabetes may be associated with metabolic and endocrine anomalies, psychosocial disadvantage or both (Lacey & Parkin, 1974). Psychotherapeutic treatment may be appropriate whether short stature was brought about by chronic poor control of the diabetes or the psychosocial antecedents of the diabetic imbalance. The course of human growth can be predicted with a relatively high level of accuracy for normal (Tanner *et al*, 1975) as well as growth disordered populations (Tanner *et al*, 1983*a*). Thus we have an opportunity to assess the effect of psychological intervention on individual patients in terms of the deviation from this predicted course.

As part of our psychotherapeutic work with brittle diabetic children we identified three children below the third percentile in height (this study is reported in more detail by Fonagy & Moran, 1990). Data on the height of these children indicated that medical intervention over the previous 2–3 years was of limited value for these children. Physical growth was assessed in the standard way at 3-month intervals (Brook, 1982). In addition, bone age was assessed once a year from the beginning of the psychotherapeutic treatment (Tanner *et al*, 1983*b*). The therapy offered to these children followed the principles outlined for the previous outcome study. All patients were in psychoanalytic psychotherapy and seen three or four times weekly on the ward. They also benefited from the ward-based educational and treatment programme which was in place over this period. The three patients' psychotherapeutic treatment continued on an out-patient basis for 2, 11 and 22 months, respectively.

To examine the relationship between the psychotherapy offered to these children and their stature, we computed three measures of growth for 6-month periods before, during and after treatment, height standard deviation (s.d.) scores for chronological age, height velocity s.d. scores for chronological age and predicted adult height from height and bone age before and 6 months after treatment.

The first case, in treatment between the ages of 8 and 9 years, showed some growth retardation from the age of 5 years. Although his height velocity remained constant (– 2.2), he was growing at a slower rate than his peers. Thus, his height standard score declined from the age of 5 years 6 months and was – 1.86 (range – 2.04 to – 1.46) when he entered treatment. During treatment his height velocity s.d. scores changed from – 2.21 to + 3.52 (range 3.26 to 4.8). Much improvement took place during the first year of treatment. Over the 2-year follow-up period he maintained a positive rate of growth and reached the 35th percentile in height. His predicted adult height prior to treatment was 161 cm. At follow-up at the age of 10 years his predicted adult height was 169 cm. In a recent 5-year follow-up of this young man, this prediction was found to be a slight underestimate. He is well on his way to be over 170 cm.

The second patient was 13 years 6 months at the start of her treatment. Her rate of growth prior to treatment was severely below normal (– 3.85). Her height s.d. was – 2.28 (range – 2.69 to – 1.89); in the 3 years before her treatment she grew only 6 cm (rather than the expected 18 cm). During the psychotherapeutic intervention her height velocity increased markedly to 3.75 (range 2.74 to 4.79) and it remained more than two s.d.s above the average over the 2-year follow-up period (range 1.53 to 3.70). As she had already passed her pubertal growth spurt by the start of treatment, our expectations of improvement were correspondingly modest. Her predicted adult height increased from 150.4 by over 5 cm (approximately one s.d.).

The third patient was 12 years 6 months when starting psychotherapy. He was 125.6 cm in height, three s.d.s below his peers. His treatment initiated a marked improvement in his speed of growth from – 1.55 to + 4.48 during the follow-up phase. His predicted adult height at the beginning of his treatment was 159.2 cm. The prediction at the end of his psychotherapy was 168.6 cm, increasing to 170.6 cm based on measures taken during the 2-year follow-up.

In our view the gain in height of these patients, clearly linked in time with their treatment, offers further evidence of the value of our psychotherapeutic approach to the management of chronically poorly controlled diabetic children. Diabetic control improved in all three patients with stature. For example the third patient's HbA_{1c} level changed from 16% to 7.8% from the time of admission to one-year follow-up. The first patient, who had three or four admissions a year to hospital for keto-acidosis prior to psychotherapy, had no admissions over the 6 years of follow-up. The second patient, the only girl in this study, reduced her M-value from 136 to 34.

Whether improvement in diabetic control, and associated endocrine changes (e.g. in growth hormone levels), entirely account for these, partial reversals of growth failure cannot be conclusively answered from these data. In evaluating the research implications of the findings, it should be noted that since we can predict height fairly accurately for both growth-retarded and normal children, we can be confident that the changes following psychotherapy did not take place coincidentally. Each of the patients' improvements are highly statistically significant relative to the error on prediction for both normal and pathological groups. For us, height as an indication of psychotherapeutic effectiveness is particularly interesting since, as was the case with HbA_{1c}, it is a 'cumulative indicator' and therefore reflects the behavioural and emotional adjustment of the child in the medium to long term. Self-rated or observer-rated psychometric measures tend to be based on time-sampling and subjective integration of observations across time. They take measurements at particular time points and ask a rater to aggregate his or her (self) observations over a specified time period. Whether individuals can be assumed to give valid information under such circumstances has always been a controversial issue (cf. Nisbett & Wilson, 1977; Mandler, 1985).

Discussion

Clinicians who work with diabetic children with chronically poor metabolic control are invariably aware that emotional problems are closely tied to instability in blood glucose regulation. In the first study we showed that this link could be demonstrated empirically using time series analysis. Further, that psychological conflicts, activated during psychoanalytic treatment, *predicted* subsequent changes in diabetic control. It appeared that the emergence of conflict themes in the material led to reductions of blood glucose levels in a girl whose brittle state was characterised by hyperglycaemia.

The second study compared two roughly equivalent series of children and adolescents with grossly abnormal blood glucose profiles. Poor metabolic control interfered with the children's daily routines and necessitated repeated admissions to hospital. The children in the treated group were managed with prolonged hospitalisation which included intensive psychotherapy, as well as psychoanalytically informed parental guidance and ward management, and manifested durable and significant improvements in metabolic control. These children stopped having serious episodes of hypoglycaemia and hyperglycaemia and, with the exception of two patients, were able to attend school or work regularly.

The third study showed that the same therapeutic approach could bring about partial but dramatic reversals of growth failure in a small group of brittle diabetic children with severe growth retardation. The three studies taken together offer support for the contention that an intensive, psychoanalytically inspired, intervention can change the course of brittle diabetes. As none of the studies involved careful controls or matching, it is naturally not possible at this stage to identify which component of the extensive intervention programme may be essential in accounting for the improvement observed. The failure of the comparison group to show change in the absence of significant psychological input underscores both the gravity of the disorder and the limited value, in the longer term, of hospital admissions beyond the restoration of homeostasis.

The present series of investigations confirm the importance of psychosocial factors in accounts of brittle diabetes. For example, the reductions in blood glucose levels observed in the outcome study was not due to over-insulinisation (see Rosenbloom & Clark, 1985); nor was possible insulin malabsorption or resistance circumvented using special methods of insulin delivery (Dandona *et al*, 1978; Williams, 1985). Rather, it seems that interpersonal irregularities (parental discord, enmeshed family relationships, parental or child psychiatric disturbance) and consequent intra-psychic conflict, observed in this group, are most probably *primary and reversible* potential aetiological factors.

It is possible that it is some metabolic abnormality that places these patients at high risk of psychological conflict and that chronic poor control may compound such abnormalities of the endocrine system (Gill *et al*, 1985*b*). However, in the light of the positive results we have achieved, and the long-term remissions observed in follow-up studies (Tattersall *et al*, 1991), we believe that 'acquired metabolic problems' such as impaired insulin absorption are medium-term consequences of chronic poor control that may be reversed with psychotherapeutic treatment of sufficient intensity and duration. Just what may be regarded as 'sufficient' in this context is clearly an appropriate target for future investigations.

The improvements we observed in the patients treated in the present programme were both clinically and statistically significant. About one-third of the children, however, were left with unacceptably high HbA_{1c} levels at the end of treatment which tended to remain high at follow-up. Gill *et al* (1985*a*) reported failure to achieve diabetic stabilisation in a similar proportion of patients following treatment. It is possible that a period of hyperglycaemic instability associated with emotional factors lead to physiological changes which alone maintain hyperglycaemic instability in the medium term despite improved general psychological status and adherence to the regimen. The relatively common pattern of spontaneous remission with maturation (Keen, 1985; Tattersall *et al*, 1991) suggests that the physiological disequilibrium, which may prolong brittle diabetes when psychosocial factors appear to have normalised, is of relatively limited duration. Nevertheless, we frequently witnessed the exasperation of brittle patients with the results of their initial attempts to manage their diabetes according to medical recommendations. Such initial failures, and consequent anxieties about having been 'irreparably damaged by non-adherence', in our experience have to be worked through. The rationalisation that "the body may take slightly longer to heal than the mind" is a helpful one for some of these patients whose sense of self-efficacy is so readily threatened. It is likely that hormonal imbalance associated with emotional arousal (Barglow *et al*, 1986) may account for the continued diabetic imbalance of youngsters whose adherence to the regimen was improved following psychotherapeutic help. In our experience, even in cases where diabetic control is seen to improve, intensive psychological treatment should continue beyond the point where the psychological cause of the brittle state has been identified and addressed if metabolic balance is to be maintained in the long term.

All the studies reported have several critical limitations. The number of patients we were able to treat in the programme was relatively small. Had we had the resources to ensure that all the patients in the comparison group crossed over into the treatment group, our findings would be more compelling. Future studies will need to be performed to contrast our intensive and probably costly service with more cost-effective forms of the same programme or programmes arising out of other psychological orientations. The quantification of change in terms of valid and reliable psychological measures was not part of our interest or the design of the studies. Thus whether or not intrapsychic considerations are essential to the improvements we observed must remain a matter for speculation. It is possible to see our intensive in-patient treatment as focused diabetic education for the child and the parents, or even as a radical intervention applied to the family system through the removal of the designated patient. Others may conceptualise our treatment effect as an unsystematic mode of enhancing specific beliefs concerning the efficacy of particular components of the regimen. Nevertheless, we believe that, taken together, the findings offer some support for our clinical intuition that the clarification of the underlying, conscious and unconscious, psychological functions of mismanagement is a critical part of the successful treatment of childhood brittle diabetes.

Acknowledgements

The research was supported by a grant from the American Philanthropic Foundation, the Alan and Babette Sainsbury Charitable Fund, and a grant from the Special Trustees of the Middlesex Hospital.

The authors would like to thank Professor C. Brook, Dr A. Bolton and Dr A. Kurtz for their direct support for the project, and gratefully acknowledge the help and advice they received from Professor A. Solnit, Dr P. Neubauer and Dr A. Higgitt.

References

ANDERSON, B. J., AUSLANDER, W. F., ACHTENBERG, N., *et al* (1983) Impact of age and parent-child and spouse responsibility sharing in diabetes management on metabolic control. *Diabetes*, **32**, 17A.

BAKER, L. & BARCAI, A. (1970) Psychosomatic aspects of diabetes mellitus. In *Modern Trends in Psychosomatic Medicine* (ed. O. W. Hill), vol. 2. London: Butterworth.

BARGLOW, P., BERNDT, D. J., BURNS, W. J., *et al* (1986) Neuroendocrine and psychological factors in childhood diabetes mellitus. *Journal of the American Academy of Child Psychiatry*, **25**, 785–793.

BARLOW, D. H. & HERSEN, M. (1984) *Single Case Experimental Designs: Strategies for Studying Behavior Change* (2nd edn). New York: Pergamon Press.

BOBROW, E. S., AVRUSKIN, T. W. & SILLER, J. (1985) Mother-daughter interaction and adherence to diabetes regimens. *Diabetes Care*, **8**, 146–151.

BOX, G. E. P. & JENKINS, G. M. (1976) *Time Series Analysis, Forecasting and Control* (2nd edn). San Francisco: Holden-Day.

BRADLEY, C. (1982) Psychophysiological aspects of the management of diabetes mellitus. *International Journal of Mental Health*, **11**, 117–132.

BRINK, S. J. & STEWART, C. (1986) Insulin pump treatment in insulin-dependent diabetes mellitus: children, adolescents and young adults. *Journal of the American Medical Association*, **255**, 617–621.

BROOK, C. (1982) *Growth Assessment in Childhood and Adolescence*. Oxford: Blackwell Scientific Publications.

CARNEY, R. M., SCHECHTER, K. & DAVIS, T. (1983) Improving adherence to blood glucose testing in insulin-dependent diabetic children. *Behavior Therapy*, **14**, 247–254.

CEDERBLAD, M., HELGESSON, M., LARSON, Y., *et al* (1982) Family structure and diabetes in children. *Pediatric Adolescent Endocrinology*, **10**, 94–98.

CLOSE, H., DAVIES, A. G., PRICE, D. A., *et al* (1986) Emotional difficulties in diabetes mellitus. *Archives of Diseases in Childhood*, **61**, 337–340.

CONNELL, F. A. (1986) Epidemiologic approaches to the identification of problems in diabetes care. *Diabetes Care*, **2**, 82–86.

COX, D. J., CARTER, W. R., GONDER-FREDERICK, L. A., *et al* (1988) Blood glucose discrimination training in insulin-dependent diabetes mellitus (IDDM) patients. *Biofeedback and Self-regulation*, **13**, 201–217.

DANDONA, P., FOSTER, M., HEALEY, F., *et al* (1978) Low dose insulin infusions in diabetic patients with high insulin requirements. *Lancet*, **ii**, 283–285.

EPSTEIN, L. H., BECK, S., FIGUEROA, J., *et al* (1981) The effects of targeting improvements in urine glucose on metabolic control in children with insulin dependent diabetes. *Journal of Applied Behaviour Analysis*, **14**, 365–375.

FAIRBURN, C. G., PEVELER, R. C., DAVIES, B., *et al* (1991) Eating disorders in young adults with insulin dependent diabetes mellitus: a controlled study. *British Medical Journal*, **303**, 17–20.

FARBEROW, N. L., DARBONNE, A. R., STEIN, K., *et al* (1970) Self-destructive behaviour of unco-operative diabetics. *Psychological Reports*, **27**, 935–946.

FEINGLOSS, M. N., HASTEDT, P. & SURWIT, R. S. (1987) Effects of relaxation therapy on patients with type I diabetes mellitus. *Diabetes Care*, **10**, 72–75.

FONAGY, P. (1991) Thinking about thinking: Some clinical and theoretical considerations in the treatment of a borderline patient. *International Journal of Psycho-Analysis*, **72**, 639–656.

——, MORAN, G. S., LINDSAY, M. K. M., *et al* (1987) Psychological adjustment and diabetic control. *Archives of Disease in Childhood*, **62**, 1009–1013.

——, —— & HIGGITT, A. C. (1989) Psychological factors in the self-management of insulin-dependent diabetes mellitus in children and adolescents. In *The Practice of Behavioral Medicine* (eds J. Wardle & S. Pearce). Oxford: Oxford University Press.

—— & —— (1990) Studies of the efficacy of child psychoanalysis. *Journal of Consulting and Clinical Psychology*, **58**, 684–695.

—— & —— (1991) Understanding psychic change in child psychoanalysis. *International Journal of Psycho-Analysis*, **72**, 15–22.

—— & —— (1993) Advances in individual case study. In *Handbook of Psychoanalytic Research and Practice* (eds L. Luborsky & N. Miller). New York: Basic Books (in press).

FREUD, A. (1965) *Normality and Pathology in Childhood*. Harmondsworth: Penguin Books.

GILBERT, B. O., JOHNSON, S. B., SILVERSTEIN, J., *et al* (1989) Psychological and physiological responses to acute laboratory stressors in insulin-dependent diabetes mellitus adolescents and nondiabetic controls. *Journal of Pediatric Psychology*, **14**, 577–591.

GILL, G. V., HUSBAND, D. J., WALFORD, S., *et al* (1985a) Clinical features of brittle diabetes. In *Brittle Diabetes* (ed. J. C. Pickup). Oxford: Blackwell.

——, WALFORD, S., ALBERTI, K. G. M. M. (1985b) Brittle diabetes – present concepts. *Diabetologia*, **28**, 579–589.

GREY, M., CAMERON, M. E. & THURBER, F. W. (1991) Coping and adaptation in children with diabetes. *Nursing Research*, **40**, 144–149.

GRIFFITH, D. N. W. & YUDKIN, J. (1989) Brittle diabetes in the elderly. *Diabetic Medicine*, **6**, 440–443.

GROEN, J. J. & PELZER, H. E. (1982) Newer concepts of teaching, learning and education and their application to the patient-donor cooperation in the treatment of diabetes mellitus. *Pediatric Adolescent Endocrinology*, **10**, 168–177.

GROSS, A. M. (1982) Self-management training and medication compliance in children with diabetes. *Child and Family Behavior Therapy*, **4**, 47–55.

——, MAGALNICK, J. & DELCHER, H. K. (1985) Blood glucose discrimination training and metabolic control in insulin-dependent diabetes. *Behaviour Research and Therapy*, **23**, 507–511.

HAMBURG, B. A. & INOFF, G. E. (1982) Relationships between behavioural factors and diabetic control in children and adolescents: A camp study. *Psychosomatic Medicine*, **44**, 321–337.

HARDY, K. J., JONES, K. E. & GILL, G. V. (1991) Deterioration in blood glucose control in females with diabetes changed to a basal-bolus regimen using a pen injector. *Diabetic Medicine*, **8**, 69–71.

HARRIS, P. L. (1989) *Children and Emotion: The Development of Psychological Understanding*. Oxford: Blackwell.

HELZ, G. W. & TEMPLETON, B. (1990) Evidence of the role of psychosocial factors in diabetes mellitus: a review. *American Journal of Psychiatry*, **107**, 1275–1282.

HOME, P. D., MASSI-BENEDETTI, M., GILL, G. V., *et al* (1982) Impaired subcutaneous absorption of insulin in 'brittle diabetes'. *Acta Endocrinologica*, **101**, 414–420.

JOHNSON, S. B. (1980) Psychosocial factors in juvenile diabetes: a review. *Journal of Behavioral Medicine*, **3**, 95–116.

—— (1984) Knowledge, attitudes, and behaviour: Correlates of health in childhood diabetes. *Clinical Psychological Review*, **4**, 503–524.

JOSEPH, B. (1982) Addiction to near-death. *International Journal of Psycho-Analysis*, **63**, 449–456.

KAAR, M. L., AKERBLOM, H. K., HUTTUNEN, N. P., *et al* (1984) Metabolic control in children and adolescents with insulin-dependent diabetes mellitus. *Acta Paediatrica Scandinavica*, **73**, 102–108.

KEEN, H. (1985) Of mind and metabolism: an overview of brittle diabetes. In *Brittle Diabetes* (ed. J. C. Pickup). Oxford: Blackwell.

LACEY, K. A. & PARKIN, J. M. (1974) Causes of short stature: a community study of children in Newcastle-upon-Tyne. *Lancet*, **i**, 42–45.

LAMMERS, C. A., NALIBOFF, B. D. & STRAATNEYER, A. J. (1984) The effects of progressive relaxation on stress and diabetic control. *Behaviour Research and Therapy*, **22**, 641–650.

LANDIS, B., JOVANOVIC, L., LANDIS, E., *et al* (1985) Effect of stress reduction on daily glucose range in previously stabilized insulin-dependent diabetic patients. *Diabetes Care*, **8**, 624–626.

LOWE, K. & LUTZKER, J. R. (1979) Increasing compliance to a medical regimen with a juvenile diabetic. *Behavior Therapy*, **10**, 57–64.

LUSTMAN, P. J., GRIFFITH, L. S., CLOUSE, R. E., *et al* (1986) Psychiatric illness in diabetes mellitus, relationship to symptoms and glucose control. *Journal of Nervous Mental Diseases*, **174**, 736–742.

MADSBAD, S., ALBERTI, K. G. M. M., SINDER, C., *et al* (1979) Role of residual insulin secretion in protecting against ketoacidosis in insulin-dependent diabetes. *British Medical Journal*, **ii**, 1257–1259.

MANDLER, G. (1985) *Cognitive Psychology. An Essay in Cognitive Science.* Hillsdale, New Jersey: Lawrence Erlbaum Associates.

MARTY, P. & DE M'UZAN, M. (1963) La 'pensée operatoire'. *Revue Française de Psychanalyse,* **27**, 1345–1536.

MAZZE, R. S., LUCIDO, D. & SHAMOON, H. (1984) Psychological and social correlates of glycemic control. *Diabetes Care,* **7**, 360–367.

MCDOUGALL, J. (1974) The psyche-soma and the psychoanalytic process. *International Review of Psycho-Analysis,* **1**, 437–460.

MCNALLY, P. G., MACIVER, D. H., JOWETT, N. I., *et al* (1987) Hypoglycaemia in insulin dependent diabetics: is advice heeded. *British Medical Journal,* **294**, 1655–1656.

MINUCHIN, S., BAKER, L., ROSMAN, B. L., *et al* (1975) A conceptual model of psychosomatic illness in children: Family organization and family therapy. *Archives of General Psychiatry,* **32**, 1031–1038.

——, ROSMAN, B. & BAKER, L. (1978) *Psychosomatic Families: Anorexia Nervosa in Context.* Cambridge, MA: Harvard University Press.

MORAN, G. S. (1984) Psychoanalytic treatment of diabetic children. *Psychoanalytic Study of the Child,* **39**, 407–447.

—— (1987) De L'interaction entre troubles psychologiques et diabète infantile. *Psychiatrie de l'enfant,* **30**, 35–58.

—— & FONAGY, P. (1987) Psychoanalysis and diabetic control: A single-case study. *British Journal of Medical Psychology,* **60**, 357–372.

——, ——, KURTZ, A., *et al* (1991) A controlled study of the psychoanalytic treatment of brittle diabetes. *Journal of the American Academy of Child and Adolescent Psychiatry,* **30**, 926–935.

MORLEY, S. (1987) Single case methodology in behaviour therapy. In *A Handbook of Clinical Adult Psychology* (eds S. J. Lindsay & G. E. Powell), pp. 699–718. London: Gower Press.

—— (1989) Single case research. In *Behavioral and Mental Health Research: A Handbook of Clinical Adult Psychology* (eds G. Parry & F. N. Watts), pp. 233–264. Hillsdale, N J: Erlbaum.

NIELSEN, S., BØRNER, H. & KABEL, M. (1987) Anorexia nervosa/bulimia in diabetes mellitus. *Acta Psychiatrica Scandinavica,* **75**, 464–473.

NISBETT, R. E. & WILSON, T. D. (1977) Telling more than we can know: verbal reports on mental processes. *Psychological Review,* **84**, 231–259.

ORR, D. P., GOLDEN, M. P., MYERS, G., *et al* (1983) Characteristics of adolescents with poorly controlled diabetes referred to a tertiary care center. *Diabetes Care,* **6**, 170–175.

——, ECCLES, T., LAWLOR, R., *et al* (1986) Surreptitious insulin administration in adolescents with insulin-dependent diabetes mellitus. *Journal of the American Medical Association,* **256**, 3227–3230.

PECK, D. F. (1985) Small N experimental designs in clinical practice. In *New Developments in Clinical Psychology* (ed. F. N. Watts), pp. 64–89. Chichester: BPS-Wiley.

PERNER, J., LEEKAM, S. R. & WIMMER, H. (1987) Three-year-olds' difficulty with false belief: the case for a conceptual deficit. *British Journal of Developmental Psychology,* **5**, 125–137.

PEYROT, M. & MCMURRY, J. F. (1985) Psychosocial factors in diabetes control: adjustment of insulin-treated adults. *Psychosomatic Medicine,* **47**, 432–537.

PICKUP, J. C. (1985) Clinical features of patients unresponsive to continuous subcutaneous insulin infusion. In *Brittle Diabetes* (ed. J. C. Pickup). Oxford: Blackwell.

POWERS, P. S., MALONE, J. I. & DUNCAN, J. A. (1983) Anorexia nervosa and diabetes mellitus. *Journal of Clinical Psychiatry,* **44**, 133–135.

ROBIN, G. M., DANEMAN, D., JOHNSON, L. E., *et al* (1985) Anorexia nervosa and bulimia in female adolescents with insulin dependent diabetes mellitus: a systematic study. *Journal of Psychiatric Research,* **19**, 381–384.

ROSE, M. I., FIRESTONE, P., HEICK, H. M., *et al* (1983) The effects of anxiety management training on the control of juvenile diabetes mellitus. *Journal of Behavioral Medicine,* **6**, 381–395.

ROSENBLOOM, A. L. & CLARKE, D. W. (1985) Excessive insulin treatment and the Somgyi effect. In *Brittle Diabetes* (ed. J. C. Pickup), pp. 103–131. Oxford: Blackwell.

SANDLER, J. & SANDLER, A-M. (1978) On the development of object relationships and affects. *International Journal of Psycho-Analysis,* **59**, 285–296.

SCHADE, D. S., DRUMM, D. A., DUCKWORTH, W. C., *et al* (1985) The aetiology of incapacitating, brittle diabetes. *Diabetes Care*, **8**, 12–20.

SCHAFER, L. C., GLASGOW, R. E. & McCAUL, K. D. (1982) Increasing the adherence of diabetic adolescents. *Journal of Behavioral Medicine*, **5**, 353–362.

SCHLICHTKRULL, J., MUNCK, O. & JERSILD, M. (1965) The M-value, an index of blood sugar control in diabetes. *Acta Medica*, **177**, 95–102.

SEEBURG, K. N. & DEBOER, K. F. (1980) Effects of EMG biofeedback on diabetes. *Biofeedback and Self-regulation*, **5**, 289–293.

SHILLITOE, R. W. (1988) *Psychology and Diabetes: Psychosocial Factors in Management and Control.* London: Chapman & Hall.

SMAIL, P. (1984) Short stature. *British Medical Journal*, **289**, 1371–1373.

SNYDER, J. (1987) Behavioral analysis and treatment of poor diabetic self-care and antisocial behavior: a single-subject experimental study. *Behavior Therapy*, **18**, 251–263.

STANCIN, T., LINK, D. L. & REUTER, J. M. (1989) Binge eating and purging in young women with IDDM. *Diabetes Care*, **12**, 601–603.

STEEL, J. M., YOUNG, J., LLOYD, G. G., *et al* (1987) Clinical apparent eating disorders in young diabetic women: associations with painful neuropathy and other complications. *British Medical Journal*, **294**, 859–862.

——, ——, ——, *et al* (1989) Abnormal eating attitudes in young insulin-dependent diabetics. *British Journal of Psychiatry*, **155**, 515–521.

STEVENSON, K., SENSKY, T. & PETTY, R. (1991) Glycaemic control in adolescents with type I diabetes and parental expressed emotion. *Psychotherapy and Psychosomatics*, **55**, 170–175.

TANNER, J. M., WHITEHOUSE, R. H., MARSHALL, W. A., *et al* (1975) Prediction of adult height from height, bone age and occurrence of menarche, at ages 4 to 16 with allowance for midparental height. *Archives of Diseases in Childhood*, **50**, 14–26.

——, LANDT, K. W., CAMERON, N., *et al* (1983a) Prediction of adult height from height and bone age in childhood. *Archives of Diseases in Childhood*, **58**, 767–776.

——, WHITEHOUSE, R. H., CAMERON, N., *et al* (1983b) *Assessment of Skeletal Maturation and Prediction of Adult Height (TW2 Method)*. New York: Academic Press.

TATTERSALL, R. B. (1985) Brittle diabetes. *British Medical Journal*, **29**, 555–557.

—— & WALFORD, S. (1985) Brittle diabetes in response to life stress: 'cheating and manipulation'. In *Brittle Diabetes* (ed. J. C. Pickup). Oxford: Blackwell.

——, GREGORY, R., SELBY, C., *et al* (1991) Course of brittle diabetes: 12 year follow up. *British Medical Journal*, **302**, 1240–1243.

TEMPLETON, B. (1967) Psychotherapeutic intervention in insulin resistance: a case report. *Diabetes*, **16**, 536.

WALLANDER, J. L., VARNI, J. W., BABANI, L., *et al* (1989) Family resources as resistance factors for psychological maladjustment in chronically ill and handicapped children. *Journal of Pediatric Psychology*, **14**, 157–173.

WARREN BOULTON, E., ANDERSON, B. J., SCHWARTZ, N. L., *et al* (1981) A group approach to the management of diabetes in adolescents and young adults. *Diabetic Care*, **1**, 620–623.

WHITE, N. H. & SANTIAGO, J. V. (1985) Clinical features and natural history of brittle diabetes in children. In *Brittle Diabetes* (ed. J. C. Pickup). Oxford: Blackwell.

WILLIAMS, G. (1985) Blood flow at insulin injection sites. In *Brittle Diabetes* (ed. J. C. Pickup). Oxford: Blackwell.

—— & PICKUP, J. C. (1985a) Continuous intravenous insulin infusion in patients unresponsive to subcutaneous insulin. In *Brittle Diabetes* (ed. J. C. Pickup). Oxford: Blackwell.

—— & —— (1985b) Subcutaneous insulin degradation. In *Brittle Diabetes* (ed. J. C. Pickup). Oxford: Blackwell.

—— & —— (1988) The natural history of brittle diabetes. *Diabetes Research*, **7**, 13–18.

WILSON, D. P. & ENDES, R. K. (1986) Compliance with blood glucose monitoring in children with type 1 diabetes mellitus. *Journal of Pediatrics*, **108**, 1022–1024.

WING, R. R., NOWALK, M. P., MARCUS, M. D., *et al* (1986) Subclinical eating disorders and glycemic control in adolescents with type I diabetes. *Diabetes Care*, **9**, 162–167.

12 Counselling challenges for women with HIV infection and AIDS

LORRAINE SHERR

The World Health Organization currently estimates that over 6 million individuals are infected with HIV, one-third of whom are women (Chin, 1991). Despite the obvious widespread nature of this virus in the female population, there are many who still see HIV as a disease of homosexual men. Such views are compounded by the readiness with which workers look at AIDS rather than HIV figures. These reflect infection anything up to 13 years ago given the long incubation period of this virus (Lemp *et al*, 1990). HIV figures can provide a more accurate picture of the future illness patterns, but are inaccurate as they often reflect HIV testing policy rather than true population prevalence. As a result, incidence of HIV in the female population is unclear and less attention is given to women in the epidemic. Their needs are sometimes overlooked and the specific consideration for their circumstances receives little or belated attention. This occurs despite the fact that heterosexually acquired AIDS in the UK increased by 98% in 1990 and AIDS in women increased by 72% for the same period (CDSC, 1991). In the USA, AIDS in women has increased by 29% which is considerably higher than increases in men for the same period, which reached 18% (Novello, 1990).

The human immunodeficiency virus (HIV) associated with acquired immune deficiency syndrome (AIDS) can be passed from men to women and women to men during sexual intercourse, indeed after a single exposure. Men are three times more likely to infect women. Women can also transmit the virus across the placenta to their unborn child. AIDS has now emerged as the leading cause of death in the age range of 20–40 years for women in most cities in central Africa and in some Western cities such as New York (Chin, 1991).

HIV infection in women closely parallels infection in children. Over 80% of infant infections can be traced to placental spread (Peckham, 1991).

This chapter examines the psychological factors associated with HIV infection in women, describes counselling intervention, and examines some of the unique facets of HIV for women, notably associated with family factors, pregnancy, termination of pregnancy, breast feeding and HIV screening.

Women are often seen only in the light of their role as mothers and child bearers. Much of the current knowledge of HIV and AIDS in women is focused on pregnancy. It is important to know that female existence transcends well beyond these roles. The multitude of pregnancy studies were perhaps triggered in the course of understanding paediatric infection and vertical transmission without full appreciation of the impact of HIV on women *per se*. The ramifications of HIV in women has lagged behind in documentation and understanding (Minkoff & Dehovitz, 1991). Problems such as AIDS often serve to highlight existing difficulties and societal barriers, as well as bringing new problems to the fore.

Gender differences have been studied in relation to survival and outcome (Rothenberg *et al*, 1987; Des Jarlais, 1988). Yet gender differences are complex and difficult to understand as they may reflect biological or environmental factors. The societal role of women may have ramifications on health behaviour and health care seeking. There is an emerging literature on specific female-related HIV manifestations and the psychological consequences of these need to be fully understood.

HIV testing

As an antibody test is available to detect exposure to HIV, it is often tempting to conduct routine screening. HIV screening is known to have a high psychological cost (Miller & Green, 1986; Perry *et al*, 1990) and to engender different reactions in women (Hutterer *et al*, 1989). Hutterer *et al* described how women attend to obtain advice for others, and often undertake testing to ensure they are not a danger to others. This may liberate them to continue sexual encounters, to put the past behind them and to bury discussion of AIDS in the future.

Pregnant women, who attend clinics in large numbers and have blood samples routinely taken for other tests, are often subjected to HIV screening (Moattie *et al*, 1990; Larsson *et al*, 1990; Sherr, 1991). Yet HIV testing should never be considered a routine test. It brings with it many problems and is limited in its usefulness.

Despite the fact that large cohorts of pregnant women worldwide have been screened for HIV, pre- and post-test counselling are rarely reported. It may simply be too costly as the numbers of pregnant women are high, yet the emotional cost of screening in the absence of testing may be unacceptable. Stevens *et al* (1989) found anxiety surrounding HIV testing in pregnancy was significantly higher than other routine antenatal tests. Furthermore, there was significantly less reassurance generated from this test when compared with other antenatal tests including blood pressure, ultrasound scanning, blood sample tests and weighing. This was confirmed by Catalan *et al* (1991). Often the decision to be tested has been taken by doctors caring for women who have little say in the testing, or who are not properly informed and consulted (Worth, 1990; Catalan *et al*, 1991). Few studies report pre-test counselling with pregnant women and in the few that do (e.g. Wenstrom & Zuidema, 1989), testing was sometimes carried out during labour. It is difficult to contemplate the logistics, yet alone the efficacy, of in-depth counselling during labour.

As maternal antibody crosses the placenta, women are placed in the unique position where their antibodies are subject to scrutiny via the testing of their infants. Indeed antibody screening of young infants can only indicate maternal HIV status with certainty and infant infection can take up to 15 months to be established (Burns & Mok, 1991), as it is only by this age that a child will shed maternal antibody. Knowledge of sero-status is often used as a factor in risk-reduction attempts (McCusker *et al*, 1988). These studies are carried out on homosexual men, and it is unclear whether the findings can be generalised to women. The high psychosocial morbidity (Coates *et al*, 1987) of confronting HIV positivity must also be taken into account with screening policies, together with increased risk behaviours (increased crack use in women in New York who were tested – whether HIV positive or HIV negative (Cancellieri *et al*, 1988) and increased injecting for heroin users (Sorrel & Springer, 1989)).

Psychological factors associated with HIV infection in women

If HIV is not recognised as a female condition there is a possibility that women may misinterpret their symptoms and that doctors may not suspect HIV as a diagnosis with some of the non-specific symptoms such as fatigue, diarrhoea, loss of weight and vaginal infections (Hankins, 1990). Indeed, in Canada women are found to be twice as likely as men to present with opportunistic infections (*Surveillance Update*, 1990). However, Kelly *et al* (1989) found drug-using women less likely to be symptomatic in a New York clinic.

Although cervical abnormalities and disease are not considered an AIDS diagnosis, the incidence of these have been noted in a number of studies (Maiman *et al*, 1988; Marte *et al*, 1990; Feingold *et al*, 1990; Minkoff & Dehovitz, 1992). The psychological impact of cervical disease has been documented as high. Good prospective studies are needed to document the full extent of cervical abnormalities and whether these are direct or indirect associates of HIV infection. Maiman examined the levels of abnormal histological findings in relation to CD4 counts, and found that the presence of HIV was predictive of more advanced cervical disease in 114 women with preinvasive and invasive cervical cancer. Recurrence was also sooner from

HIV positive women than for their HIV negative counterparts. Distress over cervical disease, treatments and cervical examinations must be taken into account when caring for women.

Psychological reactions

The knowledge of a positive HIV status has wide-reaching psychological ramifications.

Shock and denial

This can be seen on diagnosis or at other points in the course of the disease. Shock often limits the amount of reassurance that can be given at a counselling session, and also may trigger cognitive problems such as memory disturbance, high distractibility and thought implosion. Decision-making may be hampered or impaired if shock or denial reactions are excessive.

Anxiety

The unknown future often contributes greatly to anxiety states. Fear of death, and fears associated with many of the medical procedures and opportunistic infections are also anxiety-provoking. Physical manifestations of anxiety may mirror HIV-related symptoms and serve to increase fears and anxiety level.

Panic

Panic attacks are common and sometimes clients ameliorate these sensations by overuse of alcohol, drugs or sleeping tablets.

Guilt

As HIV can be sexually or transplacentally transmitted, there is often acute guilt where a loved one may be infected. Guilt may also arise for individuals who see their illness or death as "letting their loved ones down".

Secrecy

The social stigma of HIV and AIDS contributes greatly to the psychological trauma of a life-threatening illness. The burden of maintaining secrets is emotionally draining and the support of social input is correspondingly diluted.

Anger

This is a common reaction especially towards the person from whom the infection was caught and towards carers who cannot provide a cure.

Isolation

Secrecy, knowledge of status and sexual constraints often leave individuals isolated and lonely.

Depression

The course of HIV disease often marks occasional or prolonged bouts of depression. This is associated with the central role of the virus in their future life, the bleak outlook in the absence of a vaccine, relationship changes and multiple losses.

Bereavement

HIV and AIDS often heralds many losses and bereavement reactions are not only common but are often multiple.

Suicide

Ideation, attempts and completion have been monitored to varying degrees. There are no widespread reports of female attempts or completion, but this may be a time factor. All suicide comments should be taken seriously and open discussion should be encouraged.

Rape

A number of cases of rape have been documented as a transmission source of HIV infection. The fear of HIV infection may also add considerably to the trauma of rape.

Control

Many women experience a loss of control in the presence of HIV. For many this is in addition to reduced control in their everyday lives.

Counselling approaches

Counselling interventions from a variety of theoretical bases have been described. These often include the cognitive approach (Green & McCreaner,

1989), family therapy (Miller & Bor, 1988), group therapy (Hedge & Glover, 1990), couples therapy (Ussher, 1989) or individual work. Essentially individuals are viewed as normal individuals in an abnormal crisis. Cognitive counselling offers the opportunity to examine emotional reaction, vent feelings, and adopt coping strategies either based on previous strategies which have worked or on the necessity to evolve new strategies. As such the counselling sessions have an informational and a problem-solving component. Counselling can be divided into different contact points which may alter the tasks, goals and content of sessions. These are counselling pre- and post-HIV testing and ongoing counselling.

Pre-test counselling

The aim of this session should be to help a woman understand the implications of the test, its limitations and ramifications and to prepare her for all possible outcomes. It should have the specific remit of examining at-risk behaviours and exploring good risk reduction strategies so that a woman may protect herself in the future whether or not she proceeds to have the test. This is specifically in regard to safer sex, limitation of partners, resisting needle-sharing and use of condoms.

There are a number of factual items which should be included in pre-test counselling. The client needs to understand that HIV tests are limited. They can tell the presence of antibody, but cannot tell when and how infection occurred, whether the foetus will become infected or give any disease progression prognosis. As it takes up to 12 weeks for sufficient antibody to be present for a positive result, someone can be infected with HIV, transmit the virus, and not be identified during this window of infectivity.

Tests for HIV are special. Women often face HIV testing during pregnancy. Women attending antenatal care may be particularly vulnerable. Most antenatal tests are (supposedly) carried out in the best interest of the woman (Chalmers *et al*, 1989; Garcia, 1982; Hall & Chng, 1989). HIV is a different order of test and should never simply be included in a battery. The test not only has severe implications for the baby, but for the mother herself. There is little that can be offered to the mother medically. HIV testing, irrespective of outcome, is accompanied by severe anxiety and psychological trauma.

Many workers are under the (erroneous) belief that most women terminate their pregnancy in the presence of HIV. A large number of studies have shown that not only do women not tend to terminate (Johnston *et al*, 1989; Barbacci, 1991; Selwyn *et al*, 1989; Sunderland *et al*, 1992) but some are reluctant to come forward for testing in the fear that they would be forced to have a termination. Furthermore, a proportion of those who do terminate continue with a subsequent pregnancy.

Post-test counselling is always much easier if there has been adequate pre-test counselling. It is surprising how often pre-test counselling has not been provided and women have to be counselled when a positive test result is found.

Post-test counselling

Post-test counselling is divided into the session where the test result is given and all subsequent follow-up. Obviously, the first session is fraught with high anxiety and may tax the coping skills of any woman, especially if she is pregnant as she needs both to absorb this information and to consider the future of her pregnancy.

Reactions to a positive test are varied. Sometimes the result was anticipated, but most often it is a shock. Help is necessary in the face of overwhelming psychological strain, confusion, depression, anxiety and sometimes suicidal ideation.

The pregnant woman is under time pressure and termination counselling should be available if she desires it (Sherr, 1991). The essential ingredients include:

(a) discussion of the pregnancy
(b) exploration of the options
(c) examination of HIV and its implications
(d) social support
(e) exploring the impact on self and partner
(f) practical implications
(g) future
(h) regrets
(i) time to think – do not rush into a decision
(j) support through the decision and afterwards.

Women who are not pregnant may want to consider their relationships, their future sexual behaviour and the implications of a positive test for their life. When a woman is given a positive test result, she will often be in a state of shock or heightened emotional crisis. Her ability to absorb the information and think through the full implications will be limited. The value of good pre-test counselling is evident at such times. She should be given time to absorb the information with follow-up and a lifeline.

Long-term counselling

Longer-term counselling is often difficult for women to sustain (Sherr *et al*, 1993). They may place their own needs low on the list of priorities, especially if they are part of a family where other members are HIV positive.

Ongoing counselling raises a number of emotional crises. These alternate between decision-making and absorption of factual information, and adjusting to emotional trauma. The issues which many women wish to address centre around dealing with uncertainty, transmission, sexual behaviour, confidentiality and who to tell. Within the safety of the counselling setting, women can test out and think through solutions, examine the way forward, break down problems into manageable fragments, and seek out strategies to deal with some problems.

This process often highlights understanding of the interlinking of problems. For example, often sex is the route to relationship formation. Barriers to sexual activity may block off new relationships. Clients may need to explore alternatives which were previously not contemplated when relationship formation was not problematic.

Some sessions allow women to face up to, and even explore, the unthinkable, the unmentionable and the feared. Fear is often paralysing and fear reduction may lead to replacement of inaction with action. Clients may be challenged in terms of their self-esteem. Counselling can help to build up self-esteem, self-assertion and social skills in the light of her HIV status.

Women may face crisis points which require decision-making. This is often in relation to intervention (e.g. drug trials, prophylactic medication, termination of pregnancy), care options and future planning.

Factual information will vary depending on whether the woman is pregnant, contemplating pregnancy or not pregnant. Clear coverage of the factual information is required with open discussion on what is known and what is not known. If a pregnancy is at issue, the facts include:

(a) HIV, the virus associated with AIDS, has been isolated in vaginal and cervical secretions, menstrual blood, semen and seminal fluid and can be transmitted from men to women and women to men. It can do so on a single exposure.

(b) HIV has been isolated in placental tissue and breast milk.

(c) It is not known when transplacental infection occurs. HIV has been isolated in foetal tissue as early as 15 weeks.

(d) Early workers felt there may be a need to carry out Caesarean section in the presence of HIV, but this has now been seen not to be the case.

(e) The rate of vertical transmission varies in many studies. In the early days it was thought that the likelihood of transplacental infection was high (over 65%) but more recent studies which have allowed for prospective work with larger subject numbers have shown that if a mother is HIV positive and well the likelihood is much closer to 25% and as low as 12.4% in more recent studies (European Collaborative Study, 1991). The figures seem to be slightly higher in studies emerging from some centres in Africa (closer to 33%).

(f) It is also known that if a mother is symptomatic vertical transmission rate is increased.

(g) A mother who has given birth to a child previously who developed AIDS is also more likely to have a subsequent baby with HIV. These findings have particular implications for counselling and their interaction with medical care.

(h) Early studies were concerned that pregnancy itself in the presence of HIV was detrimental to the mother. There have been no longer-term data to support this, but it may well be an important factor to examine in ongoing studies.

(i) Many women infected with HIV in the West are linked directly or indirectly to drug use. This, in itself, has specific implications. Drugs themselves may act as co-factors in disease expression or maternal/foetal well-being. There is no study to date which has examined the effect of withdrawal on HIV status on an infant. Furthermore, drug users' lifestyle may have particular elements in common such as nutrition, housing, social support, access to medical care, future caretaking of the child and so on.

Barriers for women

For women there are additional and unique issues. Worth (1990) reports that women may have specific concerns about abandonment. Blachman (1988) lends some support to this. Kamenga *et al* (1991) studied discordant couples and found that HIV negative men were more likely to seek sexual partners outside of the marriage if their wives were HIV positive than HIV negative wives whose husbands were HIV positive. Marital breakdown, violence and divorce were problems faced in the above study, many of which were ameliorated by in-depth counselling. Only 6 of the 168 initial cases seroconverted in this study. With extensive counselling, use of condoms increased from 5% to over 70%, which was maintained at 18-month follow-up.

Women who are HIV positive but do not have a partner often see a bleak future where HIV represents a barrier to any future relationship (Worth, 1990).

Behaviour change

Safer sex needs to be adopted to prevent sexual transmission of HIV. This is often particularly difficult for women (Sherr & Strong, 1992). Indeed Wofsy (1988) reported that discordant couples often do not adopt safer sex. A quarter abstained from sex in this sample, a third made no changes, while the remainder responded with some incorporation of safer sex.

Traditionally the burden of contraception has been the province of women. Most methods involve women, such as the pill, IUD and cap. The condom, however, is more in the male domain. Although a female condom has been developed (Leeper, 1990) this has limited uptake at present. Most contraception under the control of women is used outside of the sexual situation. Within the sexual situation it is glib to think that women have total control and the use of condoms is simply a matter of choice (Richardson, 1990). Much counselling may be aimed at strategies to negotiate safe sex, obstacles to it and alternatives.

It is also simplistic to believe that open negotiation will occur if it is initiated. Cochran & Mays (1990) noted that many men would lie about risk behaviours and/or HIV status if questioned by a female casual partner, as would women similarly questioned.

Secrets

Unlike other life-threatening disease, HIV and AIDS still conjure up fear and secrecy (Miller & Bor, 1988). One of the major goals of counselling surrounds the issues of disclosure (Peraykla & Bor, 1990). This is often specifically problematic for women. They fear that their relationships will be jeopardised, they fear they will be abandoned. Pregnancy and procreation may become a difficult issue. Some fear that they will be forced to consider termination while others do not know how to face their family if they choose not to conceive. For some HIV heralds a childless future and this needs considerable adjustment.

Communication about sex is often absent and many encounters are typified by scant discussion and little open negotiation. It may be very difficult for a woman to initiate condom use in a relationship. This is even more difficult in a relationship in which condoms were never used (Temmerman et al, 1990). There is a high cost to women for saying no to sex generally and to unprotected sex specifically. Many women simply do not have such choices open to them, such as in cases of rape (Sherr et al, 1993) or in the more common subtle pressure and coercion which limits control. Women who provide sex for money report that they have been paid or offered extra if they consent to sex without condoms. Most studies focus on the women (Ngugi et al, 1988; Day et al, 1988) rather than on the client (Wilson et al, 1989).

Mok (1990) noted that AIDS was a closely guarded secret in her sample of women and children in Edinburgh. The practical impli-cations of such secrets often result in a reliance on a selected group of trusted health professionals when clients cannot turn to wider family for support.

Social support

For most traumatic events, social support is a predictor of subsequent adjustment. As such it is seen as desirable. Such social support for women with HIV is often difficult. Many AIDS organisations in the West have been set up by, and tend to respond to, homosexual men. Women may find it difficult to approach such organisations and to find help for themselves.

Support from medical sources may also lag. Women usually report much later with their opportunistic infections (Hankins, 1990). This could be either because they are seen as less deserving of care or less likely to be recognised as suffering from AIDS-related problems. For whatever reason, this implies later treatment, later use of possibly prophylactic drugs such as AZT and thus a potentially poorer prognosis.

Women are often the providers of social support rather than the recipients. Worth (1990) reports that male injecting drug users who lose a partner because of their own serostatus may turn to an infected woman as a last resort rather than face being alone. Crystal *et al* (1989) found women to be a major source of informal support for people with AIDS and a mediator for formal support.

Mulleady (1992) noted that drug-using men in the UK tended to seek non-drug-using partners as a risk-reduction strategy. However, from the point of view of such partners, this may represent a shift towards risk where they can become sexually exposed to HIV from a partner who is exposed via needle sharing.

Efficacy of counselling intervention

There is little literature on the comparative efficacy of different methods of input (Green, 1989). This is problematic given that it would seem unethical to withhold counselling and evidence exists that counselling does seem beneficial (Kamenga *et al*, 1991). The major goals of all counselling interventions include: assisting those infected or affected to have the optimum quality of life with minimal emotional trauma, assist those infected to adjust their risk-related behaviours to avoid transmission and to help the uninfected avoid exposure. As such the counselling should involve the infected, the potentially infected, their family and carers.

Counselling for women with HIV needs to contain the same elements as all HIV counselling (e.g. Green & McCreaner, 1989). In addition there may be particular women's issues which may emerge.

Counselling can take various forms such as individual work (Green & McCreaner, 1989), couples (Ussher, 1989), and group (Hedge & Glover, 1990). Counselling models which have been effective in HIV work include cognitive behavioural models (Miller & Green, 1986; Green & McCreaner, 1989), family therapy (Miller & Bor, 1988), brief therapy, psychodynamic approach (Gold *et al*, 1986). Therapeutic styles are rarely compared and outcome measures are often not taken. Hedge & Sherr (1992) found a high demand for crisis intervention, particularly concentrated at the time of diagnosis and again at onset of symptoms. Pre- and post-test anxiety, depression, coping and quality of life measures for a subsample of 39 individuals receiving cognitive–behavioural intervention showed an improvement. However, no controls or comparisons were drawn.

Carers and counselling

In order to provide counselling or to operate with a counselling model of care, many health-care staff need training (Sherr & McCreaner, 1989; Sherr *et al*, 1991).

Avenues for care may be limited for women. Sherr (1987) showed that most people would turn to the medical profession in the first instances for worries and concerns surrounding HIV. As a precondition for effective reaction, the professions need to be fully aware of the factual background, willing to receive such approaches, and knowledgeable as well as skilled in counselling approaches. Sherr (1987) examined obstetric and gynaecological staff and found many knowledge gaps about HIV/AIDS as it applied to women, specifically concerning the spread and ramifications of HIV in pregnancy at the start of the epidemic in the UK. The position had not altered dramatically at 2-year follow-up (Sherr, 1989). Short input was effective in increasing knowledge, reducing staff anxiety, and affecting screening policy. Roderick *et al* (1990) addressed the educational needs of general practitioners in one district health authority in the UK (with the highest concentration of HIV cases) and found that GPs were specifically requesting information about pregnancy (47%), paediatric HIV (47%) and allied issues such as vaccination (44%), risk to self (40%), family planning (31%) and safer sex (22%). In addition, these GPs (Sherr *et al*, 1991) reported considerable anxiety about counselling pregnant women with a specific desire for education. Midwifery staff generally may be the front-line workers who have initial contact with pregnant women and need to respond to this challenge (Meadows *et al*, 1990).

Burnout has been monitored in carers (Miller, 1991) and the findings suggest that unremitting exposure to patients may limit staff coping in the long term (Bennett *et al*, 1991).

Paediatric issues

Infection with HIV, and AIDS, is of direct concern to parents. Women with HIV need to face the fact that their infants will either be infected or affected.

Multiple illness may pose particular counselling challenges. The infant's mother, and perhaps father, may be ill with HIV and the possibility of transplacental infection may herald many months of uncertainty coupled with tests and worry. For example, of the 288 children born to HIV-infected mothers in the European Cohort Study (as at 31 March 1991), 83 were infected, 125 had indeterminate HIV status and 80 were not infected (Peckham, 1991).

In an infant, AIDS is more severe than in an adult. Living with uncertainty is traumatic for the family and may continue for the first 2 years of a child's life. AIDS is a terminal illness, often with a poor prognosis. Children who are diagnosed under one year of age fare less well than those who are diagnosed after one year. Infection in the older group is often accompanied by loss of developmental milestones which can be particularly depressing for parents to observe. The distress caused by developmental delay and loss of milestones together with the educational and developmental implications for the child must be discussed and planned with the parents.

Treatments are often limited, but the drug trials of AZT may present decision-making challenges for parents who have often had to undergo a similar process for themselves.

Input for this group is demanding. The range of psychological trauma is often concentrated around the stresses of long-term uncertainty, illness of a child in the presence of family illness, the wider effects of HIV on the siblings and grandparents, all exacerbated by constant hospitalisation, medicalisation and unpleasant medical procedures. The issue of AIDS orphans and the future care of the children on parental death, whether the children are HIV positive or not, is a further challenge.

At all times it must be remembered that AIDS and HIV infection is still veiled in secrecy. As few people in the wider community are confided in, social support is not forthcoming. This increases the burden on parents, tries their coping ability and also has implications for the team of health care workers who often need to provide such support. Often children are unaware of their diagnosis. This creates a challenge of what to tell the child, who should tell, how it should be introduced and handled and when such information should be given. In the long term, bereavement issues may be paramount as they extend to loss of a family member, facing death and multiple bereavement.

Conclusion

As the epidemic unfolds the medical and psychological problems of this group will increase dramatically. The way forward must involve an integration between the psychological and physical care. This new disease must signify extensive uncertainty for both professionals and women, and counselling under such conditions of uncertainty may reduce psychological morbidity in this population.

Acknowledgement

This chapter was written drawing on part of the development of the project for the European Commission entitled ''AIDS: Ethics, Justice and European Policy''. The author acknowledges the stimulus and support provided by the Commission.

References

BARBACCI, M., REPKE, J. & CHAISSON, R. (1991) Routine prenatal screening for HIV infection. *Lancet*, *i*, 709–711.

BENNETT, L., MICHIE, P. & KIPPAX, S. (1991) Quantitative analysis of burnout and its associated factors in AIDS nursing. *AIDS Care*, **3**, 181–192.

BLACHMAN, M. (1988) Seropositive women. Clinical issues and approaches. *Focus*, **3**, 2–3.

BURNS, S. & MOK, J. (1991) Diagnosis of HIV infection. In *Caring for Children with HIV Infections and AIDS* (eds R. Claxton & T. Harrison). London: Edward Arnold.

CANCELLIERI, R. F. R., HOLMAN, S., SUNDERLAND, A., *et al* (1988) Psychiatric and behavioural impact of HIV testing in pregnant drug users. 4th Int AIDS Conference, Stockholm Sweden June 12–16.

CATALAN, J., MEADOWS, J., STONE, Y., *et al* (1991) Antenatal testing for HIV. *British Medical Journal*, *i*, 1400.

CDSC (1991) *Communicable Disease Surveillance Centre Reports*.

CHALMERS, I., ENKIN, M. & KEIRSE, M. (1989) *Effective Care in Pregnancy and Childbirth*. Oxford: Oxford University Press.

CHIN, J. (1991) Current and future dimensions of the HIV AIDS pandemic in women and children. *Lancet*, **336**, 221–224.

COATES, T. J., MORIN, S. F. & McKUSICK, L. (1987) Behavioural consequences of AIDS antibody testing among gay men. *Journal of the American Medical Association*, **258**, 1889.

COCHRAN, S. D. & MAYS, V. M. (1990) Sex, lies and HIV. *New England Journal of Medicine*, **322**, 774–775.

CRYSTAL, S., SCHILLER, N., DEJOWSKI, E., *et al* (1989) Female family members as mediators of utilization of health and social services. International AIDS Conference Montreal THDP 15.

DAY, S., WARD, H. & HARRIS, J. R. W. (1988) Prostitute women and public health. *British Medical Journal*, **297**, 1585.

DES JARLAIS, D. & FRIEDMAN, S. (1988) Gender differences in response to HIV infection. In *Psychological Neurological and Substance Abuse Aspects of AIDS* (eds T. Bridge, A. Mirsky & F. Goodwin), pp. 159–163. New York: Raven Press.

EUROPEAN COLLABORATIVE STUDY (1988) Mother to child transmission of HIV infection. *Lancet*, *ii*, 1039–1042.

—— (1991) Children born to women with HIV 1 infection natural history and risk of transmission. *Lancet*, **337**, 253–260.

FEINGOLD, P. R., VERMUND, S. H. & BURK, R. A. (1990) Cervical cytologic abnormalities and papilloma virus in women infected with HIV. *Journal of Acquired Immune Deficiency Syndrome*, **3**, 896–903.

GARCIA, J. (1982) Womens' views of antenatal care. In *Effectiveness and Satisfaction in Antenatal Care* (eds M. Enkin & I. Chalmers), pp. 81–92. London: Spastics International Medical Publications/Heinemann Medical Books.

GOLD, M., SEYMOUR, N. & SAHL, J. (1986) Counselling HIV seropositives. In *What To Do About AIDS* (ed. L. McKusick). Berkeley: California Press.

GREEN, J. (1989) Counselling for HIV Infection and AIDS. *AIDS Care*, **1**, 5–11.

—— & McCREANER, A. (1989) *Counselling in HIV Infection and AIDS*. Oxford: Blackwell Scientific Publications.

HALL, M. & CHNG, P. (1982) Antenatal care in practice. In *Effectiveness and Satisfaction in Antenatal Care* (eds M. Enkin & I. Chalmers). London: Spastics International Medical Publications/Heinemann Medical Books.

HANKINS, C. (1990) Women and HIV infection and AIDS in Canada: should we worry. *Canadian Medical Association Journal*, **143**, 1171–1173.

HEDGE, B. & GLOVER, L. F. (1990) Group intervention with HIV seropositive patients and their partners. *AIDS Care*, **2**, 147–154.

—— & SHERR, L. (1992) Psychological services for People with HIV infection and AIDS. Paper presented at the International Health Psychology Conference, Lausanne.

HUTTERER, J., BLASS, P., OBERAVER, C., *et al* (1989) Differences in HIV AIDS counseling for women and for men. In Abstracts V Int Conference on AIDS, Montreal Canada June 8. Abstract THDP 18.

JOHNSTON, F., BRETTLE, R., MACCALLUM, R., *et al* (1989) Womens' knowledge of their HIV antibody state its effect on their decision whether to continue the pregnancy. *British Medical Journal*, **300**, 23–24.

JOHNSTONE, F. D., McCALLUM, L. R., BRETTLE, R. P., *et al* (1989) Testing for HIV in pregnancy 3 years experience in Edinburgh City. *Scottish Medical Journal*, **34**, 561–563.

KAMENGA, M., RYDER, R. W., JINGU, M., *et al* (1991) Evidence of marked sexual behaviour change associated with low HIV 1 seroconversion in 149 married couples with discordant HIV 1 serostatus experience at an HIV counselling center in Zaire. *AIDS*, **5**, 61–67.

KELLY, P., GRAHAM, V., HALL, L., *et al* (1989) Differences between symptomatic HIV + ve female and male patients. *Abstracts of the International AIDS Conference*, Montreal, THDP 9.

LARRSON, G., SPANGBERG, L., LINDGREN, S., *et al* (1990) Screening for HIV in pregnant women a study of maternal opinion. *AIDS Care*, **2**, 223–228.

LEEPER, M. A. (1990) Preliminary evaluation of "Reality" a condom for women. *AIDS Care*, **2**, 287.

LEMP, G. F., PAYNE, S. F., RUTHERFORD, G. W., *et al* (1990) Projections of AIDS morbidity and mortality in San Francisco. *Journal of the American Medical Association*, **263**, 1497–1501.

MAIMAN, M., FRUCHTER, R. G., SERUR, E., *et al* (1988) Prevalence of HIV in a colposcopy clinic. *Journal of the American Medical Association*, **260**, 2214–2215.

MARTE, C., COHEN, M., FRUCHTER, R. G. (1990) Pap test and STD finding in HIV + ve women at ambulatory caresites. VI International AIDS Conference, San Francisco.

McCUSKER, J., STODDARD, A. M., MAYER, K. H., *et al* (1988) Effects of HIV antibody test knowledge on subsequent sexual behaviours in a cohort of homosexually active men. *American Journal of Public Health*, **78**, 462–467.

MEADOWS, J., JENKINSON, S., CATALAN, J., *et al* (1990) Voluntary HIV testing in the antenatal clinic: differing uptake rates for individual counselling midwives. *AIDS Care*, **2**, 229–234.

MILLER, D. & GREEN, J. (1986) Organizing a counselling service for AIDS related problems. *Genitourinary Medicine*, **62**, 116–122.

MILLER, R. & BOR, R. (1988) *AIDS: A Guide to Clinical Counselling*. London: Science Press.

MILLER, D. (1991) Occupational morbidity and burnout. *International Review of Psychiatry*, **3**, 439–450.

MINKOFF, H. L. & DEHOVITZ, J. A. (1991) Care of women infected with the human immunodeficiency virus. *Journal of the American Medical Association*, **266**, 2253–2258.

MOATTI, J. P., LE GALES, C., SEROR, V., *et al* (1990) Social acceptability of HIV screening among pregnant women. *AIDS Care*, **2**, 213–222.

MOK, J. (1990) Paper presented at the VI International AIDS Conference, San Francisco.

MULLEADY, G. (1992) *HIV and AIDS in Drug Users*. Oxford: Blackwell Scientific Publications.

NGUGI, E. E., PLUMMER, F. A., SIMONSEN, J. N., *et al* (1988) Prevention of transmission of HIV in Africa. Effectiveness of condom promotion and health education among prostitutes. *Lancet*, **ii**, 887–890.

NOVELLO, A. C. (1991) Women and HIV infection. *American Medical Association*, **265**, 1805.

PECKHAM, C. (1991) AIDS and Children, Paper presented at the AIDS and Children Conference, London.

—— & NEWELL, M. L. (1990) HIV-1 infection in mothers and babies. *AIDS Care*, **2**, 205–212.

PERAKYLA, A. & BOR, R. (1990) Interactional problems of addressing dreaded issues in HIV counselling. *AIDS Care*, **2**, 325–338.

PERRY, S., JACOBSBERG, L., FISHMAN, B., *et al* (1990) Psychological responses to serological testing for HIV. *AIDS*, **4**, 145–152.

RICHARDSON, D. (1990) *Women and the AIDS Crisis*. London: Pandora Press.

RODERICK, P., VICTOR, C. R. & BEARDOW, R. (1990) Developing care in the community GPs and the HIV epidemic. *AIDS Care*, **2**, 127–132.

ROTHENBERG, P., WOELFEL, M., STONEBURNER, R., *et al* (1987) Survival with the acquired immunodeficiency syndrome. *New England Journal of Medicine*, **317**, 1297–1302.

SELWYN, P. A., CARTER, R. J., SCHOENBAUM, E. E., *et al* (1989) Knowledge of HIV antibody status and decision to continue or terminate pregnancy among intravenous drug users. *Journal of the American Medical Association*, **261**, 3567–3571.

SHERR, L. (1987) The impact of AIDS in obstetrics on obstetric staff. *Journal of Reproductive and Infant Psychology*, **5**, 87–96.

———— (1989) Communication and anxiety in obstetric care. PhD Thesis, Warwick University.

———— (1991) *AIDS and HIV in Mothers and Babies*. Oxford: Blackwell Scientific Publications.

———— & McCREANER, A. (1989) Summary evaluation of national AIDS counselling training. *Counselling Psychology Quarterly*, **2**, 21–32.

————, STRONG, C. & DAVEY, T. (1991) Anxiety and depression in AIDS and HIV/infection. *Counselling Psychology Quarterly*, **4**, 27–35.

———— & ———— (1992) Safe sex and women. *Genito-urinary Medicine*, **68**, 1.

————, MELVIN, D., PETRAK, J., *et al* (1993) The psychological trauma of HIV for women. *Counselling Psychology Quarterly*, **6**, 99–119.

SORREL, S. & SPRINGER, E. (1989) The argument against HIV antibody testing in chemical dependency treatment programme. *Journal of Psychoactive Drugs*, **21**, 419–421.

STEVENS, A., VICTOR, C., SHERR, L., *et al* (1989) HIV testing in antenatal clinics: the impact on women. *AIDS Care*, **1**, 165–171.

SUNDERLAND, A., MINKOFF, H., HANDTE, J., *et al* (1992) The impact of HIV serostatus on reproductive decisions of women. *Obstetrics and Gynecology*, **79**, 1027–1031.

SURVEILLANCE UPDATE (1990) AIDS in Canada. *Surveillance Update*, 4 September. Federal Centre for AIDS, Ottawa.

TEMMERMAN, M., MOSES, S., KIRAU, D., *et al* (1990) Impact of single session post partum counselling of HIV infected women on their subsequent reproductive behaviour. *AIDS Care*, **2**, 247–252.

TURNER, C. F., MILLER, H. G., MOSES, L. E. (eds) (1989) *AIDS: Sexual Behaviour and Intravenous Drug Use*. Washington DC: National Academy Press.

USSHER, J. M. (1989) Cognitive behavioural couples therapy with gay men referred for counselling in an AIDS setting: a pilot study. *AIDS Care*, **2**, 43–52.

WENSTROM, K. D. & ZUIDEMA, L. J. (1989) Determination of the seroprevalence of HIV infection in Gravidas by non anonymous versus anonymous testing. *Obstetrics and Gynecology*, **74**, 558–561.

WILSON, D., CHIRORO, P., LAVELLE, S., *et al* (1989) Sex workers client sex behaviour and condom use in Harare, Zimbabwe. *AIDS Care*, **1**, 269–280.

WOFSY, C. (1988) Women and the acquired immunodeficiency syndrome. An interview. *Women in Medicine*, **149**, 687–690.

WORTH, D. (1990) Women at high risk of HIV Infection. In *Behavioural Aspects of AIDS* (ed. D. G. Ostrow). New York: Plenum Medical Books.

13 Family therapy for anorexia nervosa

IVAN EISLER

The notion that anorexia nervosa is a disorder that can only be fully understood if it is placed in the context of the patient's family is by no means new. Thus Lasegue stated (1873):

> ". . . it must not cause surprise to find me thus always *placing in parallel* the morbid condition of the hysterical subject and the preoccupations of those surrounding her. These are intimately connected and we should acquire an erroneous idea of the disease by confining ourselves to examining the patient."

The italics are mine, in order to stress the neutrality of the quote as to the direction of influence – patient to family, family to patient. This is important because all too often those writing about families suggest, at least implicitly, that families cause anorexia nervosa and that it is the family rather than the individual who needs treatment. Bliss & Branch (1960) write:

> "one can conclude that a large number of these patients are nurtured in family environments which tend to produce emotionally impaired individuals."

The idea of families being linked to the problem of anorexia nervosa gained a fresh impetus with the development of family therapy, most notably through the work of Mara Selvini-Palazzoli (1974) and of Minuchin and his co-workers from the Philadelphia Child Guidance Clinic (Minuchin *et al*, 1978). Minuchin, in particular, produced a very elegant description of families containing an anorexic youngster. Minuchin characterised what he termed the "psychosomatic family" as having four specific features:

(a) *Enmeshment* – the overclose relationships in the family are typically manifested by frequent intrusions on each others' thoughts and feelings, speaking for each other and 'mind reading'. Closeness and loyalty are valued more than autonomy and self-realisation. There are poor inter-generational boundaries resulting in cross-generational alliances, e.g. a parent and a child joining together, excluding the other parent, who becomes peripheral in the family. This undermines effective parental functioning and may place an inappropriate burden on a child who has taken on a 'parental' role.

(b) *Lack of conflict resolution* – the difficulties in dealing with conflict are often initially masked to the outside observer because overt conflict is generally avoided or it is only short lived. The families develop a range of transactional patterns that enable them to side-step potential conflicts before they actually develop. In some families overt conflict does emerge but when that happens it is quickly pushed aside so that it is seldom resolved.

(c) *Overprotectiveness* – the heightened sensitivity to the needs of the other family members lead to frequent protective responses. While this is most apparent in the attitudes and behaviours aimed at the anorexic youngster, it also characterises other interactions in the family. The anorexic child will often feel a great responsibility to protect the family. The illness, while being perceived as a great burden to the family, also has the effect of binding the family together, protecting it from the feared break-up.

(d) *Rigidity* – the family tends to have a rather limited and fixed pattern of interaction and remains unchanged, even in the face of external change. The family's response to changing circumstances (e.g. the changing needs of its pubertal child) is to try to absorb them rather than to adapt to them.

Minuchin views the psychosomatic family model as both the setting condition for anorexia nervosa, as well as the interactional system with which the symptomatic behaviour becomes inextricably linked. The account is clinically cogent and provides important insights into the family dynamics in which anorexia becomes frequently embedded. Nevertheless, it would be simplistic to view any of the features of the 'psychosomatic' family (or indeed all of them together) as being the *cause* of anorexia nervosa. This is not only because a comprehensive aetiological model of anorexia nervosa must include a variety of factors ranging from genetic, through biological to family and social factors (Garfinkel & Garner, 1982) but also because there is a constant interaction between the symptomatic behaviour of the anorexic youngster and the transactional patterns within the family. The anorexic behaviour provides the adolescent with a sense that she has found a way of challenging the enmeshed relationships in the family. At the same time it makes her more dependent on her parents, reinforcing her child-like position. The illness brings the parents together, often masking any short-comings in the marital relationship, but the sense of failure in not achieving the desired task, leads to feelings of guilt and blame which makes them again feel distant and alone. The increasing anxiety reinforces the wish to avoid conflict at all cost which has a paralysing effect on the family. The rigidity and narrowness of the transactional repertoire of the family will often give the impression of a 'frozen' family where time has virtually come to a standstill. The family seems poised in a balancing act, where putting one foot wrong could bring everything crashing down. The anorexic behaviour may superficially challenge the family's wish to maintain the status quo but the family's way of regaining balance is to increase the rigidity and narrowness of its transactional repertoire (Eisler, 1988). Trying to decide what is cause and what is effect becomes a somewhat arbitrary exercise as the process just described is a continuous, circular one with no obvious starting or end point.

Even though Minuchin's account of the 'psychosomatic family' has been criticised for lacking a firm empirical base (Kog *et al*, 1985) it has been very influential, primarily because it has formed the basis for the development of a treatment approach to anorexia nervosa with striking claims about its efficacy (Minuchin *et al*, 1978). The importance of the results reported by Minuchin and his colleagues stands out most clearly when it is contrasted with follow-up data from other treatment centres.

During the 1970s a number of important follow-up studies of individuals suffering from anorexia nervosa were published (Theander, 1970; Halmi *et al*, 1973; Morgan & Russell, 1975; Cantwell *et al*, 1977; Minuchin *et al*, 1978; Hsu *et al*, 1979). In most of these studies the patients received a combination of treatments in which specialised in-patient care generally played a central role. A variety of other treatments including psychodynamic psychotherapy, behaviour therapy and family therapy were also used but in most cases not as the main or only treatment. There is a degree of variation in the results of these studies, as can be expected given the different population samples and different methodologies that were utilised. Nevertheless, the overall picture that emerges from these studies is relatively clear. In the short term, the majority of patients respond very favourably to specialised in-patient nursing care. The follow-up studies quoted above, however, show that the medium- to long-term outcome is much less favourable. At a 4–5-year follow-up between 30 and 40% of the patients can be said to have recovered. Approximately one-third will have improved significantly, without making a full recovery, and the remaining third will have become chronically ill or they will have died.

The one study that stands out from the other follow-up studies is the study by Minuchin *et al* (1978). This study describes the outcome of the treatment of a series of 53 patients who were treated at the Philadelphia Child Guidance Clinic using family therapy as the main therapeutic intervention. At the follow-up, of between 1.5 and 7 years, over 85% of the patients were deemed to have recovered. Minuchin's findings were challenging for anybody working in the field of anorexia nervosa and could not be dismissed easily. There were, of course, a number of criticisms of this study (e.g. Swift, 1982): it was an uncontrolled study, the length of follow-up was in some cases quite short, the patients were all 'easy' patients in the sense that they were young, mostly with a short duration of illness. It is known from other follow-up studies (e.g. Morgan & Russell, 1975; Hsu *et al*, 1979) that this would give most of the patients in the study a relatively good prognosis.

Nevertheless, the findings had to be taken seriously, indicating the need for carefully controlled evaluation of family therapy for the treatment of eating disorder. This was the starting point of a research programme carried out at the Maudsley Hospital in London, which is the subject matter of this chapter. The chapter focuses primarily on the family therapy of the younger anorexic patient, where the clearest results have been obtained and where our understanding of the treatment has made the greatest progress. The results for the older and more chronic patients are only mentioned in passing.

A controlled trial of family therapy and individual supportive therapy in anorexia nervosa

The first controlled trial of family therapy for anorexia nervosa confirmed some but not all of the claims made for the efficacy of family therapy (details of this study can be found in Szmukler *et al*, 1985; Russell *et al*, 1987; Dare *et al*, 1990). In this study 80 consecutive admissions to the in-patient Eating Disorder Unit at the Maudsley Hospital were enrolled. The treatment programme was in two parts. During the first phase the patients first took part in a carefully structured ward-based programme (lasting approximately 10–12 weeks), during which their weight was restored to a healthy level. Following this, each patient was randomly assigned either to family therapy or an individual supportive therapy out-patient follow-up treatment, which lasted for one year.

Table 13.1 shows the results at the end of the one-year treatment for the 54 anorexic patients in the trial who received one of the two follow-up treatments.[1] The results confirm some of the doubts about the Philadelphia study. It is clearly *not* the case that family therapy is a universally effective treatment for every sufferer from anorexia nervosa. The sample of anorexic patients studied at the Maudsley Hospital was quite heterogeneous; the patients covered a wide age range (14–55 years) and the age of onset of their illness varied considerably (9–50 years) as did its duration (3 months – 14 years). Over 80% had had previous psychiatric treatment on an in-patient or out-patient basis. Table 13.1 shows that for the group as a whole there is no clear difference between the two treatments and that family therapy is, therefore, by no means a universal treatment for anorexia nervosa.

The study does, however, show that there are important differences between subgroups of patients who respond differently to different treatments. This is most apparent with the younger group of patients

---

1. Table 13.1 excludes those patients in the study who had a concurrent diagnosis of bulimia nervosa (*n* = 23) and those anorexic patients who refused any follow-up treatment.

TABLE 13.1
First Maudsley trial of family therapy for anorexia nervosa – one-year follow-up

| Therapy | Outcome at the end of the one-year follow-up treatment | | | Prognostic group |
	Good	Intermediate	Poor	
Family	6	3	1	*Subgroup 1**
Individual	1	1	9	Onset ≤18
				Duration <3 years
Family	2	2	6	*Subgroup 2*
Individual	2	1	4	Onset <18
				Duration >3 years
Family	0	1	6	*Subgroup 3*
Individual	2	1	4	Onset >18
Family	8	6	13	*All patients*
Individual	5	3	19	

*Good v. (intermediate + poor): $>P<0.02$.
 (Good + intermediate) v. poor: $>P<0.002$.

(i.e. with an onset of the illness before the age of 18 years and who were ill for less than 3 years – in other words precisely the group studied by Minuchin) who not only benefit from family therapy but do significantly better than if they are seen on their own. Nine out of 10 patients in this

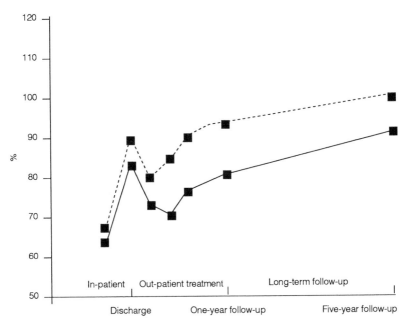

*Fig. 13.1. Weights of patients (as a percentage of matched population mean weight) in subgroup 1
(■——■ , individual therapy; ■ · · · · · ■ family therapy)*

group treated with family therapy had a good or intermediate outcome and only one patient had a poor outcome. In comparison, the results for the patients in the individual supportive therapy group are virtually reversed. Nine out of 11 of these patients at the end of the treatment had a poor outcome. The preliminary results of a recently completed follow-up at 5 years confirm the earlier results. Figure 13.1 shows the average weight of the patients from subgroup 1 in the two treatments over the 5-year period. Those who received family therapy continued to do well (with the exception of the one patient who had done badly at the one-year follow-up). The good outcome in terms of symptomatic improvement is also reflected in other areas of the patients' lives – several of them are married, they have children and in all other ways are doing well. Those in the supportive therapy group have also continued to improve, as one would expect in a group of patients with a generally good prognosis. But even at 5 years, the overall outcome of the patients seen in individual therapy is significantly worse than for those treated with family therapy.

Overall, this result confirms, that at least for the younger, non-chronic patient, family therapy is indeed a very effective form of treatment. It is important to stress that the results for the other subgroups are not nearly so striking. The more chronic patients in subgroup 2 did not do particularly well at the end of treatment and a number of them have continued to do badly at the 5-year follow-up. The patients with an onset of the illness in adulthood (subgroup 3) have done, if anything, better in individual treatment, though these results are nowhere near as clear-cut as the results for the younger patient.[2]

Proponents of different forms of psychotherapy often tend to see their particular brand of treatment as the 'treatment of choice'. Family therapists are certainly not immune to this. However, even with the clear-cut results that we obtained for the younger patient with anorexia nervosa it would be risky to claim that family therapy has now shown to be the treatment of choice for this group. It is risky, because it begs the question: what is family therapy? A brief trawl through the family therapy literature would quickly reveal at least a dozen definitions of what is family therapy.

Strictly speaking all that we can conclude from our results is that a particular form of family therapy was shown to be highly effective with a subgroup of anorexic patients in preventing relapse after hospital treatment. This naturally leads to the following question: what is it about the specific form of family therapy that we use that makes it effective?

---

2. The psychotherapy of this older group of patients is being investigated in two further studies. An MRC study of individual and family therapy following in-patient treatment is nearing completion and a new study funded by the Leverhulme Trust of out-patient treatments for older patients is in its early phase.

Family therapy, like other treatments, is a complex package of interventions which has developed over time, and even in the hands of a particular practitioner is always a conglomerate of various techniques, strategies and theories. In the approach developed at the Maudsley Hospital (which is described in more detail below), there were at least two quite distinct components. One is a problem-solving aspect, through which the parents are helped to make the first step in reversing their daughter's weight loss and take firm control of her eating behaviour. The other aspect, in common with other family therapy approaches, is a focus on the family as a unit, to try to understand its transactional style, structure, beliefs etc. Fundamental to all family therapy approaches is a belief that an understanding of the way the family functions provides the therapist with insights that are not available when the patient is considered in isolation, and that intervening in the interactional system surrounding the symptomatic behaviour is a powerful vehicle for change. While some family therapists would argue that acquiring an understanding of the patient's family context does not necessarily require the whole family to be present during treatment (cf. Jenkins & Asen, 1992), being able to observe the interaction in the family and making direct interventions in the family is central to most family therapy approaches.

Two forms of family treatment – family therapy and family counselling

In order to separate the 'problem solving' and 'family systems' components of the treatment we decided to compare two different ways of working with families: our customary conjoint family therapy and a form of family treatment, which we have called family counselling, which retains the problem solving aspect of the treatment but where the family is not seen together. In this latter treatment, the parents are seen as a couple and the anorexic youngster is seen, by the same therapist, but separately, on her own.

The treatment model, of both the conjoint family therapy and the family counselling, puts a strong emphasis on helping the parents to become effective parents once more, so that they can take control of the eating problem. Put somewhat simplistically, in the early stages of treatment the message to the parents is: "You've got a sick daughter, who is in danger of dying – your family, and in particular you as parents, have the resources to help her – our task is to help you use your own resources to the best effect." In engaging the family in treatment, it is vital that the therapist does it in a way that gets across another message, which is: "the illness is not the fault of the family". Addressing disabling feelings of guilt and blame early on in treatment is particularly important when the treatment being offered involves the whole family. When people are offered family therapy, it is very easy for them to think that what you are saying is that "The real problem isn't your daughter, the real problem is you. The real problem is that there is something wrong with your family or with your marriage." An important task for the therapist is to help the parents regain their belief in themselves as parents – implying that they are the root cause of the problem is unlikely to help them achieve this.

As the parents take charge of the symptomatic behaviour, other issues start to emerge, that are more directly concerned with adolescent development, individuation, separation, etc. (cf. Dare, 1983; Eisler, 1988; Dare & Eisler, 1992). In the early phases of treatment the therapist will be careful not to allow the discussion of these issues to deflect the parents from their central task of managing the anorexic behaviour of their daughter. To succeed, the family needs to develop quite a rigid and single-minded approach to deal with the eating problem. The effect of the consistency of the transactions around eating is that the anorexia loses its central role in the family system. Family interactions and relationships can no longer be mediated by the anorexic symptom and the family's response to the symptom. Instead, the family has to start finding new ways of addressing the usual issues that families at that particular life-cycle stage have to deal with. At this point the therapy moves into a new phase where the family issues are addressed more directly or in some cases the family may decide that they no longer need to come for treatment.

How does family counselling differ from family therapy?

In comparing two quite similar family treatments, our aim was to ascertain the extent to which the availability of the whole family for observation and direct intervention would determine the course of the therapy. For the family therapist, observing the moment-to-moment interaction between family members and identifying recurrent patterns of interactions is an important source of information for the understanding of the way a particular family functions. Many family therapy interventions aim to modify directly the process of family interaction in the here-and-now. Neither of these are available to the therapist in the family counselling situation. The most obvious example of this is in how the therapist helps the parents take charge of the eating behaviour.

In the family therapy situation the therapist will invite the family to bring a picnic lunch to see how they actually try to tackle the eating problem and will help the parents to get their daughter to eat, even if this might entail an unpleasant conflict. The therapist might start by asking the parents to decide how much the daughter should eat at this meal. If the daughter interrupts this discussion, there are a number of ways in which the therapist might intervene. He might say: "I want your parents to make that decision on their own; they are going to find it hard to ignore what you are saying but that's what they have to do if they are to save your life"; at other times a gentle silencing gesture will have the same effect. The therapist will be sympathetic to the daughter's needs to intervene but will gently and persistently encourage the parents not to let her side-track them. When one of the parents during a family meal is encouraging the daughter to eat and the other parent is wavering, finding the whole process too painful, the therapist will look for ways of helping both parents to maintain the parental coalition.

In the family counselling, such interventions are not available to the therapist, because the interaction between parents and daughter are happening away from the therapy session. The therapist can only *talk about* what is likely to happen when they go home and try to get their daughter to eat. The therapist may predict to the parents that their daughter will feel that she has no alternative but to look for a way of trying to split them, that they will have to have a united front as parents, that she will have to find ways of fighting for herself and that she will probably do it by trying to get them to take a different approach and not pull together. What the therapist cannot do in the counselling situation is actually intervene directly in the process of that kind of interaction. Inevitably, the therapy sessions then have a different pace; they are less likely to be confrontational and the whole process seems much gentler.

A pilot study comparing family therapy and family counselling

To test some of our hypotheses a controlled treatment trial was set up to compare family therapy with family counselling for adolescent anorexia nervosa. This study is now nearing completion and the data from it are not yet available. What is being reported here are the results of a pilot study and a two-year follow-up of this pilot.

We had expected that the family counselling would prove a somewhat simpler but still quite effective treatment for many of our patients. We had hypothesised that with the more difficult cases, the therapist might be at a disadvantage compared with the whole family interventions. We thought that however firm and authoritative the therapist was in the parental sessions, in some cases this would be undermined by the family's inability to put the advice into practice.

The results, so far, do not bare this out. Figure 13.2, showing the average weight gain in the two treatment groups over 6 months of treatment that was offered during the pilot study, shows that both treatments proved quite effective in restoring the patients to physical health and that the differences between the treatments were small. The differences between the two groups are not significant, but the family counselling certainly appears at least as effective as family therapy.

There are some further data from the follow-up of the pilot study (Squire *et al*, in preparation) which are also of interest. In the follow-up, the family

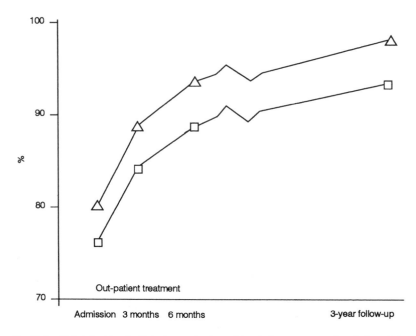

Fig. 13.2. Pilot study of two family treatments showing weight gain (as a percentage of matched population mean weight) during treatment and follow-up (∆——∆ family counselling; □ —— □ family therapy)

members were asked what they had found helpful, and what was unhelpful about the treatment that they had received. Their experience of the therapy was very revealing. The majority of the families mentioned two things that they had found most helpful. First was the fact that they were made aware of how seriously and dangerously ill their daughter was. This does not mean that they were naïve or unaware of the dangers of self-starvation or indeed that they had not been told before. But there was something about the process of being referred to a specialist treatment centre, the prolonged assessment and the often very forceful manner in which the therapists spoke about the terrible risks their daughter was exposing herself to that enabled the family to accept in full what was being said to them. Coupled with that was the second thing most often listed as helpful, which was being told that it was the parents who had to do something about the problem. This finding caused surprise, because at the time of treatment such advice was often quite strongly resisted. These aspects of treatment were endorsed by parents as well as the daughters in both treatment groups. Where the two treatment groups differed was in what they had felt was unhelpful about the treatment. In the family therapy group, a number of the family members, particularly the youngsters (and occasionally the parents), felt that the family or the parents in particular were being blamed. This is in spite of the fact that the same therapists conducted both forms of treatment and always worked hard at reducing feelings of guilt and blame. It seems that for some families, simply being seen together as a whole family in therapy or perhaps the style of the sessions, which sometimes could lead to open conflict, made them feel guilty or blamed by the therapist. In spite of that, most of the families (including those who said that they felt they were blamed) said they found the therapist was understanding. The second difference between the family therapy and family counselling group was that a proportion of the families in the family therapy group reported how, in the family therapy session, or after they left the hospital, they had conflicts which they found very distressing. None of the families in the family counselling group reported such experiences.

What makes family therapy effective?

In spite of the preliminary nature of these results they raise important questions about our notions of what makes family therapy effective. Implicit in much of our thinking about family therapy (Dare, 1983; Eisler, 1988; Dare *et al*, 1990) was an acceptance that the families of anorexic youngsters have a particular transactional style and that one of the aims of the treatment was to help the families to change in ways which would make the family environment more conducive to healthy development. Our clinical experience, confirmed by the results of our research showing the efficacy of the treatment, reinforced this view. Minuchin's model, for instance, emphasises very strongly that psychosomatic families are bad at dealing with conflict: they either try to avoid it or if it happens they have difficulties in resolving it. It is a common belief that sometimes conflict is a useful and healthy thing – if we can resolve it. Exhorting parents to take control of a resistant, starving youngster can often lead the family into open conflict. Our experience has been that however much the family fear such conflict they can usually be helped to manage it effectively. The pain that they experience seems a small price to pay for saving their daughter's life. We would often talk with the family about the life-saving battle that the parents will have to undertake with their daughter and that it is a battle that they will have to win. Generally, parents can and do win the battle.

There is another aspect of the psychosomatic family model that is relevant to this discussion. The overclose, enmeshed relationships in the family are manifested most powerfully in the parents' feeling of being paralysed by their daughter's fear that she will be overwhelmed by them and lose her identity if she gives in to them and starts eating. The parents can only win the battle at the point when they stop listening to their daughter saying ''don't make me eat'', and instead start acting on their own fear, which is that she will die. Paradoxically, therefore, pushing the parents into taking very firm control and making the anorexic daughter eat, instead of taking away her "last bit of independence", leads to greater differentiation within the family.

There were, therefore, theoretical reasons, backed up by clinical experience as well as empirical evidence, to suggest that challenging the conflict avoidance style of the family around the central issue of the eating behaviour was a crucial component of our treatment. The efficacy of the family counselling approach makes such an explanation much less tenable.

It may be in one sense a truism that for one member of a family to change, the family as a whole has to change. But the family change may not be of the kind or degree that we expect. Our clinical experience of observing families during the course of treatment and also at follow-up research interviews, is that families can and do change. The most obvious change takes place when the anorexia nervosa stops being the hub of the family's life, when food, eating and weight are no longer the main or only currency for negotiating personal relationships. The family then starts to address the various developmental issues that have been dormant, such as growing up, leaving home, sexuality and in this process, like all other families, they inevitably change.

How such changes are made possible varies from family to family. With the families of the younger anorexic a crucial turning point seems to be when the parents find a way of not being organised by their daughter's fears and pains. In the families of the older anorexic we have observed similar changes taking place when the parents truly 'give up' and make it clear that their daughter's anorexia is no longer their problem, while at the same time their daughter makes sure that they have no knowledge of how she is getting on. In both cases the disconnection of the anorexia nervosa from personal relationships within the family seems to have a similar, liberating effect.

This does not, however, mean that the effect of treatment is to change the family from being 'psychosomatic' into a 'normal' family. Indeed, our clinical experience is that descriptively the post-treatment family is probably no less 'psychosomatic' than the pre-treatment family. They still tend to avoid conflict, they still highly value closeness and the observed family structure may also have undergone only little change. Of course, once these characteristics are no longer intertwined with anorexia nervosa they look much more like a normal variation of family life and are more likely to continue to evolve as the family moves through its life-cycle. What our research is teaching us is that while we may be successful in helping families move away from the position of being stuck when no change seems possible, the families themselves are perhaps better at finding the best direction for them to move in than we are.

Before drawing some final conclusions several caveats have to be made. The first one, already mentioned earlier, is that a number of the points made in this chapter are based on preliminary data. It is possible for instance that the differences that we found in the perceptions of our two treatments only apply to certain types of family. We have some evidence (Le Grange *et al*, 1992) that the negative perceptions of family therapy are primarily found in families where feelings of guilt are high and which tend towards overt criticism (as measured by the expressed emotion scales, Leff & Vaughn, 1985). The ongoing, main study is designed in such a way so as to allow for the testing of this hypothesis.

The second caveat is to do with the nature of the family therapy being utilised in this study. There is no such thing as generic family therapy and it would be wrong to assume that our findings are somehow about family therapy *per se*. Many family therapies are very different from ours. For instance 'Systemic' or 'Milano' family therapy (Campbell & Draper, 1985), in which the therapist has a very neutral role, would be neither confrontational nor directive in asking the parents to take control of their daughter's eating problem. Such approaches have been used reportedly with some effect for the treatment of eating disorder, though the findings reported by Stierlin *et al* (1989) suggest that they are possibly more effective in bringing about change in the family than in securing symptomatic change in the anorexic youngster.

Many family therapists would argue that what we term family counselling is just another form of family therapy. We are happy to concede that point but would stress the importance of the differences between the two approaches described earlier. Indeed, our findings would support the notion that what may make the two treatments different is not the format (i.e. conjoint v. separate interviews) but rather the therapeutic stance that the two formats engender.

Dare (this volume) challenges the idea that theoretical models of aetiology go hand in hand with explanatory models of therapy. However, these models are necessary, as their development is very much part of the learning process that helps us gain an understanding of what we do. Clinical experience and empirical research data can be integrated to lead to a revision of our theoretical models.

Our experience of doing research on family therapy in anorexia nervosa is a good illustration of this process. It started from asking questions about the efficacy of a particular form of family therapy. It showed persuasively that it was highly effective for the younger anorexic and that its effects are lasting even after 5 years. We felt we had a good understanding of why it was effective. However, the more we have looked into the mechanics of the treatment, the more we are realising that it works only partly for the reasons we thought and partly for other reasons.

References

BLISS, E. L. & BRANCH, C. H. H. (1960) *Anorexia Nervosa*. New York: Hoeber.
CAMPBELL, D. & DRAPER, R. (1985) *Applications of Systemic Family Therapy*. London: Grune & Stratton.

CANTWELL, D., STURZENBERGER, S., BURROUGH, J., *et al* (1977) Anorexia nervosa: an affective disorder. *Archives of General Psychiatry*, **34**, 1087–1093.

DARE, C. (1983) Family therapy for families containing an anorectic youngster. In *Understanding Anorexia Nervosa and Bulimia* (ed. G. J. Bargman), pp. 28–34. Columbus, OH: Ross.

———, EISLER, I., RUSSELL, G. F. M., *et al* (1990) Clinical and theoretical impact of a controlled trial of family therapy in anorexia nervosa. *Journal of Marital and Family Therapy*, **16**, 39–57.

——— & ——— (1992) Family therapy for anorexia nervosa. In *Feeding Problems and Eating Disorders in Children and Adolescents* (eds P. J. Cooper & A. Stein), pp. 147–160. Chur: Harwood Academic Press.

EISLER, I. (1988) Family therapy approaches to anorexia. In *Anorexia and Bulimia Nervosa, Practical Approaches* (ed. D. Scott), pp. 95–107. London: Croom Helm.

GARFINKEL, P. E. & GARNER, D. M. (1982) *Anorexia Nervosa: A Multidimensional Perspective*. New York: Brunner/Mazel.

HALMI, K., BRODLAND, G. & LOONEY, J. (1973) Progress in anorexia nervosa. *Annals of Internal Medicine*, **78**, 907–909.

HSU, L. K. G., CRISP, A. H. & HARDING, B. (1979) Outcome of anorexia nervosa. *Lancet*, i, 61–65.

JENKINS, H. & ASEN, K. (1992) Family therapy without the family: a framework for systemic practice. *Journal of Family Therapy*, **14**, 1–14.

KOG, E., VANDEREYCKEN, W. & VERTOMMEN, H. (1985) The psychosomatic family model: A critical analysis of family interaction concepts. *Journal of Family Therapy*, **7**, 31–44.

LEFF, J. & VAUGHN, C. (1985) *Expressed emotion in families*. New York: Guilford Press.

LE GRANGE, D., EISLER, I., DARE, C., *et al* (1992) Evaluation of family treatments in adolescent anorexia nervosa: a pilot study. *International Journal of Eating Disorders*, **12**, 347–357.

LASEGUE, C. (1873) On hysterical anorexia. *Medical Times Gazette*, **2**, 367–369.

MINUCHIN, S., ROSMAN, B. L. & BAKER, L. (1978) *Psychosomatic Families: Anorexia Nervosa in Context*. Cambridge, MA: Harvard University Press.

MORGAN, H. G. & RUSSELL, G. F. M. (1975) Value of family background and clinical features as predictors of long-term outcome in anorexia nervosa: four year follow up study of 41 patients. *Psychological Medicine*, **5**, 355–371.

RUSSELL, G. F.M., SZMUKLER, G. I., DARE, C., *et al* (1987) An evaluation of family therapy in anorexia nervosa and bulimia nervosa. *Archives of General Psychiatry*, **44**, 1047–1056.

SELVINI-PALAZZOLI, M. (1974) *Self Starvation*. London: Chaucer.

STIERLIN, H. & WEBER, G. (1989) Anorexia nervosa: lessons from a follow-up study. *Family Systems Medicine*, **7**, 120–157.

SWIFT, W. J. (1982) The long-term outcome of early onset anorexia nervosa – a critical review. *Journal of the American Academy of Child Psychiatry*, **21**, 38–46.

SZMUKLER, G. I., EISLER, I., RUSSELL, G. F. M., *et al* (1985) Anorexia nervosa: parental "expressed emotion", and dropping out of treatment. *British Journal of Psychiatry*, **147**, 265–271.

THEANDER, S. (1970) Anorexia nervosa: a psychiatric investigation of 94 female patients. *Acta Psychiatrica Scandinavica* (suppl. 214), 24–31.

Index

Compiled by LINDA ENGLISH